by

Robert H. Marshall

Donald H. Jacobs

AGS Publishing
Circle Pines, Minnesota 55014-1796
800-328-2560

About the Authors

Robert H. Marshall, M.Ed., teaches high school physics and algebra for the Baltimore School for the Arts. He is coauthor of several AGS textbooks including *Earth Science, General Science,* and *Matter, Motion, and Machines.*

Donald H. Jacobs, M.Ed., taught mathematics for many years in the Baltimore City Public Schools. He is currently with the Upton Home and Hospital School Program in the technology department. Other AGS textbooks that he has coauthored include *Basic Math Skills, Life Skills Math,* and *General Science.*

Photo credits for this textbook can be found on page 398.

The publisher wishes to thank the following consultants and educators for their helpful comments during the review process for *Physical Science.* Their assistance has been invaluable.

Rebecca Abreu, Science Teacher, Timber Creek High School, Orlando, FL; **Bonnie Buratti,** Research Astronomer, Jet Propulsion Laboratory, California Institute of Technology, Pasadena, CA; **Barbara Cassius,** Science Resource Teacher, Hoover High School, San Diego, CA; **Norman Gelfand,** Physicist, Fermi National Accelerator Laboratory (Fermilab), Batavia, IL; **Brian P. Johnson,** Science Teacher, Centennial High School, Centerville, MN; **Gary A. Mansergh,** Ph.D., Inquiry-Science Coach, Professional Development Center for Academic Excellence, St. Paul, MN; **Thomas E. Rock,** Teacher, John Marshall High School, San Antonio, TX; **Lorraine S. Taylor,** Ph.D., Professor of Special Education, State University of New York at New Paltz, New Paltz, NY; **Katherine L. Turley,** Specific Learning Disabilities Teacher/Ex. Ed. Curriculum Leader, Timber Creek High School, Orlando, FL; **Dr. Alex Vera,** Science Teacher, Templeton Secondary School, Vancouver, BC, Canada

Editorial services provided by General Learning Communications.

Publisher's Project Staff

Vice President, Product Development: Kathleen T. Williams, Ph.D., NCSP; Associate Director, Product Development: Teri Mathews; Senior Editor: Julie Maas; Development Assistant: Bev Johnson; Senior Designer/Illustrator: Diane McCarty; Creative Services Manager: Nancy Condon; Project Coordinator/Designer: Laura Henrichsen; Purchasing Agent: Mary Kaye Kuzma; Senior Marketing Manager/Secondary Curriculum: Brian Holl

Printed in the United States of America
ISBN 0-7854-3624-3
Product Number 93920
A 0 9 8 7 6 5 4 3 2

Contents

How to Use This Book: A Study Guide

Welcome to *Physical Science.* Science touches our lives every day, no matter where we are—at home, at school, or at work. This book covers the area of physical science. It also focuses on science skills that scientists use. These skills include asking questions, making predictions, designing experiments or procedures, collecting and organizing information, calculating data, making decisions, drawing conclusions, and exploring more options. You probably already use these skills every day. You ask questions to find answers. You gather information and organize it. You use that information to make all sorts of decisions. In this book, you will have opportunities to use and practice all of these skills.

As you read this book, notice how each lesson is organized. Information is presented in a straightforward manner. Examples, tables, illustrations, and photos help clarify concepts. Read the information carefully. If you have trouble with a lesson, try reading it again.

It is important that you understand how to use this book before you start to read it. It is also important to know how to be successful in this course. Information in this first section of the book can help you achieve these things.

How to Study

These tips can help you study more effectively.

◆ Plan a regular time to study.

◆ Choose a quiet desk or table where you will not be distracted. Find a spot that has good lighting.

◆ Gather all the books, pencils, paper, and other equipment you will need to complete your assignments.

◆ Decide on a goal. For example: "I will finish reading and taking notes on Chapter 1, Lesson 1, by 8:00."

◆ Take a five- to ten-minute break every hour to stay alert.

◆ If you start to feel sleepy, take a break and get some fresh air.

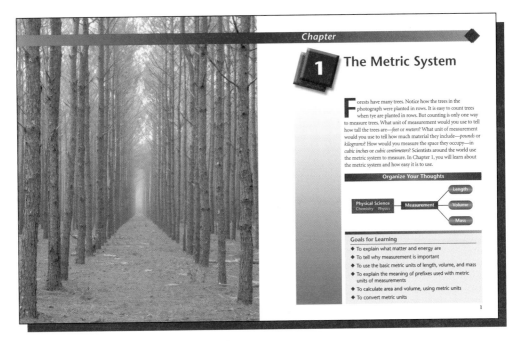

The Metric System

Forests have many trees. Notice how the trees in the photograph were planted in rows. It is easy to count trees when tye are planted in rows. But counting is only one way to measure trees. What unit of measurement would you use to tell how tall the trees are—*feet* or *meters*? What unit of measurement would you use to tell how much material they include—*pounds* or *kilograms*? How would you measure the space they occupy—in *cubic inches* or *cubic centimeters*? Scientists around the world use the metric system to measure. In Chapter 1, you will learn about the metric system and how easy it is to use.

Organize Your Thoughts

Physical Science
Chemistry Physics → Measurement → Length
Volume
Mass

Goals for Learning
◆ To explain what matter and energy are
◆ To tell why measurement is important
◆ To use the basic metric units of length, volume, and mass
◆ To explain the meaning of prefixes used with metric units of measurements
◆ To calculate area and volume, using metric units
◆ To convert metric units

Before Beginning Each Chapter

◆ Read the chapter title and study the photograph. What does the photo tell you about the chapter title?
◆ Read the opening paragraphs.
◆ Study the Goals for Learning. The Chapter Review and tests will ask questions related to these goals.
◆ Look at the Chapter Review. The questions cover the most important information in the chapter.

Note These Features

Note
Points of interest or additional information that relates to the lesson

Did You Know?
Facts that add details to lesson content or present an interesting or unusual application of lesson content

Science Myth
Common science misconceptions followed by the correct information

Technology Note

Technology information that relates to the lesson or chapter

Science in Your Life

Examples of science in real life

Achievements in Science

Historical scientific discoveries, events, and achievements

Science at Work

Careers in science

Investigation

Experiments that give practice with chapter concepts

Before Beginning Each Lesson

Read the lesson title and restate it in the form of a question.

For example, write:
Why use metric measurements to find area?

Look over the entire lesson, noting the following:
◆ bold words
◆ text organization
◆ notes in the margins
◆ photos and illustrations
◆ lesson review questions

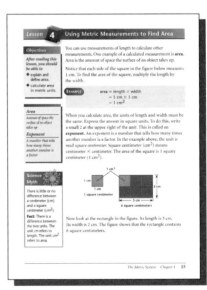

As You Read the Lesson

◆ Read the lesson title.
◆ Read the subheads and paragraphs that follow.
◆ Read the content in the Examples.
◆ Before moving on to the next lesson, see if you understand the concepts you read. If you do not understand the concepts, reread the lesson. If you are still unsure, ask for help.
◆ Practice what you have learned by completing the Lesson Review.

Using the Bold Words

Bold type

Words seen for the first time will appear in bold type

Glossary

Words listed in this column are also found in the glossary

Knowing the meaning of all the boxed vocabulary words in the left column will help you understand what you read.

These words are in **bold type** the first time they appear in the text. They are often defined in the paragraph.

> **Physical science** is the study of matter and energy.

All of the words in the left column are also defined in the **glossary.**

> **Physical science** (fiz´ə kəl sī´əns) the study of matter and energy (p. 2)

Word Study Tips

◆ Start a vocabulary file with index cards to use for review.
◆ Write one term on the front of each card. Write the chapter number, lesson number, and definition on the back.
◆ You can use these cards as flash cards by yourself or with a study partner to test your knowledge.

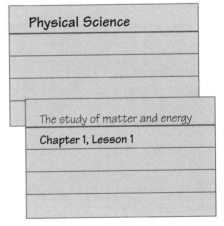

Physical Science

The study of matter and energy

Chapter 1, Lesson 1

Using the Summaries

◆ Read each Chapter Summary to be sure you understand the chapter's main ideas.

◆ Make up a sample test of items you think may be on the test. You may want to do this with a classmate and share your questions.

◆ Read the vocabulary words in the Science Words box.

◆ Review your notes and test yourself on vocabulary words and key ideas.

◆ Practice writing about some of the main ideas from the chapter.

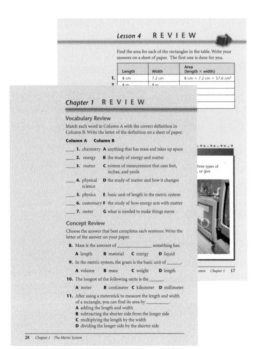

Using the Reviews

◆ Answer the questions in the Lesson Reviews.

◆ In the Chapter Reviews, answer the questions about vocabulary under the Vocabulary Review. Study the words and definitions. Say them aloud to help you remember them.

◆ Answer the questions under the Concept Review and Critical Thinking sections of the Chapter Reviews.

◆ Review the Test-Taking Tips.

Preparing for Tests

◆ Complete the Lesson Reviews and Chapter Reviews.

◆ Complete the Investigations.

◆ Review your answers to Lesson Reviews, Investigations, and Chapter Reviews.

◆ Test yourself on vocabulary words and key ideas.

◆ Use graphic organizers as study tools.

Using Graphic Organizers

A graphic organizer is a visual representation of information. It can help you see how ideas are related to each other. A graphic organizer can help you study for a test or organize information before you write. Here are some examples.

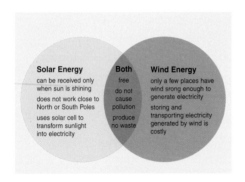

Venn Diagram

A Venn diagram can help you compare and contrast two things. For example, this diagram compares and contrasts solar energy and wind energy. The characteristics of solar energy are listed in the left circle. The characteristics of wind energy are listed in the right circle. The characteristics that both have are listed in the intersection of the circles.

Column Chart

Column charts can help you organize information into groups, or categories. Grouping things in this format helps make the information easier to understand and remember. For example, this four-column chart groups information about each of the four biomes. A column chart can be divided into any number of columns or rows. The chart can be as simple as a two-column list of words or as complex as a multiple-column, multiple-row table of data.

Four Biomes

Tundra	Grassland	Tropical Rain Forest	Desert
cold, dry frozen below the surface	temperate humid	warm wet	very dry
lichens, low shrubs	grasses	palms, tree ferns, vines	cacti
polar bears, caribou, wolves	antelopes, bison, coyotes	bats, birds, monkeys	lizards, snakes, kangaroo rats

Network Tree

A network tree organizer shows how ideas are connected to one another. Network trees can help you identify main ideas or concepts linked to related ideas. For example, this network tree identifies concepts linked to the concept of conservation. You can also use network trees to rank ideas from most important to least important.

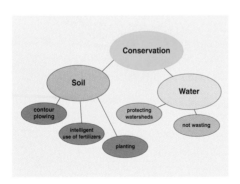

The Nature of Science

Science is an organized body of knowledge about the natural world. It encompasses everything from atoms to rocks to human health. Scientific knowledge is important because it solves problems, improves everyday life, and uncovers new opportunities. For example, scientists develop vaccines and antibiotics to prevent and cure diseases. Scientific knowledge helps farmers grow better and more crops. Science is behind the electricity we depend on every day. And science has launched space exploration, which continues to offer new opportunities.

Scientists use a logical process to explore the world and collect information. It is called the scientific method, and it includes specific steps. Scientists follow these steps or variations of these steps to test whether a possible answer to their question is correct.

1. Ask a question.
2. State a hypothesis, or make a prediction, about the answer.
3. Design an experiment, or procedure, to test the hypothesis.
4. Perform the experiment and gather information.
5. Analyze the data and organize the results.
6. State a conclusion based on the results, existing knowledge, and logic. Determine whether the results support the hypothesis.
7. Communicate the results and the conclusion.

As a scientist researches a question, he or she may do these steps in a different order or may even skip some steps. The scientific method requires many skills: predicting, observing, organizing, classifying, modeling, measuring, inferring, analyzing, and communicating.

Communication is an important part of the scientific method. Scientists all over the world share their findings with other scientists. They publish information about their experiments in journals and discuss them at meetings. A scientist may try another scientist's experiment or change it in some way. If many scientists get the same results from an experiment, then the results are repeatable and considered reliable.

Sometimes the results of an experiment do not support its hypothesis. Unexpected observations can lead to new, more interesting questions. For example, penicillin was discovered accidentally in 1928. Alexander Fleming observed that mold had contaminated one of his bacteria cultures. He noticed that the mold had stopped the growth of the bacterium. Since the mold was from the penicillium family, he named it penicillin. A decade later, researchers found a way to isolate the active ingredient. Since then, penicillin has been used to fight bacteria and save people's lives.

Once in a while, scientists discover something that dramatically changes our world, like penicillin. But, more often, scientific knowledge grows and changes a little at a time.

What scientists learn is applied to problems and challenges that affect people's lives. This leads to the development of practical tools and techniques. Tools help scientists accurately observe and measure things in the natural world. A new tool often provides data that an older tool could not. For example, computers help scientists analyze data more quickly and accurately than ever before. Our science knowledge grows as more advanced tools and technology make new discoveries possible.

Scientists use theories to explain their observations and data. A theory is a possible explanation for a set of data. A theory is not a fact. It is an idea. Theories are tested by more experiments. Theories may be confirmed, changed, or sometimes tossed out. For example, in 1808, John Dalton published a book describing his theory of atoms. His theory stated that atoms are solid spheres without internal structures. By the early 1900s, however, new tools allowed Ernest Rutherford to show that atoms are mostly empty space. He said that an atom consists of a tightly packed nucleus with electrons whizzing around it. This theory of the atom is still accepted today.

Theories that have stood many years of testing often become scientific laws. The law of gravity is one example. Scientists assume many basic laws of nature.

In this book, you will learn about physical science. You will use scientific skills to solve problems and answer questions. You will follow some of the steps in the scientific method. And you will discover how important physical science is to your life.

1

The Metric System

Forests have many trees. Notice how the trees in the photograph were planted in rows. It is easy to count trees when they are planted in rows. But counting is only one way to measure trees. What unit of measurement would you use to tell how tall the trees are—*feet* or *meters*? What unit of measurement would you use to tell how much material they include—*pounds* or *kilograms*? How would you measure the space they occupy—in *cubic inches* or *cubic centimeters*? Scientists around the world use the metric system to measure. In Chapter 1, you will learn about the metric system and how easy it is to use.

Organize Your Thoughts

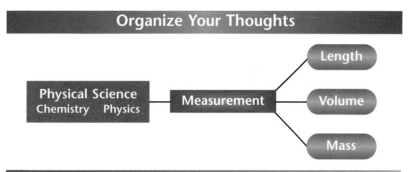

Goals for Learning

◆ To explain what matter and energy are

◆ To tell why measurement is important

◆ To use the basic metric units of length, volume, and mass

◆ To explain the meaning of prefixes used with metric units of measurements

◆ To calculate area and volume, using metric units

◆ To convert metric units

Have you ever wondered how a camera or a computer works? Do you listen to music on the radio or a boombox? Do you know how the sound is produced? Have you ever noticed that your body seems to weigh less in water? Do you know why?

All of these questions—and many more—can be answered by studying **physical science.** Physical science is the study of the things around you. It deals with **matter** and energy. Matter is anything that has mass and takes up space.

The Study of Matter and Energy

Look around you. What do you have in common with all the objects you see—your desk, the floor, the air? At first, you might think you have very little in common with these objects. But, in fact, all of them—including you—are made of matter. Other examples of matter appear in the photograph.

Physical science

The study of matter and energy

Matter

Anything that has mass and takes up space

Mass

The amount of material an object has

All matter has **mass.** Mass is the amount of material that an object has. All of the objects in the photo have mass. The cat has more mass than the potted plant.

What do all these objects have in common?

Science and technology are not the same thing. Science is a study of the world in which we live. Technology uses science to create tools and techniques that solve practical problems.

Energy is different from matter. You cannot hold energy or measure it with a ruler. Energy is needed to make things move. You use it to move your body. A car uses energy to move, too. You will learn more about energy in Chapter 8.

Two Areas of Physical Science

Physical science can be divided into two areas. One area is **chemistry.** Chemistry is the study of matter and how it changes. Chemistry can explain how a cake rises or how acid rain forms. Chemistry is also the study of how matter can be made into new materials. By studying chemistry, scientists have made new medicines, food, clothing, fragrances, and soaps. They have even made artificial skin and bones for people.

A second area of physical science is **physics.** Physics is the study of energy and how it acts with matter. Physics can explain why helium balloons rise or how lasers work. Scientists studying physics have developed television, cellular phones, stereo systems, computers, space satellites, microwave ovens, and jet airplanes.

Computers and cell phones are among the many products physical scientists have developed.

The Tools of Physical Scientists

Physical scientists—and all scientists—use many different skills. The skills they use include observing, classifying, measuring, organizing, inferring, predicting, modeling, analyzing, and communicating. Scientists need to be curious. They need to ask questions such as "Why does sugar dissolve in water when sand does not?" Scientists want to know how and why things are the way they are.

Scientists answer their questions by doing experiments. You will also do experiments to answer questions. In this book, these experiments are called Investigations.

Scientists have to know how to use scientific tools. In the figure below, you can see some of the tools scientists use. You will use many of these tools as you do the Investigations.

Scientists also need to know how to make measurements. Measurements are an important part of the information scientists gather. In the following lessons, you will learn how to measure like a scientist.

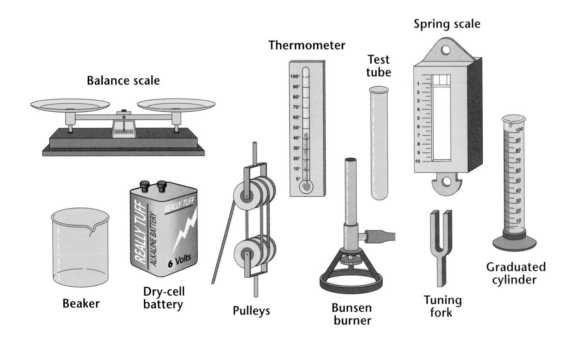

Write your answers to these questions in complete sentences on a sheet of paper.

1. What is physical science?

2. What are two examples of matter?

3. What are two areas of physical science?

4. What kinds of things do scientists in each area study?

5. What are three tools that scientists use to do experiments?

6. List three skills that scientists use.

7. How do scientists answer questions?

8. What is matter?

9. What area of physical science would be involved in the search for a cure for the common cold?

10. Name three tools that scientists could use to measure liquids.

Technology Note

In the 1960s, the U.S. government created what we now call the Internet. The Internet was designed to maintain government communications in case of a national emergency. In 1990, the World Wide Web portion of the Internet was born. The WWW was invented to meet the needs of some particle physicists located around the world. These scientists were looking for a faster, more effective way to communicate and share ideas. Though it was originally designed as a collaboration tool for scientists in the high-energy physics community, the Web is now available to everyone.

Unit

A known amount used for measuring

Look at the poles in the photo. Which one is the tallest? Use a ruler to measure each one.

Are the poles the same height?

Though some look taller than others, in reality the poles are the same height. Measurements are important because we cannot always trust observations made with our eyes. Measurements help us gather exact information. Exact measurements are especially important to a scientist.

Units of Measurement

When you measured the poles in the photo above, you probably measured with a ruler marked in inches. You compared the length of the pole to a known measurement, the inch. A known amount in measurement, such as the inch, is called a **unit.** Other units you might be familiar with are the yard, mile, minute, and day.

If you had lived thousands of years ago, you most likely would have used units of measurement that were based on the length of certain parts of your body.

For example, Egyptians used the cubit to measure length. A cubit was the distance from the elbow to the tip of the middle finger. The Romans used the width of their thumb to measure length. This unit of measurement was called an uncia.

Compare the widths of the thumbs of each person in your classroom. Do you think they are all the same? Probably not. So you can see why using units of measurement based on body parts does not work very well. The exact length of an uncia or a cubit could vary from person to person.

In order for a unit of measurement to be useful, it has to be the same for everybody. When one scientist tells another scientist that something is a certain length, that measurement should mean the same thing to both of them.

Systems of Measurement

You probably measure in units based on the **customary** system. Some customary units for measuring length are the inch, foot, yard, and mile. Customary units also can be used to measure time, weight, and other amounts.

In the customary system of measurement, it is difficult to convert one unit to another because the units are very different. The units of measure also are not clearly related to each other.

Scientists and most other people throughout the world use a different system of measurement. They use the **metric system.** Metric units are the most common units of measurement in the world. The metric system is simpler to use and easier to remember than the customary system. You will use the metric system in this book. You will find conversion information about some metric and customary measurements in Appendix C on pages 380–381.

Write your answers to these questions in complete sentences on a sheet of paper.

1. Why are measurements important?

2. Why is it important to use units of measurement that are the same for everyone?

3. What are some common units in the customary system of measurement?

4. What is the name of the system of measurement that scientists use?

5. Name the unit of measurement you would use to measure the length of your finger.

Answer these questions to find out how familiar you are with the customary system.

6. How many inches are in 1 foot?

7. How many feet are in 1 yard?

8. How many minutes are in 1 hour?

9. How many seconds are in 1 minute?

10. How many seconds are in 1 hour?

Technology Note

Digital measurers use sound waves to measure distance. A laser beam points at the spot from which you want to measure. At the same time, a sound wave bounces off that spot. The measurer calculates the distance the sound wave traveled. Then it displays the measurement digitally.

Objectives

After reading this lesson, you should be able to

◆ identify and explain the common metric units of length.

◆ explain the meaning of prefixes used with metric units of measurement.

The metric system is similar to the money system used in the United States. As the figure shows, there are 10 pennies in a dime, 10 dimes in a dollar, and 10 dollars in a 10-dollar bill. You can say that the money system is based on a system of tens. Likewise, you will see that the metric system is based on a system of tens.

Meter, m

The basic unit of length in the metric system; it is about 39 inches

Using Meters

In the metric system, you measure length in **meters** or parts of a meter. A meter is a little more than 39 inches, or a bit longer than a yard.

1 meter

The length from the tip of a man's nose to the tip of his middle finger is about one meter. A football field is just over 90 meters long. The abbreviation for meter is *m*. A period is not used with abbreviations for metric units.

The common tool for measuring length in the metric system is the **meterstick.** It is one meter long.

The figure below shows part of a meterstick. Notice that it is divided into equal units. Each of these units is a **centimeter.** A centimeter is $\frac{1}{100}$ of a meter. You can use centimeters when the meter is too long a unit. For example, it might be difficult to measure the width of your book in meters, but you could easily use centimeters. The abbreviation for centimeter is *cm*.

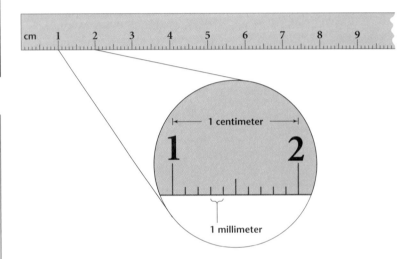

Sometimes, even the centimeter is too large a unit to measure an object. You need a smaller unit. Look at the meterstick again. Notice that each centimeter is divided into 10 smaller units. Each of these smaller units is a **millimeter.** A millimeter is $\frac{1}{1,000}$ of a meter. You would measure the width of a pencil in millimeters. Use *mm* as an abbreviation for millimeter.

Using meters to describe the distance from your school to your home would likely result in a large number of units. It would be more convenient to use a unit larger than a meter. The **kilometer,** which is equal to 1,000 meters, would be more useful. The abbreviation for kilometer is *km*.

Length Equivalents	
10 millimeters	1 centimeter
1,000 millimeters	1 meter
100 centimeters	1 meter
1,000 meters	1 kilometer

Using Metric Prefixes

Did You Know?

Only three countries do not use the metric system as their official measurement system. They are the United States, Myanmar (Burma), and Liberia.

Once you understand how the meterstick is divided, you know how to use other units of measurement in the metric system. The prefixes in front of the word *meter* have special meanings. They are used to show how many times the meter is multiplied or divided. Just as a cent is $\frac{1}{100}$ of a dollar, a centimeter is $\frac{1}{100}$ of a meter. The prefix *centi-* means $\frac{1}{100}$. You will learn how to use the prefixes shown in the table with other units of measurement later in this chapter.

Any measurement of a physical quantity must include two things. The measurement must include a number followed by a unit.

Some Metric Prefixes		
Prefix	**Meaning**	**Unit and Its Abbreviation**
kilo- (k)	1,000 ×	kilometer (km)
centi- (c)	$\frac{1}{100}$ (0.01)	centimeter (cm)
milli- (m)	$\frac{1}{1,000}$ (0.001)	millimeter (mm)

Write your answers to these questions in complete sentences on a sheet of paper.

1. Which letter in the figure below marks 1 millimeter?

2. Which letter shows 1 centimeter?

3. How many millimeters are there in 1 centimeter?

4. How many millimeters are there in 10 centimeters?

5. What is the measurement in millimeters of the match? What is it in centimeters?

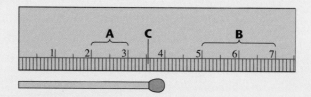

Achievements in Science

Measurement Standards

Every measurement compares an unknown quantity with a standard. A measurement standard defines the size of a unit. People based early standards on local customs. They sometimes used body parts to create standards. They also used objects like grains and stones.

In the 1400s, King Edward I of England created what may have been the first uniform standards. He ordered a measuring stick made of iron to be a master yardstick. The first metric standards were a standard meter bar and kilogram bar. The French government officially adopted them in 1799. The international kilogram bar and meter bar are made of a mixture of metals.

The Bureau of Weights and Measures in France keeps standards of length and mass. In the United States, the National Institute of Standards and Technology keeps these same standards. All metersticks and scales are checked against these standards.

Hands Instead of Feet

Purpose

Can you think of a measuring system that would be more useful than the metric system? In this investigation, you will create a system of measuring length and compare it to the metric system.

Materials
◆ meterstick

Procedure

1. Copy the data table on a sheet of paper.

Object	Length in Hands	Length in Centimeters

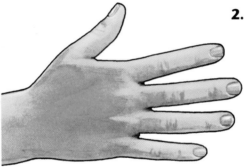

2. Measure several objects in your classroom. Your teacher will tell you which objects to measure. Each member of the class will measure the same objects.

3. Use your stretched out right hand as a measuring tool. The length of this hand from your wrist to the end of your longest finger will equal one unit of length in "hands."

4. Measure the length, in hands, of each object. Estimate to the nearest length of a hand. Record this information in the table.

5. After you have measured all the objects, compare your results with those of at least five other students.

6. Measure the objects again, using a meterstick instead of your hand. Record your measurements in centimeters.

7. Compare your results with those of other students in your class.

Questions and Conclusions

1. Did your length in hands match those of other students? Explain your answer.

2. Did your length in centimeters match those of other students? Explain your answer.

3. Do you think a system such as the metric system is more useful than one that uses units such as hands? Explain your answer.

Explore Further

Develop your own system of measurement. Determine the units you will use. Share your system with the class.

Objectives

After reading this lesson, you should be able to

◆ explain and define area.

◆ calculate area in metric units.

You can use measurements of length to calculate other measurements. One example of a calculated measurement is **area.** Area is the amount of space the surface of an object takes up.

Notice that each side of the square in the figure below measures 1 cm. To find the area of the square, multiply the length by the width.

EXAMPLE   area = length × width
              = 1 cm × 1 cm
              = 1 cm^2

Area

Amount of space the surface of an object takes up

Exponent

A number that tells how many times another number is a factor

When you calculate area, the units of length and width must be the same. Express the answer in square units. To do this, write a small 2 at the upper right of the unit. This is called an **exponent.** An exponent is a number that tells how many times another number is a factor. In the example above, the unit is read *square centimeter.* Square centimeter (cm^2) means centimeter × centimeter. The area of the square is 1 square centimeter (1 cm^2).

Science Myth

There is little or no difference between a centimeter (cm) and a square centimeter (cm^2).

Fact: There is a difference between the two units. The unit *cm* refers to length. The unit *cm^2* refers to area.

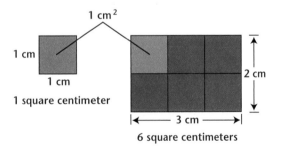

1 cm^2

1 cm

1 cm

1 square centimeter

2 cm

3 cm

6 square centimeters

Now look at the rectangle in the figure. Its length is 3 cm. Its width is 2 cm. The figure shows that the rectangle contains 6 square centimeters.

You can find the area of the rectangle by using the same formula you used to find the area of the square.

EXAMPLE

area = length × width
     = 3 cm × 2 cm
     = 6 cm²

The area of the rectangle is 6 square centimeters.

What is the area of a rectangle with a length of 8.5 mm and a width of 3.3 mm?

EXAMPLE

area = length × width
     = 8.5 mm × 3.3 mm
     = 28.05 mm²

The area is 28.05 square millimeters.

Science in Your Life

Do you have enough paint?

If you have ever gone to a store to buy paint, you know that first you have to figure out how much paint you need. It is easy to do if you use what you learned about calculating area.

Suppose you have a wall that measures 3.5 m long and 8 m high. You want to paint it. The instructions on the paint can say that the paint will cover 32 m² of surface area. Do you have enough paint to cover the wall?

3.5 meters

8 meters

Find the area for each of the rectangles in the table. Write your
answers on a sheet of paper. The first one is done for you.

	Length	Width	Area (length × width)
1.	8 cm	7.2 cm	8 cm × 7.2 cm = 57.6 cm²
2.	8 m	8 m	
3.	3.4 mm	5.2 mm	
4.	2.6 m	4.7 m	
5.	13 m	5.1 km	

▼◄▲▼◄▲▼◄▲▼◄▲▼◄▲▼◄▲▼◄▲▼◄▲▼◄▲▼◄▲▼◄▲▼◄▲▼◄▲▼◄▲▼◄▲▼◄▲▼◄▲▼

Science at Work

Instrument Calibration Technician

Instrument calibration technicians calibrate, or check the accuracy of, three types
of instruments. The instruments make measurements, control equipment, or give
information about what equipment
is doing. All these instruments must
be exact.

Instrument calibration technicians
first test an instrument by comparing
it with another instrument. They study
the test results and keep a record.
Instrument calibration technicians
maintain and repair instruments
so they stay calibrated.

Instrument calibration technicians
must earn a two-year degree in
electronics technology.

They must be able to handle details
and must have strong fine-motor skills.
They also must understand electronics.

INVESTIGATION

1-2

Counting Squares and Calculating Area

Purpose

How is area related to square units? This investigation will show the relationship between area and the number of square units.

Procedure

1. Copy the data table on a sheet of paper.

	Length	Width	Area (length × width)	Total Number of Squares
original paper				
rectangle 1				
rectangle 2				

2. Put on your safety glasses. Obtain a small sheet of paper from your teacher. The size of your paper will be larger or smaller than your classmates' papers. Use a ruler to measure the length and width of the paper. Record these two measurements in centimeters in your table.

3. Use the following formula to calculate the area of the paper.

$$\text{area} = \text{length} \times \text{width}$$

Record this area. Remember that the units should be square centimeters (cm^2).

4. Use the ruler to mark off all four sides of the paper in 1-cm units. Using the ruler as a straightedge, draw straight lines to connect the marks from side to side. Now connect them from top to bottom. You will create a grid of squares similar to the one on the next page.

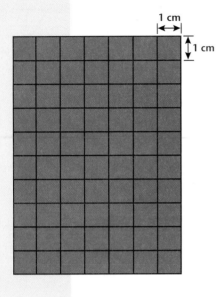

1 cm

1 cm

5. Count the squares on the paper. The area of each square is 1 square centimeter. That is because area = length × width = 1 cm × 1 cm = 1 cm². The area of the sheet of paper is the number of squares. Record that number in your table. The answer should be in square centimeters.

6. Cut the paper into squares along the lines you drew. Use all the individual squares to make two smaller rectangles of different lengths and widths. To do this, carefully place the squares next to each other in rows and columns. Make sure the squares have almost no space between them and that they do not overlap.

7. Measure the length and width of each new rectangle you create. Find the area of each one.

Questions and Conclusions

1. Does the area for the original paper in step 5 match the area calculated in step 3? Do you think it should? Explain your answer.

2. How does the sum of the areas of the two new rectangles compare to the total number of squares in the two rectangles? How does it compare to the calculated area of the original sheet of paper? Explain these results.

Explore Further

Repeat steps 1 through 5. Divide the grid in half. Use a ruler to draw a line from one corner to the opposite corner. Cut along the diagonal line. Measure the area of each triangle using the following formula.

$$\text{area} = \text{base} \times \frac{\text{height}}{2}$$

Calculate the sum of the two triangles. How does it compare to the area of the rectangle?

Objectives

After reading this lesson, you should be able to

◆ explain what volume is.

◆ calculate volume in metric units.

◆ convert metric units of volume.

Volume

The amount of space an object takes up

Cubic centimeter, cm³

A metric unit of measure that means centimeter × centimeter × centimeter

In 1975, the United States Congress passed the Metric Conversion Act. The act made the metric system the preferred system of measurement for U.S. commerce. It also directed government agencies to use the metric system.

Another calculation that you can make using metric measurements is **volume.** Volume describes the amount of space an object takes up.

Volume of a Rectangle

The small green box in the figure below measures 1 cm on each edge. You can find out how much space the box takes up—its volume—by using a simple formula.

> **EXAMPLE**
>
> $$\text{volume} = \text{length} \times \text{width} \times \text{height}$$
> $$= 1 \text{ cm} \times 1 \text{ cm} \times 1 \text{cm}$$
> $$= 1 \text{ cm}^3$$

The small 3 written to the upper right of the centimeter unit means cubic. It is read ***cubic centimeter*** or *centimeter cubed.* Cubic centimeter means centimeter × centimeter × centimeter. The volume of the small green box is 1 cubic centimeter.

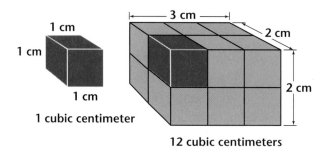

1 cubic centimeter

12 cubic centimeters

Now look at the larger box above. Its length is 3 cm. Its width is 2 cm. Its height is 2 cm. You can see that 12 small boxes will fit into the larger box. If each small box is 1 cm³, then the large box would have a volume of 12 cm³.

You also can use the formula to find the volume of the larger box.

EXAMPLE volume = length × width × height
= 3 cm × 2 cm × 2 cm
= 12 cm³

Volume of a Liquid

You might be familiar with another unit of volume in the metric system—the **liter.** You can see liter containers at the supermarket, especially in the soft-drink section. A liter is slightly more than a quart. The abbreviation for liter is *L*. The liter is the basic unit of volume in the metric system. It is often used to measure the volume of liquids.

As you can see in the figure, one liter of water will exactly fill a box that measures 10 cm on each side. A liter occupies the same amount of space as 1,000 cubic centimeters.

1,000 cubic centimeters = 1 liter

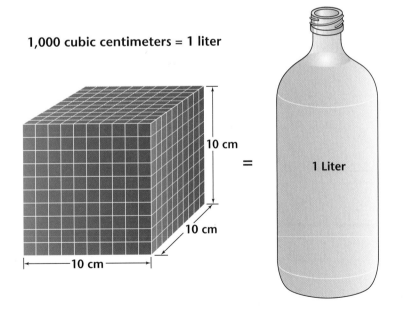

10 cm

10 cm

10 cm

=

1 Liter

You learned earlier in this chapter that you can use the same prefixes you used with the meter to form other units of measurement. The only prefix that is commonly used to measure volume is *milli-*. Remember that *milli-* means $\frac{1}{1,000}$. A **milliliter** is $\frac{1}{1,000}$ of a liter. The abbreviation for milliliter is *mL*. There are 1,000 milliliters in a liter. Since there are also 1,000 cubic centimeters in one liter, a milliliter is the same as one cubic centimeter.

Volume Equivalents	
1 liter (L)	1,000 cubic centimeters
1 cubic centimeter (cm^3)	$\frac{1}{1,000}$ liter (0.001 L)
1 milliliter (mL)	$\frac{1}{1,000}$ liter (0.001 L)
1 milliliter (mL)	1 cubic centimeter (cm^3)

Sometimes you will have to convert cubic centimeters to liters. Since one cubic centimeter is $\frac{1}{1,000}$ of a liter, you can convert by dividing by 1,000.

EXAMPLE   Express 1,256 cm^3 as liters.
$1,256 \div 1,000 = 1.256$ L

You can also convert liters to cubic centimeters. Simply multiply by 1,000.

EXAMPLE   Express 4.3 L as cubic centimeters.
$4.3 \text{ L} \times 1,000 = 4,300 \text{ cm}^3$

You cannot measure the volume of liquids by using the formula you used to find the volume of a rectangle. In Chapter 2, you will learn how to use special equipment to find the volume of a liquid.

Lesson 5   R E V I E W

Write your answers to these questions in complete sentences on a sheet of paper.

1. A box measures 8 cm by 9 cm by 12 cm. What is its volume?

2. What is the volume of a stainless-steel container with a length of 18 mm, width of 20 mm, and height of 10 mm?

3. Find the volume of a cabinet that measures 1.20 m by 5 m by 75 cm. (Hint: Convert meters to centimeters. Remember that 1 m = 100 cm.)

4. A box is 5 cm high, 4 cm wide, and 9 cm long. What is the volume in cubic centimeters? What is the volume in milliliters?

Convert each of these measurements. Write the answers on your paper.

5. 3 L = _____ mL

6. 5.5 L = _____ mL

7. 3,000 cm^3 = _____ L

8. 3,700 cm^3 = _____ L

9. 0.72 L = _____ mL

10. 350 mL = _____ cm^3

Achievements in Science

The Metric System

The metric system is the first standardized system of measurement based on the decimal. Before the metric system, units of length, area, and weight varied from country to country. Ways of measuring were sometimes different even within a country. England had three different systems. In order to trade goods fairly, merchants and tradesmen needed a uniform system. Scientists needed a way to exchange information.

In France, the idea of the metric system first was suggested around 1670. No action was taken, however, for more than 100 years. In the 1790s, the French Academy of Sciences proposed a new system of measurement. The French revolutionary assembly adopted the metric system in 1795.

At first, the people of France had a hard time changing to a new system. For a time in the early 1800s, France went back to the old units of measure. But in 1837, the metric system became the rule in France. Soon other countries throughout the world began using the metric system.

After reading this lesson, you should be able to

◆ identify the basic metric unit of mass.

◆ convert metric units of mass.

You learned earlier in this chapter that all matter has mass. Remember that mass is the amount of material an object has. But how can you measure mass?

In the metric system, the **gram** is the basic unit of mass. Look at the figure below. One gram equals the mass of one cubic centimeter of water. That is about the same mass as a large wooden match or a small paper clip. There are 454 grams in one pound. The abbreviation for gram is *g*.

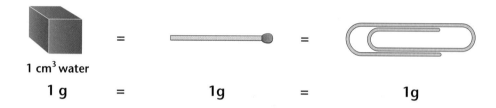

1 cm³ water
1 g = **1g** = **1g**

Gram, g

Basic unit of mass in the metric system

Mass Equivalents

Recall that the meter sometimes is too large or too small to measure the length of certain objects. The same is true for the gram. For example, a person may have a mass of 85,000 grams. That's a large number!

You can use the same prefixes you use with meters to show parts of a gram or multiples of a gram. The table on the next page shows these units of mass.

Kilogram, kg

A unit of mass in the metric system that equals 1,000 grams

Milligram, mg

A unit of mass in the metric system that is $\frac{1}{1,000}$ of a gram

Centigram, cg

A unit of mass in the metric system that is $\frac{1}{100}$ of a gram

To measure the mass of a person, you probably would use **kilograms.** One kilogram equals 1,000 grams. The abbreviation for kilogram is *kg.* However, the mass of a single hair from your head would be measured in smaller units called **milligrams.** A milligram is $\frac{1}{1,000}$ of a gram. The abbreviation for milligram is *mg.* A **centigram** is $\frac{1}{100}$ of a gram. The abbreviation for centigram is *cg.*

Mass Equivalents	
1 kilogram (kg)	1,000 g
1 centigram (cg)	$\frac{1}{100}$ g (0.01 g)
1 milligram (mg)	$\frac{1}{1,000}$ g (0.001 g)

If 1 cubic centimeter of water has a mass of 1 gram, then 1,000 cubic centimeters will have a mass of 1,000 grams, or 1 kilogram. Remember that there are 1,000 cubic centimeters in 1 liter. Therefore, as the figure below shows, 1 liter of water will have a mass of 1 kilogram.

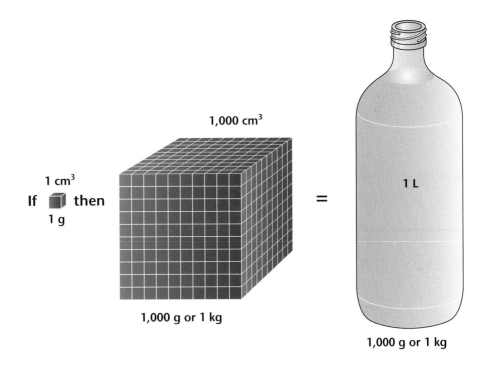

Convert each of these measurements. Write the answers on a sheet of paper.

1. 6 g = _____ mg

2. 80,000 g = _____ kg

3. 90 g = _____ cg

4. 3,000 cg = _____ mg

5. 25,300 mg = _____ kg

6. 10 g = _____ mg

Write the answers to these questions on your paper.

7. Which is larger—5 g or 49 cg?

8. Which is smaller—850 g or 0.9 kg?

9. A boy weighs 45 kg. What is his weight in grams?

10. Arrange these measurements from smallest to largest.

   A 125 g   **B** 1,203 mg   **C** 0.123 kg

Chapter 1 SUMMARY

- Physical science is the study of matter and energy.

- Matter is anything that has mass and takes up space. Mass is the amount of material in an object.

- Measurements are important because we cannot always trust observations made with our eyes. Measurements help scientists gather exact information.

- In order for a unit of measurement to be useful, it has to be the same for everyone.

- Scientists use the metric system. The metric system is based on a system of tens.

- The meter is the basic unit of length in the metric system.

- You can measure length with a meterstick. A meterstick is divided into 100 smaller units, called centimeters. Each centimeter is divided into 10 units, called millimeters.

- You can use a system of prefixes in the metric system to show multiples or parts of a unit.

- Area is the amount of space the surface of an object takes up. The formula *length* × *width* is used to calculate area.

- Volume is the amount of space an object takes up. The volume of a rectangle can be calculated by using the formula *length* × *width* × *height*.

- A liter is the basic unit of volume in the metric system.

- You can convert from one unit to another in the metric system.

- The gram is the basic unit of mass in the metric system.

Science Words

area, 15	exponent, 15	matter, 2	millimeter, 10
centigram, 25	gram, 24	meter, 9	physical science, 2
centimeter, 10	kilogram, 25	meterstick, 10	physics, 3
chemistry, 3	kilometer, 11	metric system, 7	unit, 6
cubic centimeter, 20	liter, 21	milligram, 25	volume, 20
customary, 7	mass, 2	milliliter, 22	

Chapter 1 REVIEW

Vocabulary Review

Match each word in Column A with the correct definition in Column B. Write the letter of the definition on a sheet of paper.

Column A

_____ **1.** chemistry

_____ **2.** unit

_____ **3.** matter

_____ **4.** physical science

_____ **5.** physics

_____ **6.** customary

_____ **7.** meter

Column B

A anything that has mass and takes up space

B the study of energy and matter

C ordinary

D the study of matter and how it changes

E basic unit of length in the metric system

F the study of how energy acts with matter

G known amount used for measuring

Concept Review

Choose the answer that best completes each sentence. Write the letter of the answer on your paper.

8. Mass is the amount of _____ something has.

    A length   **B** material   **C** energy   **D** liquid

9. In the metric system, the gram is the basic unit of _____.

    A volume   **B** mass   **C** weight   **D** length

10. The longest of the following units is the _____.

    A meter   **B** centimeter **C** kilometer   **D** millimeter

11. After using a meterstick to measure the length and width of a rectangle, you can find its area by _____.
    A adding the length and width
    B subtracting the shorter side from the longer side
    C multiplying the length by the width
    D dividing the longer side by the shorter side

12. The measurement _____ describes the area of a solid object.

    A 25 mm   **B** 25 cm   **C** 25 cm^2 **D** 25 cm^3

13. The amount of space an object takes up is its _____.

    A volume   **B** area   **C** mass   **D** length

14. The basic unit of volume is _____.

    A quart   **C** liter

    B cubic centimeter   **D** A and C

15. If 1 cubic centimeter of water has a mass of 1 gram, then a liter of water has a mass of _____ gram(s).

    A 1   **B** 10   **C** 100   **D** 1,000

Critical Thinking

Write the answer to each of these questions on your paper.

16. Some ancient civilizations used units of measure based on the length of certain seeds. What kinds of problems might you expect with such a system?

17. How is the relationship between units in the money system in the United States similar to the metric system?

18. For each of the following objects, tell which unit of measurement you would use:

    A length of an ant   **C** volume of a large jug of milk

    B mass of a postage stamp   **D** mass of a truck

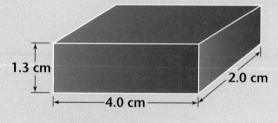

1.3 cm   2.0 cm   4.0 cm

19. Calculate the volume of the rectangular object shown in the figure.

20. If one candle weighs 2.5 g, how many candles are in a 1-kg box of candles?

Test-Taking Tip Drawing pictures and diagrams is one way to help you understand and solve problems.

2 The Properties of Matter

ook at the snow under the trees and on the tree branches in the photograph. Notice the patches of ice in the stream. Both snow and ice are forms of water. So is the substance in the stream. What words would you use to describe these forms of water? You might say that snow and ice are frozen water. You might say that the water in the stream is liquid. In Chapter 2, you will learn ways to describe the properties of matter. You will also learn how to measure various substances.

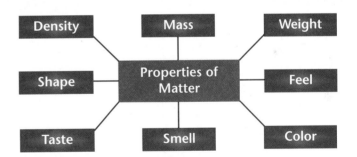

Organize Your Thoughts

Density · Mass · Weight

Shape · **Properties of Matter** · Feel

Taste · Smell · Color

Goals for Learning

◆ To describe various objects by listing their properties

◆ To measure the mass of different objects

◆ To measure the volume of a liquid, using a graduated cylinder

◆ To measure the volume of an object, using the displacement of water method

◆ To calculate density

Property

A characteristic that helps identify an object

Matter has many properties. One property of matter is the temperature at which something melts. Another property of matter is how it dissolves. How well something conducts electricity is also a property of matter.

If someone asked you to describe sugar, what would you say? You might say "It is a solid made of small, individual pieces." Each part of that description tells a **property** of sugar. A property is a characteristic that helps identify an object. The above description identifies two properties of sugar.

◆ It is a solid.
◆ It is made of small individual pieces.

This description of sugar is correct. But it isn't enough to accurately identify sugar. As you can see in the photo, sand has the same properties. The description could be made more useful by adding other properties. For example, you might add color and taste. Your description of sugar becomes, "It is a white solid made of small, individual pieces that have a sweet taste." Sand could be described as "a tan solid made of small, individual pieces that have no taste."

Sugar and sand have some of the same properties.

Scientists group the properties of matter into two categories. Properties that describe how one kind of matter reacts with another are called chemical properties. All other properties are called physical properties.

Technology Note

Electronic noses have sensors that "sniff" different odors. Scientists use them in many ways. Electronic noses can detect the freshness of fish and identify chemical spills. They can even detect some illnesses, such as pneumonia. Scientists have also used electronic noses to measure air quality on the space shuttle.

Some Common Properties

The photo on this page shows some of the more common properties that you might use to describe matter. Scientists prefer to use some properties more than others. For example, scientists often use mass. The reason is because mass can be measured easily. If someone asked you to describe a rock you saw, you might say it was big. But how big is big? And would someone else think the same rock was big? By using specific measurements of mass, everyone can agree on the measurement. For example, everyone can find the mass of the rock and agree on its mass. Another property that can be measured easily is volume (length, width, and height).

Color: yellowish-red
Shape: almost round
Volume: about 20 mL
Feel: fuzzy, soft

Size: similar to a baseball
Mass: about 0.023 kg
Taste: sweet
Smell: pleasant, sweet

Which of these properties are easy to measure?

Some properties, such as color, cannot be measured as easily. Because of this, descriptions based on color can be misunderstood. For example, how would you describe the color of the fruit in the photo above? One person might describe the color as "pink," while another would call it "yellowish-red." When describing properties, it is important to be as exact as you can. Use measurements whenever possible.

Write your answers to these questions on a sheet of paper.

1. For each of the following statements, tell whether it is a good description. Explain your answer.
   A It is a large, colorful box.
   B The rock has a mass of 25 kilograms.
   C The solid that formed was dark, shiny, and lumpy.

2. A baseball has several properties. Write one property that a baseball has.

3. Could the property you wrote for question 2 also be a property for another object? If yes, write a second property that a baseball has.

4. Choose an object. Write a detailed description of the object.

5. Read your description to the class. Can classmates identify the object from your description?

▼ ◄ ▲ ▼ ◄ ▲ ▼ ◄ ▲ ▼ ◄ ▲ ▼ ◄ ▲ ▼ ◄ ▲ ▼ ◄ ▲ ▼ ◄ ▲ ▼ ◄ ▲ ▼ ◄ ▲ ▼ ◄ ▲ ▼ ◄ ▲ ▼ ◄ ▲ ▼

Science at Work

Perfumer

Perfumers create formulas for fragrances and other scented products such as soaps and candles. Perfumers also set quality and production standards for perfumes. Each batch of a product must have exactly the same properties as earlier batches. Perfumers evaluate the smell, color, strength, and other properties of fragrances.

There are two different ways to become a perfumer. Some perfumers earn a four-year degree in chemistry. Other perfumers receive on-the-job training. They usually work for five years as an assistant to an experienced perfumer.

Perfumers must recognize and remember smells, must understand chemistry, and must be creative.

INVESTIGATION

2-1

Identifying Properties

Purpose

Why is it important to provide a clear description of an object? In this investigation, you will learn to write clear descriptions of objects.

Procedure

1. Copy the data table on a sheet of paper.

Object Number	Properties
1	color >
2	shape >
3	feel >
4	size >
5	taste/smell > >

2. Obtain a bag from your teacher. You will find five objects in your bag.

3. Study the five objects in your bag carefully. On another sheet of paper, make a list of the objects in your bag. Number the objects from 1 to 5.

4. Now describe each object by writing as many of its properties as you can. Write the information in your table. Be sure to describe each object clearly and completely. Do not tell what the object is or what it is used for.

5. When you have completed your descriptions, give your table to a classmate. Ask your classmate to read your descriptions and identify the objects.

Questions and Conclusions

1. How many objects did your classmate identify correctly?

2. Which objects did your classmate identify?

3. Which objects did your classmate identify incorrectly?

4. What could you have done to make your descriptions more useful?

Explore Further

Work with five other students. Combine the objects from the bags of everyone in your group. Place objects with similar properties in a group. Identify the properties that describe all the objects in each group. Then list the property of each object in a group that makes it different from all the other objects. Elect someone in your group to share the list with the class.

Weight

The measure of how hard gravity pulls on an object

Newton

The metric unit of weight

You know from Chapter 1 that all matter has mass. Mass is a property of matter that you can measure. For example, the mass of the man in the figure is 65 kg. But what is the man's weight? Are mass and weight the same?

Mass and Weight

Mass and *weight* are often used to mean the same thing. However, scientists have different meanings for these two words. Mass measures how much matter is in an object. **Weight** is a measure of how hard gravity pulls on an object. The force of gravity depends on the mass of an object. Objects with a large mass will have a strong pull of gravity.

You may have seen a scale like the one shown here at the grocery store or supermarket. You can use a scale like this to measure the weight of produce such as grapes or tomatoes.

Scientists use the **newton** when describing weight. A mass of 1 kg has a metric weight of 9.8 newtons. You will find more information about the newton in Chapter 8.

This astronaut weighs less on the moon than on Earth.

The mass of an object never changes under normal conditions. But the weight of an object can change when it is moved to some other place. For example, the pull of gravity on the moon is less than the pull of Earth's gravity. So when the astronaut in the photograph went to the moon, he weighed less on the moon than he did on Earth. But his mass did not change.

Measuring Solid Mass

Recall from Chapter 1 that in the metric system, mass is measured in units called grams. The mass of a small paper clip is about 1 g. How many grams do you think a large paper clip might be? How could you find out?

Balance

An instrument used to measure mass

Standard mass

A small object that is used with a balance to determine mass

You can use an instrument called a **balance** to measure mass. There are many different kinds of balances. But the simplest kind often looks like the one in the figure below. When you use this kind of balance, you find the mass of an object by balancing it with objects of known masses.

A **standard mass** is a small object that is used with a balance to determine mass. The object is usually a brass cylinder with the mass stamped on it. Look at the standard masses in the figure. Most people use standard masses when they use a balance. You can place standard masses on the pan opposite the object to be measured until the two pans are balanced. The mass of the object is equal to the total of the standard masses.

Did You Know?

Deimos, a moon of Mars, has very low mass. This makes its gravity much less than the Earth's gravity. On Deimos, you would weigh very little. You could jump off the surface on a pogo stick.

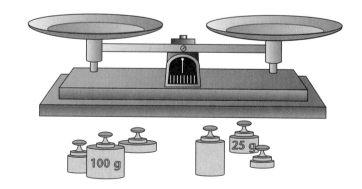

The table below lists some planets of the solar system. It also tells each planet's force of gravity compared to the earth's. Copy the chart on a sheet of paper. Then calculate the weight of a 100-pound person on each of the planets. The first two items are done for you. Write your answers in your chart.

	Planet	Force of Gravity Compared to Earth	Weight on Earth	Weight on this Planet	Method
1.	Earth	1.00	100 lbs	100 lbs	1.00 x 100
2.	Jupiter	2.54	100 lbs	254 lbs	2.54 x 100
3.	Mars	0.379	100 lbs		
4.	Saturn	1.07	100 lbs		
5.	Mercury	0.378	100 lbs		
6.	Venus	0.894	100 lbs		

Write your answers to these questions in complete sentences on your paper.

7. How does mass differ from weight?

8. Are you measuring mass or weight when you use a grocery scale?

9. Why would you weigh less on the moon than on Earth?

10. What is the weight in newtons of a 5 kg mass?

Technology Note

Most electronic scales have a load cell. A load cell changes force or weight into an electrical signal. An indicator reads the signal. The indicator shows how much an object weighs. Scales in grocery stores have load cells. So do scales used to weigh large trucks on highways.

You can find the mass of a solid by using a balance. But how do you find the mass of a liquid? A balance is made to hold solids, not liquids.

To help answer the question, think about the following example. Suppose a boy uses a scale to find his weight. The scale shows that he weighs 100 pounds. Then the boy picks up his dog and weighs himself again while holding the dog. The scale now reads 120 pounds. Why? It is because the scale is measuring the weight of both the boy and the dog.

The boy knows that his weight is 100 pounds. He knows that his and the dog's weight together is 120 pounds. Now he can easily find the weight of the dog.

120 pounds – 100 pounds = 20 pounds
(weight of boy and dog) – (weight of boy) = (weight of dog)

120 lbs　　　　　　　**100 lbs**

Measuring Liquid Mass

You can use a similar procedure to find the mass of a liquid.

1. Measure the mass of an empty container, such as a beaker.

2. Pour the liquid you want to measure into the beaker.

3. Measure the mass of the liquid plus the beaker.

4. Subtract the mass of the empty beaker from the mass of the beaker plus liquid. The answer will be the mass of the liquid.

mass of liquid   =   mass of liquid plus beaker   −   mass of beaker

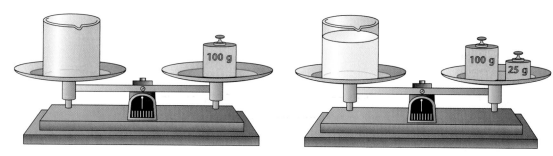

Mass of empty beaker = 100 g   **Mass of beaker plus liquid = 125 g**

The mass of the liquid is 125 g − 100 g = 25 g

Achievements in Science

Balances

The first scales were used more than 4,500 years ago in ancient Egypt. The oldest kind of scale is the balance.

The first balance was the equal-arm balance. Egyptians made the equal-arm balance around 2,500 B.C. An equal-arm balance has a bar with a pan hanging from each end. The bar is held up at the center by a piece of metal or other hard material. The object whose mass is being measured is put in one pan. Standard masses are placed in the other pan until the two pans balance. A pointer shows that the pans are balanced.

About 2,500 years later, the Romans invented the steelyard balance. A steelyard balance has a bar with arms that are not the same length. The shorter arm has a pan or hook to hold the object that is being measured. A small standard mass is moved along the longer arm until it balances. Markings on the arm show the object's weight.

Write your answers to these questions in complete sentences on your paper.

1. A container has a mass of 150 g. What is the mass of a liquid if the container plus the liquid has a mass of 185 g?

2. A container has a mass of 125 g. When a liquid is added, the mass becomes 163 g. What is the mass of the liquid?

3. Suppose the mass of a certain liquid is 35 g. You place it in a beaker that has a mass of 75 g. What is the mass of the beaker plus the liquid?

4. A beaker has a mass of 100 g. Liquid is poured into the beaker. The mass of the liquid and the beaker is 135 g. What is the mass of the liquid?

5. Using this information, find the mass of the liquid:
   mass of liquid and beaker = 250 g
   mass of beaker = 150 g
   mass of liquid = _____

Objectives

After reading this lesson, you should be able to

◆ explain how to use a graduated cylinder to measure the volume of a liquid.

Graduated cylinder

A round glass or plastic cylinder used to measure the volume of liquids

Meniscus

The curved surface of a liquid

In Chapter 1, you learned that the unit of volume in the metric system is the liter. Usually, the liter is too large a unit to use in a laboratory, so scientists often use the milliliter. Remember that 1 milliliter has the same volume as 1 cubic centimeter. Liquid volumes are sometimes measured in cubic centimeters rather than milliliters.

To measure the volume of a liquid, you can use a **graduated cylinder.** Graduated cylinders come in many different sizes. The largest ones usually hold 1 L of a liquid. More common sizes hold 100 mL, 50 mL, or 10 mL. You can see two sizes of graduated cylinders in the figure on page 44.

Measuring with a Graduated Cylinder

To measure the volume of a liquid, follow this procedure.

1. Pour the liquid into the graduated cylinder.

2. Position yourself so that your eye is level with the top of the liquid. You can see the correct position in the figure below.

3. Read the volume from the scale that is on the outside of the cylinder. The top of the liquid usually is curved. This curve is called a **meniscus.** You can see the meniscus in the figure to the right. Read the scale on the bottom of the curve as shown. The volume of this liquid is 16 mL.

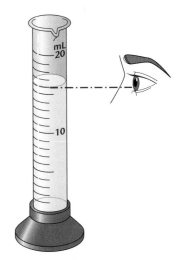

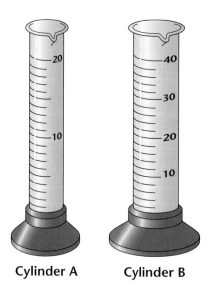

Cylinder A　　**Cylinder B**

If you look carefully at the two graduated cylinders to the left, you will see that they are marked differently. Notice that Cylinder A on the left can hold 20 mL of a liquid. Cylinder B on the right can hold 40 mL. The number of spaces between the numbers on the cylinders is also different.

Reading a Scale

In order to measure the volume of a liquid in a graduated cylinder, you need to know what the spaces between each line represent. In other words, you must be able to read the scale. It is easy to do if you follow this procedure.

1. Subtract the numbers on any two long lines that are next to each other. In the figure below, the two long lines are labeled *20* and *10*. When you subtract these numbers (20 mL – 10 mL) you get 10 mL.

2. Count the number of spaces between the two long lines. In the figure, you can see 5 spaces between the two long lines.

3. Divide the number you got in Step 1 by the number you counted in Step 2. This will tell you how much of an increase each line represents from the line below. In the figure below, each space equals 2 mL.

Step 1
20 mL – 10 mL = 10 mL

Step 2
5 spaces

Step 3
10 mL ÷ 5 spaces =
2 mL/space

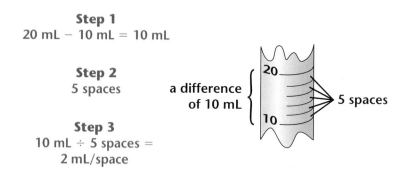

a difference
of 10 mL

5 spaces

Write your answers to these questions on a sheet of paper.

Read the volume of liquid in each cylinder. Write the volumes for A and B on the lines.

1. Cylinder A: _____

2. Cylinder B: _____

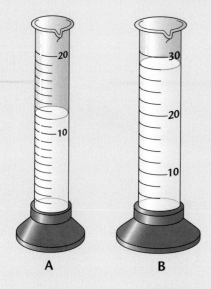
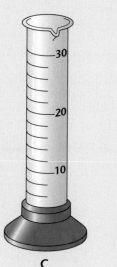

A   B

Draw the three cylinders shown here on your paper. Shade each one to show these volumes:

3. Cylinder C: 26 mL

4. Cylinder D: 13 mL

5. Cylinder E: 8 mL

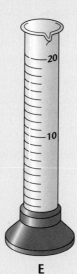

C   D   E

The volume of solid objects cannot be measured using a graduated cylinder. However, you can measure the volume of solids in two different ways, depending on the shape of the solid.

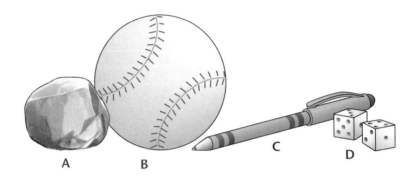

A   B   C   D

Regular and Irregular Shapes

Displacement of water

Method of measuring the volume of an irregularly shaped object

You can describe some solids as having a regular shape. Objects B and D in the figure above have a regular shape. When a solid has a regular shape, you can find the volume by using a formula. You have already learned the formula for finding the volume of objects that have a rectangular shape.

volume = length × width × height

Some solids have regular shapes other than rectangular. Examples are spheres and cylinders. You can use different formulas for finding the volumes of objects with these shapes.

Objects A and C in the figure have irregular shapes. You cannot use a formula to find the volume of a solid with an irregular shape. Instead, you can use the **displacement of water** method to find the volume of irregularly shaped objects.

Using Displacement of Water

If a glass is partially filled with water and you place an object in the glass, the level of the water will rise. In fact, the water level will rise by an amount equal to the volume of the object that was placed in the glass. To accurately measure the volume, use a graduated cylinder. The object must be completely under the water.

To measure the volume of a small, solid object using the displacement of water method, follow the procedure below. Remember to cover the object completely with water.

1. Pour water into a graduated cylinder. Record the volume of the water. (Figure A)

$$volume = 10 \text{ cm}^3$$

2. Place the object in the cylinder. The water level will then rise. Record this new volume. (Figure B)

$$volume = 16 \text{ cm}^3$$

3. Subtract the volume of the water from the volume of the water and the object. The difference will be the volume of the object.

$$16 \text{ cm}^3 - 10 \text{ cm}^3 = 6 \text{ cm}^3$$

The volume of the object is 6 cm^3.

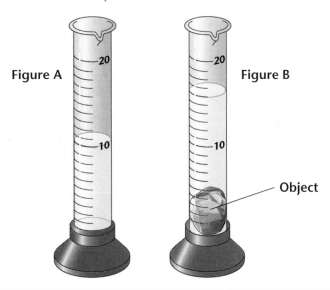

Figure A

Figure B

Object

Write your answers to these questions in complete sentences on your paper.

1. What is the volume of an object 10 cm long, 5 cm wide, and 2 cm high?

2. A stone is placed in a graduated cylinder, which has been filled to the 35-mL mark. The level rises to 42 mL. What happens to the volume of the stone?

3. What is the volume of the stone in question 2?

4. A red marble is placed in a graduated cylinder, which has been filled to the 25-mL mark. The level rises to 41 mL. A blue marble is placed in another graduated cylinder, which has been filled to the 25-mL mark. The level rises to 52 mL. Which marble has the greater volume?

5. Explain how you would find the volume of a pencil.

Science in Your Life

Is your aquarium large enough?

Suppose you are setting up an aquarium. You have seen 10 fish at the pet store that you would like to include in your aquarium. The store owner tells you that the 10 fish you have chosen will live together well, but they need at least 40,000 cm^3 of water.

You already own a fish tank that you would like to use. It measures 30 cm wide, 50 cm long, and 30 cm high. Is this tank large enough to provide the fish with the amount of water they need?

30 cm   50 cm   30 cm

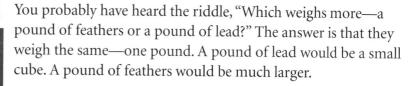

Objectives

After reading this lesson, you should be able to

◆ explain and define density.

◆ calculate density.

◆ explain how to use density to identify a substance.

Density

A measure of how tightly the matter of a substance is packed into a given volume

Buoyancy makes objects seem lighter under water. The force of the water that is displaced or spilled out is the buoyant force. The buoyant force pushes in the opposite direction of the force of gravity.

You probably have heard the riddle, "Which weighs more—a pound of feathers or a pound of lead?" The answer is that they weigh the same—one pound. A pound of lead would be a small cube. A pound of feathers would be much larger.

1 pound of feathers   **1 pound of lead**

But what if you made 1-cm cubes from both materials? Would they be equally heavy? No, the lead cube would be much heavier. The reason is that lead has more matter packed in the cube than the feathers. The lead has a higher **density**. Density is a measure of how tightly the matter of a substance is packed into a given volume.

Calculating Density

If you know the volume and mass of a substance, you can find its density. You just have to use the following formula.

$$\text{density} = \frac{\text{mass}}{\text{volume}} \left(\frac{m}{v}\right)$$

Suppose you know the mass of an object is 30 g and its volume is 15 cm³. What is the object's density?

EXAMPLE

$$\text{density} = \frac{\text{mass}}{\text{volume}} \quad \left(\frac{m}{v}\right)$$

$$= \frac{30 \text{ g}}{15 \text{ cm}^3}$$

$$= 2 \text{ g/cm}^3$$

Density = 2 g/cm³. A mass of 2 grams of this object has a volume of 1 cubic centimeter.

Density Is a Property

The density of a particular substance is always the same. It does not matter how large or what shape the piece of the substance is. As the figure shows, the density of lead is always 11.3 g/cm³.

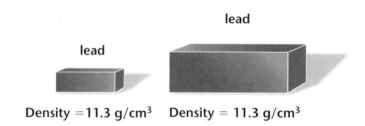

lead

lead

Density = 11.3 g/cm³   Density = 11.3 g/cm³

Material	Density (g/cm³)
gold	19.3
mercury	13.6
lead	11.3
silver	10.5
aluminum	2.7
rubber	1.1
water	1.0
cork	0.24
air	0.0013

The lead block on the right has more mass. It also has a larger volume. But the density of both blocks is the same.

Look at the different kinds of material and their densities in the table. You can use density to identify a material.

Suppose you have a small piece of metal and you want to find out what it is. You can measure its mass and volume, and then use the formula to find its density.

Suppose you measure the mass of the metal on a balance. Its mass is 8 g. Then you use a graduated cylinder to find the volume of the metal. The volume is 3 cm^3. Using the formula, you find the density of the metal is 2.7 g/cm^3. Now look at the table on page 50. What metal do you have?

Sink or Float

Matter that has a greater density than water will sink in water. Matter with a density that is less than water will float.

Look at the glass of water. It holds an ice cube and a silver ball. You know from the table on page 50 that the density of silver is 10.5 g/cm^3. That density is greater than the density of water, which is 1.0 g/cm^3.

But what about the ice cube ? It floats on the water. What does that tell you about the density of ice compared to water? It tells you that ice has a lower density than liquid water. Ice expands, increasing the volume. Since density is mass divided by volume, the density becomes less because the denominator is bigger. The mass stays the same.

Technology Note

Have you ever seen a liquid motion lamp? A liquid motion lamp contains two kinds of matter. One is a liquid. The other is a "blob" that has a different density from the liquid. When the lamp is on, the density of the blob decreases and the blob rises. When the blob cools, it sinks.

Lesson 6   R E V I E W

Write your answers to these questions in complete sentences on your paper.

1. What is density?

2. Which would have more matter—a 1-cm cube of lead or a 1-cm cube of rubber?

3. Suppose you have a metal bar. Its mass is 57.9 g and its volume is 3 cm^3. What is its density?

4. If you cut the metal bar from question 3 in half, what would the density of each half be?

5. If you put a piece of cork in a container of water, would it sink or float? Why? (Hint: Use the table on page 50 to answer the question.)

Achievements in Science

Archimedes' Principle of Displacement

Archimedes was a Greek inventor and mathematician who lived from about 287 to 212 B.C. He is best known for his discovery of the displacement of an object in water. Here is Archimedes' principle: Any object in water displaces, or spills out, the same amount of water as the object's volume.

As the story goes, Archimedes made his discovery while getting into the bathtub. He noticed that as he got into the tub, the water began overflowing. The more he lowered himself into the water, the more the water overflowed the tub. He looked at the amount of water that overflowed. He realized that the amount of his body that was in the water was the same. He was so excited about his discovery, he cried out "Eureka!" or "I have found it!" Archimedes had discovered the principle of displacement.

Archimedes' principle applies both to objects that are under water and objects that float. The principle explains why steel ships float and why helium-filled balloons rise.

2-2

INVESTIGATION

Finding Density

Materials
- safety glasses
- 2 graduated cylinders
- balance
- cooking oil
- water

Purpose

Do you think cooking oil and water have the same density? In this investigation, you will calculate and compare the densities of cooking oil and water.

Procedure

1. Copy the data table on a sheet of paper.

Measurements	Cylinder with Water	Cylinder with Cooking Oil
A mass of empty cylinder		
B mass of cylinder and liquid		
C mass of liquid (B–A)		
D volume of liquid		
E density (E = $\frac{C}{D}$)		

2. Put on your safety glasses.

3. Obtain two identical graduated cylinders. Use a balance to find the mass of each cylinder. Record the masses on line A of your table.

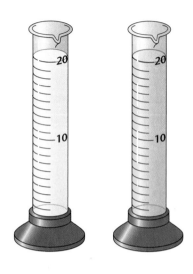

4. Fill one graduated cylinder with water and the other with cooking oil. Fill each one to the same level. You now have equal volumes of water and oil. Record this volume on line D of your data table.

5. Find the mass of the cylinder and the water. Record your data on line B.

6. Subtract the mass of the graduated cylinder from the mass of the graduated cylinder and water (line B – line A). The answer tells you the mass of the water. Write the mass on line C.

7. Repeat steps 5 and 6, using your data for the cooking oil.

8. Use the equation for density to find the densities of the water and the cooking oil.

$$density = \frac{mass}{volume}$$

Questions and Conclusions

1. Which substance—the water or the cooking oil—has the greater density?

2. Liquids with lesser densities will float on liquids with greater densities. If you pour cooking oil and water together, which liquid will float on top?

Explore Further

Corn syrup has a density of 1.3 g/cm³. If you pour corn syrup into a cylinder of cooking oil and water, what will happen?

Chapter 2 SUMMARY

- Mass measures how much matter is in an object.

- Weight can change when moving from one place to another, but mass generally stays the same.

- Properties are used to describe an object.

- Mass, volume, and density are important properties of matter.

- Mass is measured using a balance. A common unit of mass is the gram.

- Volume of liquids is measured by using a graduated cylinder.

- When measuring the mass of liquids, first measure the mass of an empty beaker. Then pour the liquid into the beaker and measure the mass again. Subtract these two figures to find the mass of the liquid.

- The volume of regularly shaped objects can be found by using formulas.

- The volume of irregularly shaped objects is measured by using the displacement of water method.

- Density is a property of matter that tells how tightly the matter of a substance is packed into a given volume.

- Density can be used to identify substances.

- Liquids that are less dense than water will float on water. Liquids that are more dense will sink.

Science Words

balance, 38	graduated cylinder, 43	property, 32
density, 49	meniscus, 43	standard mass, 38
displacement of water, 46	newton, 37	weight, 37

Chapter 2 REVIEW

Vocabulary Review

Word Bank

displacement of water

graduated cylinder

meniscus

property

standard mass

weight

Choose a word or words from the Word Bank that best complete each sentence. Write the answers on a sheet of paper.

1. You measure volume with a _____.

2. The _____ is the curved surface of a liquid.

3. You use a _____ with a balance to determine mass.

4. The measure of how hard gravity pulls on something is _____.

5. A characteristic that helps identify an object is a _____.

6. The _____ method is used to measure the volume of irregularly shaped objects.

Concept Review

Choose the answer that best completes each sentence. Write the letter of the answer on your paper.

7. The mass of an object can change if _____.

    A the object is moved to a different height

    B the object is put under water

    C the object is moved to place where the gravity is different

    D none of the above

8. A balance can measure the mass of _____.

    A solids   **C** solids and liquids

    B liquids   **D** only very heavy things

9. If you place a marble in a half-filled glass of water, the water level will _____.

    A rise   **C** stay the same

    B fall   **D** overflow

10. To find the density of a substance, you must know

_____.

    A what it is made of   **C** its mass and volume

    B how much it weighs   **D** its length and width

Critical Thinking

Write the answer to each of these questions on your paper.

11. Why is the following statement *not* a good one for a scientist to use in a report? "The material was made of small, colorful pieces."

12. Explain how to find the mass of a liquid.

13. How would you measure the volume of each of the objects shown here?

14. Cork has a density of 0.24 g/cm^3 and water has a density of 1.0 g/cm^3. If you put a piece of cork in water, will it sink or float? Explain your answer.

15. Suppose a scientist has two solid substances that look alike. How could the scientist use density to see if the substances are the same?

Test-Taking Tip   When studying for a test, use a marker to highlight important facts and terms in your notes. For a final review, read over highlighted areas.

3

The Structure of Matter

The snowflake in the photograph looks like one large ice crystal. In fact, a snowflake is made up of thousands of small particles of matter called molecules. Each molecule is made of even smaller parts called atoms. In Chapter 3, you will learn more about the particles that make up matter—molecules, atoms, elements, and compounds.

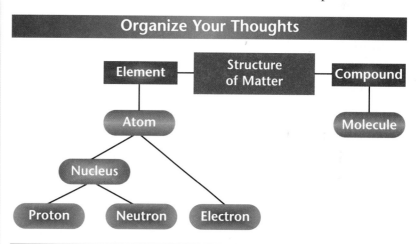

Organize Your Thoughts

Element — Structure of Matter — Compound

Atom

Molecule

Nucleus

Proton   Neutron   Electron

Goals for Learning

◆ To explain molecules, elements, and compounds

◆ To tell how scientists use models

◆ To describe the parts of an atom

◆ To explain the meaning of atomic number and mass number

◆ To calculate the number of protons, electrons, and neutrons in an element using its atomic number and mass number

Objectives

After reading this lesson, you should be able to

◆ describe the size of molecules.

◆ explain what a molecule is.

◆ explain how molecules move in each of the three states of matter.

◆ describe plasma.

Molecule

The smallest particle of a substance that has the same properties as the substance

How would you describe the sugar shown in the figure below? You might mention that sugar is a material made of matter. You might tell about its properties, such as its color, taste, or texture. Now think about how you might describe a single grain of sugar. You probably would say that it is very small. But how small is the smallest piece of sugar?

Size of Molecules

Each grain of sugar is made of even smaller particles that are too tiny for you to see. These tiny particles are called **molecules.** Molecules are the smallest particles of a substance that still have the properties of that substance. Each molecule of sugar has exactly the same properties. How small can molecules be? Molecules of some substances are so small that billions of them could be placed side by side on a line one centimeter long.

Describing Molecules

Atom

The building block of matter

Look at the water spraying out of the fountain in the photo. Imagine dividing one drop of this water into smaller and smaller drops. The smallest drop you could make that still had the properties of water would be one molecule of water.

This fountain contains billions of molecules of water.

In general, all water molecules are alike. A water molecule from the fountain is the same as a water molecule in a raindrop, in a lake, or in the water you drink. The figure on the left shows a molecule of water. You can see that each water molecule has three parts—one large part and two smaller parts.

Molecule of water

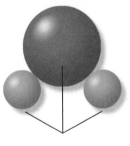

Atoms

If you divided a water molecule into its three parts, it would no longer be a molecule of water. The parts would no longer have the properties of water. When a water molecule is divided into its separate parts, each individual part is called an **atom.** An atom is a building block of matter. A water molecule has three atoms. Each kind of atom has its own properties. All matter is made of atoms.

States of Matter

You can describe matter by telling about its properties. For example, you might tell about its mass or density. The form that matter has is another one of its properties.

There are three forms of matter in the photo below. Can you find them? The boats and rocks are **solids.** A solid is a form of matter that has a definite shape and volume. The molecules in a solid attract, or pull toward, each other. In a solid, molecules vibrate, which means that they move back and forth quickly, but stay close together. For this reason, a solid keeps a certain shape and volume.

How many solids, liquids, and gases do you see?

The water in the picture is a **liquid.** A liquid is a form of matter that has a definite volume but no definite shape. The pull between the molecules is weaker in liquids than it is in solids. The molecules can slide past each other. A liquid can change its shape because its molecules can move around easily.

Suppose you had a liter of water in a container. If you poured the liter of water into a container that had a different shape, the water would still take up one liter of space. But its shape would be different. The water would take the shape of the new container.

Notice the shape of the helium balloon in the photo on page 62. Helium is a **gas** that fills the balloon. Gas is a form of matter that has no definite shape or volume. The molecules of a gas are much farther apart than they are in a liquid or a solid. The attraction between the molecules in a gas is very weak. A gas takes the same shape as its container because its molecules move around freely. The gas molecules will always fill a container completely. A container of water can be half full, but a container of a gas will always be completely full. The volume of a gas can change.

Solid   Liquid   Gas

These forms of matter—solid, liquid, and gas—are called the **states of matter.** The figure illustrates how the molecules move in each of these three states of matter.

Plasma

Matter can exist in a fourth state of matter called **plasma.** Plasma is a very hot gas made of particles that have an electric charge. The particles of plasma shake violently at very high temperatures. Plasma is very rare on Earth. But all stars, including the sun, are balls of plasma. Scientists estimate that 90 percent of all matter in the universe is plasma.

Write your answers to these questions in complete sentences on a sheet of paper.

1. Can you see a single molecule of sugar? Explain your answer.

2. What parts make up a molecule of water?

3. Describe how molecules move in each of the three states of matter.

4. What is plasma?

5. In which form of matter are the molecules close together?

6. Which form of matter has a definite shape and volume?

7. Which form of matter has no definite shape, but has a definite volume?

8. Which form of matter takes the shape of its container?

9. Where is most plasma located?

10. In which state of matter is the attraction between molecules weakest?

Technology Note

The scanning electron microscope, or SEM, uses electron beams to look at very small items. The SEM makes a sharply detailed, 3–D picture. An SEM picture can show an item up to 200,000 times bigger than it is. The item is magnified so much that you can see molecules.

Element

Matter that has only one kind of atom

In Lesson 1, you learned that atoms are very tiny. In fact, they are one of the smallest particles that make up matter. Remember the balloon that was filled with helium? A balloon as small as a softball would hold many billions of atoms of helium.

One Kind of Atom

Most of the matter you see around you is made up of many different kinds of atoms. However, some matter has only one kind of atom. Matter that is made of only one kind of atom is called an **element.** All atoms of the same element are alike. For example, all atoms of oxygen are the same. The atoms of oxygen are different from the atoms of all other elements.

The foil you might use to wrap a sandwich is made of atoms of the element aluminum. Gold, silver, and copper are other elements that are used to make jewelry and other common items.

Natural Elements

Scientists know of about 109 different kinds of elements. Of these elements, 92 are called **natural elements.** Natural elements are those that are found in nature. For example, oxygen is an element that you get from the air you breathe. Your body is made of atoms of many different elements. Atoms of the element calcium help keep your bones and teeth strong.

Not all elements are natural elements. Scientists are able to produce a few elements in specialized laboratories. Some of the elements that scientists produce last only a short time—a fraction of a second—before they change into other elements.

The table lists some natural elements and tells what they can be used for. Can you think of other uses for some of these elements?

Did You Know?

Look at the tip of your pencil. It is made of a soft, black material that is a form of the element carbon. The small pencil point has billions of carbon atoms.

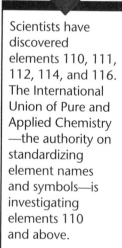

Scientists have discovered elements 110, 111, 112, 114, and 116. The International Union of Pure and Applied Chemistry —the authority on standardizing element names and symbols—is investigating elements 110 and above.

Some Natural Elements	
Name	**Element Is Used or Found in These Items**
copper	coins, frying pans, electrical wire
silver	jewelry, photography
carbon	pencils, charcoal, diamonds
helium	balloons, airships
nitrogen	air that we breathe, fertilizers
chlorine	bleach, table salt
aluminum	airplanes, cookware, soft-drink cans
neon	"neon" signs
gold	jewelry, seawater, dentistry
mercury	thermometers, drugs, pesticides
iron	steel, eating utensils

Elements in Water

You have learned that a molecule of water is made of three parts like those in the figure below. These parts are elements. The large part of the molecule, shown in blue, is an atom of the element oxygen. The two small parts, shown in green, are atoms of the element hydrogen. The atoms of the element oxygen are different from the atoms of the element hydrogen.

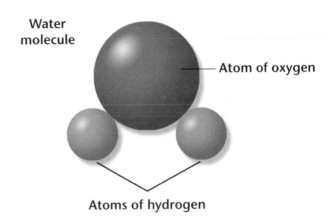

Water molecule

Atom of oxygen

Atoms of hydrogen

Science Myth

The properties of a material's atoms are the same as the properties of the material.

Fact: Gold atoms are not shiny. Silver atoms are not silver in color. If we could see them, we would find that all individual atoms look about the same. The differences are not noticeable until billions of atoms are together.

How are elements important to health?

Your body needs many natural elements in order to stay healthy and work properly. There are two groups of elements in your body. The major elements are the elements your body needs in large amounts. Your body needs trace elements in smaller amounts. Your body cannot produce any of these elements. You must get them from food.

The table below lists some of the major elements and tells how they are important for your health. The table also lists some foods that contain these elements. Write a menu for a day. Include healthful foods in your menu that provide a variety of natural elements.

Element	Purpose in the Body	Food That Contains the Element
calcium	builds and maintains teeth and bones; helps blood clot; helps nerves and muscles work properly	cheese, milk, dark green vegetables, sardines, legumes
phosphorus	keeps teeth and bones healthy; helps release energy from the food you eat	meat, poultry, fish, eggs, legumes, milk products
magnesium	aids breaking down of foods; controls body fluids	green vegetables, grains, nuts, beans, yeast
sodium	controls the amount of water in body; helps nerves work properly	most foods, table salt
potassium	controls the fluids in cells; helps nerves work properly	oranges, bananas, meats, bran, potatoes, dried beans
iron	helps move oxygen in the blood and in other cells	liver, red meats, dark green vegetables, shellfish, whole-grain cereals
zinc	helps move carbon dioxide in the body; helps in healing wounds	meats, shellfish, whole grains, milk, legumes

Write your answers to these questions in complete sentences on a sheet of paper.

1. What is an element?

2. What is a natural element?

3. Give three examples of natural elements.

4. Table salt is made up of one sodium atom and one chlorine atom. Is table salt an element? Explain your answer.

5. Name two elements that we need to build and maintain bones in our body.

Achievements in Science

Quarks

A fundamental particle is a particle that is not made up of anything else. An electron is a fundamental particle. Protons and neutrons are made of subnuclear particles called quarks.

There are six types of quarks. Scientists usually discuss them as pairs. The up and down quarks are the first and lightest pair. The strange and charm quarks are the second pair. The last pair is made up of the bottom and top quarks. The existence of the top quark was hypothesized for 20 years before scientists discovered it in 1995. It is the most massive quark and was the last to be discovered.

Quarks are different from protons and electrons. Protons and electrons have a charge that is always a whole number. Quarks have a fractional charge. Protons and neutrons are made of up quarks and down quarks. All of the everyday matter in our world is made of electrons, up quarks, and down quarks. The other quarks usually are found only in particle accelerators.

Compound

A substance that is formed when atoms of two or more elements join together

All the substances in the figure are different from the elements you learned about in Lesson 2. The substances in the figure are each made of two or more different kinds of atoms. When two or more atoms of different elements join together, the substance that forms is called a **compound**. A compound has properties that are different from the properties of the elements that form the compound.

 + =

Hydrogen + Oxygen = Water
(gas)   (gas)   (liquid)

Think again about a molecule of water. The drawing shows that an atom of oxygen combines with two atoms of hydrogen to form a molecule of the compound water. Water is different from the elements that form it. Water is a liquid. Both oxygen and hydrogen are gases. You will learn more about breaking down the compound water into its elements when you do the Investigation on pages 73 and 74.

Another compound that probably is familiar to you is The chemical name of salt is sodium chloride. It is fo when the element sodium is combined with the elen chlorine. Sodium chloride is very different from each of elements it contains. Sodium is a solid. You might be surprised to learn that chlorine is a poisonous gas. However, when chlorine is combined with sodium to form sodium chloride, chlorine no longer has its poisonous property. Remember that a compound can have completely different properties from the elements that form it.

Most kinds of matter on Earth are compounds. In fact, there are more than 10 million known compounds. The table lists some common compounds and tells the elements that make up each compound.

Some Common Compounds		
Name	Elements in this Compound	How/Where It Is Used
table salt	sodium, chlorine	cooking
water	hydrogen, oxygen	drinking
sugar	carbon, hydrogen, oxygen	cooking
baking soda	sodium, hydrogen, carbon, oxygen	baking
Epsom salts	magnesium, sulfur, oxygen	medicine

You might wonder if you can tell by looking at a substance whether it is an element or a compound. An unknown substance must be tested in a laboratory to determine whether it is an element or a compound.

Write your answers to these questions in complete sentences on a sheet of paper.

1. Explain what a compound is.

2. Give two examples of compounds.

3. Suppose you test a gas in the laboratory. You learn that the gas is made up of carbon atoms and oxygen atoms. Is the gas a compound? Explain your answer.

4. Name two common compounds that contain sodium.

5. Name four compounds that contain oxygen.

▼◀▲▼◀▲▼◀▲▼◀▲▼◀▲▼◀▲▼◀▲▼◀▲▼◀▲▼◀▲▼◀▲▼◀▲▼◀▲▼

Science at Work

Accelerator Technician

Accelerator technicians help build, maintain, repair, and operate particle accelerators and related equipment. They are responsible for recording meter readings. Accelerator technicians also keep track of parts and move heavy equipment.

Accelerator technicians need vocational training to learn to make and maintain electrical or mechanical equipment.

Accelerator technicians must be able to follow instructions and keep records. They must be able to use hand tools and electronic instruments. Accelerator technicians also must know how to measure and calculate dimensions, area, volume, and weight.

3-1 **INVESTIGATION**

Materials

- safety glasses
- beaker or wide-mouth jar
- water (distilled water preferred)
- two 50-cm long pieces of copper wire (about 3 cm of insulation removed at ends)
- one 15-cm long piece of copper wire (about 3 cm of insulation removed at ends)
- 2 six-volt batteries
- 1 teaspoon table salt
- stirring rod
- salt water
- 2 test tubes

Breaking Down Water

Purpose

How can you tell that water is a compound? This investigation will show that water is made from two different substances and is therefore a compound.

Procedure

1. Copy the data table on a sheet of paper.

Setup	After 10 Minutes
wire connected to positive (+) terminal	
wire connected to negative (−) terminal	

2. Put on your safety glasses.

3. Fill a 500 mL beaker with water.

4. Attach the end of one long copper wire to the negative (−) terminal of one battery, as shown on the next page. Attach the end of the other long copper wire to the positive (+) terminal of the second battery. **Safety Alert: The ends of the wires are sharp. Handle them carefully.**

5. Use the short copper wire to connect the positive (+) terminal of the first battery to the negative (−) terminal of the second battery.

6. Put one end of each longer wire in the beaker so that the ends are about 4 cm to 5 cm apart, as shown.

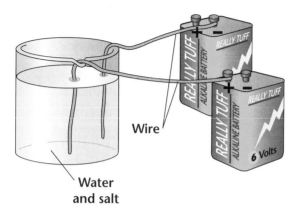

Wire

Water
and salt

6 Volts

7. Sprinkle a few grains of salt into the water. Stir with the stirring rod until the salt dissolves. Observe the ends of the wires in the water. Continue adding a few grains of salt to the water. Stir until the salt dissolves. When small bubbles appear at the wire ends, stop adding salt.

8. Observe the ends of both wires in the water for about 10 minutes. Record your observations in the table.

Questions and Conclusions

1. Which of the wires had more bubbles around it? Identify the wire by telling whether it was connected to the positive (+) terminal or the negative (−) terminal.

2. Describe what you observed at the end of each wire after 10 minutes.

3. The gas you observe comes from the water. The electricity from the batteries breaks down the water into hydrogen gas and oxygen gas. How does this production of gases show that water is a compound?

Explore Further

Bend the two wires in the beaker upward. Fill two test tubes with salt water. Hold your thumb over the top of one test tube and turn it upside down. Put the test tube in the water and remove your thumb. Place the test tube over a wire. Repeat with the other test tube. What happens in each of the test tubes?

Objectives

After reading this lesson, you should be able to

◆ describe what a model is and explain how scientists use it.

◆ explain how models of the atom have changed.

◆ describe the electron cloud model.

Model

A picture, an idea, or an object that is built to explain how something else looks or works

Since atoms are too small to be seen with the eyes alone, people have wondered for a long time what atoms look like. In fact, scientists have been studying atoms since the 1800s. But if scientists can't see an atom, how do they know what atoms look like?

Using Models

Sometimes scientists can tell what things look like by studying how they act. For example, have you ever seen wind? What does it look like? You might say that wind is leaves blowing or your hair getting messed up. If you say that you are describing what wind does, not what it looks like. You use the effects of wind to describe it. You know that wind is there because of its effects even though you can't see it. You use evidence.

Scientists use the same kind of evidence to study things they can't see, such as atoms. Scientists study how atoms act and then decide what an atom must look like. Scientists make **models.**

You have probably seen models of cars or airplanes or buildings. In science, a model is an idea, a picture, or an object that is built to explain how something else looks or works. The model may not look exactly like the object it is built to describe, but it helps people understand the way the object acts.

Models of Atoms

Nucleus

The central part of an atom

Proton

A tiny particle in the nucleus of an atom

Electron

A tiny particle of an atom that moves around the nucleus

Science Myth

An atom is solid.

Fact: Atoms are mostly empty space. Imagine an atom the size of a football field. What would you put in the center to model the size of the nucleus? A grapefruit? A grape? The nucleus would be the size of one grape seed. Between the grape and the outside diameter of the field would be emptiness.

Scientists use models of atoms to show how atoms look and act without having to actually see them. Many scientists have developed models of atoms. The first model was developed over 2,000 years ago. But as scientists gather new information about atoms, they change their models.

In the early 1900s, a scientist developed a model of an atom like those shown at the bottom of the page. Although scientists know more about atoms today, this kind of model is still useful for describing atoms.

Find the center of each atom. This central part of an atom is called a **nucleus.** The nucleus of an atom contains small particles called **protons.** Protons are labeled with the letter p. Another symbol for a proton is a plus ($+$) sign. Protons have a positive charge. Look for the letter e in the figures below. This letter stands for **electrons.** Electrons are particles in an atom that move around the outside of the protons. The mass of an electron is much less than the mass of a proton. Another symbol for an electron is a minus ($-$) sign. Electrons have a negative charge. The protons and electrons of an atom stay together because they attract each other.

Notice that the numbers of protons and electrons in the models are different. Figure A shows a model of an atom of hydrogen. You can see that hydrogen has one proton and one electron. Figure B shows an atom of helium, a gas that is often used to fill balloons. How many protons and electrons does helium have?

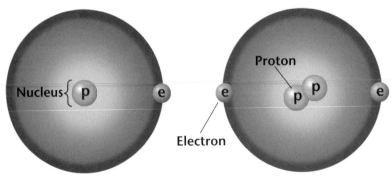

Figure A
An atom of hydrogen

Figure B
An atom of helium

In 1827, Robert Brown found the first sign that atoms exist. While studying pollen under a microscope, he noticed that particles were always moving. This *Brownian* motion comes from the movement of atoms and molecules.

In 1932, scientists had evidence that the nucleus of an atom had another kind of particle. This particle is called a **neutron**. It is similar to a proton in size. Because of the new evidence, scientists changed the model of the atom. In Figure C, an atom of boron shows how the model changed. Find the neutrons, labeled with the letter *n*.

You can see in Figure C that the electrons seem to be on certain paths around the nucleus of the atom. Scientists thought that electrons moved in different layers around protons, sometimes jumping from one layer to another.

Today scientists use another model of atoms. You can see this new model—the electron cloud model—in Figure D. The dark center area represents the nucleus. However, you can't see different layers of electrons like you see in the models in figures A, B, and C. The electron cloud model was developed because of evidence that electrons behave in more complicated ways than scientists previously thought. Because of this new evidence, scientists are not sure how electrons move around the nucleus. As scientists continue to learn more about atoms, perhaps the model will change again.

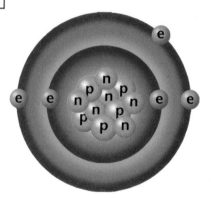

Figure C
An atom of boron

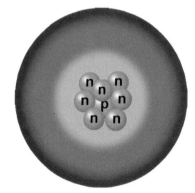

Figure D
Electron cloud model of an atom

In an electrically neutral atom, the number of protons equals the number of electrons. When an atom gains electrons or loses electrons, the charge becomes unbalanced.

You have looked at models showing the number of protons and electrons in the atoms of a few different elements. The table below lists some other elements and tells the numbers of protons and electrons in each. Find the number of protons in the element carbon. How many electrons does carbon have? Compare the numbers of protons and electrons in nitrogen. How many of each does it have? Now look at the numbers of protons and electrons in each of the elements listed. What do you notice? The number of protons in an atom is equal to the number of electrons in the atom.

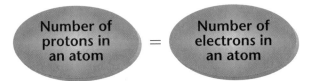

Number of Protons and Electrons for Some Elements		
Element	Number of Protons	Number of Electrons
hydrogen	1	1
helium	2	2
lithium	3	3
beryllium	4	4
boron	5	5
carbon	6	6
nitrogen	7	7
oxygen	8	8
fluorine	9	9
neon	10	10

Lesson 4   R E V I E W

Write your answers to these questions in complete sentences on a sheet of paper.

1. If scientists cannot see atoms, how do they know what they look like?

2. How do scientists use models?

3. How many protons are in the element shown in the figure?

4. How many electrons are in the element?

5. What is the name of the element? (Hint: Use the table on page 78.)

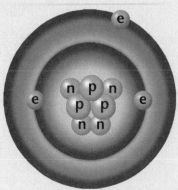

Achievements in Science

The History of the Atom Model

Democritus, a Greek philosopher, first used the term atom around 400 B.C. In 1803, English schoolteacher John Dalton showed that materials were made of atoms. Ideas about the atom have continued to change. Scientists, at different times in history, have thought about what an atom looks like. In recent years, scientists have done experiments to prove information about atoms.

Over the years, scientists discovered that atoms were made of smaller parts. They also created models for the atom. In the late 1800s, English physicist J. J. Thompson discovered the electron. He also suggested the "plum pudding" model of the atom. He imagined the electrons scattered inside an atom like bits of plum in plum pudding. Fourteen years later New Zealand physicist Ernest Rutherford disproved the plum pudding model. He showed that atoms have a nucleus in the center with electrons on the outside.

Later, Danish scientist Niels Bohr offered his planetary model of the atom. It was based on speculation that seemed to be supported by experiments. Later, however, mathematical calculations led to the electron cloud model.

INVESTIGATION

3-2

Making Models of Atoms

Materials

- safety glasses
- 3 different colored pieces of modeling clay
- craft sticks
- metric ruler

Purpose

What three things must every atom have? You will make a model of an atom of a particular element in this investigation.

Procedure

1. Copy the data table on a sheet of paper.

Name of Element:	
Picture of Element:	

2. Put on your safety glasses.

3. Choose an element from the table on page 78. Find the numbers of protons, neutrons, and electrons in your element.

4. Place three different colors of modeling clay on your desk. Choose one color of clay for protons. Pull off a small piece of clay for each of the protons in your element. Roll each piece into a ball about 1 cm in diameter.

5. Use another color of clay for neutrons. Make clay balls the same size as the protons. Be sure to make the same number of balls as there are neutrons in your element.

6. With the third color of clay, make smaller clay balls to represent electrons. Make the same number of balls as the protons you made.

7. Press the protons and neutrons together gently to make the nucleus of your model atom.

8. Gently put the craft sticks into the nucleus of your model. Put the same number of sticks as there are electrons in your element.

9. Place the clay electrons on the ends of the craft sticks.

10. Write the name of the element in your table. Then draw a picture of your model.

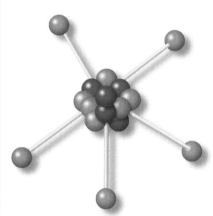

Questions and Conclusions

1. What is the name of your element?

2. How many protons are in the nucleus?

3. How many neutrons does it have?

4. How many electrons does your element have?

5. Write at least four things that your model shows about atoms.

Explore Further

Work with other students who have made models of different atoms. Find the mass number of each atom. The mass number is a number equal to the sum of the number of protons and neutrons in an atom. (You will learn more about mass number in the next lesson.) Put the atoms in order from lowest to highest mass number. What happens to the number of protons and neutrons as mass number increases?

Lesson 5 Identifying Elements

Objectives

After reading this lesson, you should be able to

◆ explain what the atomic number of an element is.

◆ explain how the mass number of an element is determined.

Atomic number

A number equal to the number of protons in the nucleus of an atom

Did You Know?

All atoms are recycled. You constantly breathe atoms in and out of your body. Some atoms stay in your body for a while. Then they move on to become part of someone or something else.

Because more than 100 elements are known, scientists need a way to identify them. One way scientists can identify elements is by knowing their **atomic numbers.**

Atomic Number

The table below shows the same 10 elements listed in the table on page 78. However, a column labeled Atomic Number has been added to the table. The atomic number of an element tells the number of protons in each atom of the element.

Some Elements and Their Atomic Numbers			
Element	Atomic Number	Number of Protons	Number of Electrons
hydrogen	1	1	1
helium	2	2	2
lithium	3	3	3
beryllium	4	4	4
boron	5	5	5
carbon	6	6	6
nitrogen	7	7	7
oxygen	8	8	8
fluorine	9	9	9
neon	10	10	10

Notice that each element has a different number of protons, and therefore a different atomic number. For example, the element hydrogen has one proton. Its atomic number is also one. According to the table, how many protons does boron have? What is the atomic number of boron? For all the elements, the atomic number of the element is equal to the number of protons it has.

$$ \text{Atomic number} = \text{Number of protons} $$

Mass number

A number equal to the sum of the numbers of protons and neutrons in an atom of an element

Did You Know?

Hydrogen and helium are the two lightest elements. They exist in great quantities in the universe. Stars are composed mostly of these two elements.

The Mass of an Element

You learned in Chapter 1 that mass is the amount of matter in an object. Protons and neutrons have a greater mass than electrons have. In fact, the mass of a proton or a neutron is about 1,800 times the mass of an electron. Yet protons and neutrons are still so small that it would not be possible to measure their mass on a balance scale. Instead, scientists tell about the mass of an element by using its **mass number.** The mass number of an element is equal to the sum of the numbers of protons and neutrons in an atom of the element.

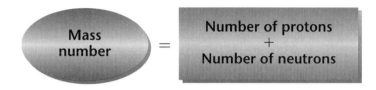

The figure shows an atom of beryllium. You can see that it has 4 protons and 5 neutrons. The atomic number of beryllium is 4, the same as the number of protons. To determine the mass number of beryllium, add the number of protons, 4, and the number of neutrons, 5. The mass number of beryllium is 9 ($4 + 5 = 9$).

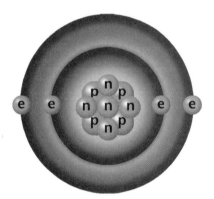

An atom of beryllium

You have learned about protons, neutrons, and electrons. You also have learned about atomic numbers and mass numbers of elements. The table below gives a summary of information for the first 10 elements.

The First 10 Elements					
Element	Atomic Number	Mass Number	Number of Protons	Number of Electrons	Number of Neutrons
hydrogen	1	1	1	1	0
helium	2	4	2	2	2
lithium	3	7	3	3	4
beryllium	4	9	4	4	5
boron	5	11	5	5	6
carbon	6	12	6	6	6
nitrogen	7	14	7	7	7
oxygen	8	16	8	8	8
fluorine	9	19	9	9	10
neon	10	20	10	10	10

Remember that you can use information you know about an element to determine other information. For example, look at this figure of an atom of sodium. Find the numbers of protons and neutrons. How many protons are in the nucleus? You know that the number of electrons in an element is equal to its number of protons. How many electrons does sodium have? You also know that the atomic number of an element is equal to the number of protons it has. What is the atomic number of the element sodium?

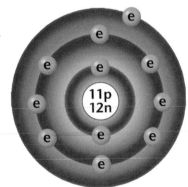

An atom of sodium

Antimatter particles can be made in laboratories. Some antimatter particles are antielectrons and antiprotons. Antiprotons and protons are exactly the same, except their charges are opposite. This is also true for antielectrons and electrons.

Technology Note

Particle accelerators make protons or electrons move very fast and collide with targets. These collisions create new types of particles. Accelerators let physicists see what's inside particles. You have a particle accelerator at home. A TV works like a particle accelerator, only on a much smaller scale.

The box below shows the relationships between the mass number of an element and the numbers of protons and neutrons it has. Notice that Relationship 1 explains how to find the mass number of an element. Simply add the number of protons and neutrons it has in its nucleus.

Relationship 1:	Mass number	=	Number of protons	+	Number of neutrons
Relationship 2:	Number of neutrons	=	Mass number	−	Number of protons
Relationship 3:	Number of protons	=	Mass number	−	Number of neutrons

Suppose you know the mass number of an element and the number of protons it has. Can you determine the number of neutrons it has? Find Relationship 2 in the box. This relationship explains how you can use the information you know to find the number of neutrons in the nucleus of an atom.

Finally, suppose you know the mass number of an element and its number of neutrons. For example, the element aluminum has a mass number of 27. You can see in the figure that aluminum has 14 neutrons in its nucleus. You can use Relationship 3 to determine the number of protons it has. How many protons are in the nucleus of the element aluminum?

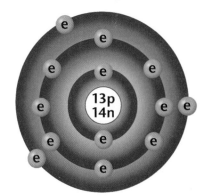

An atom of aluminum

Lesson 5   R E V I E W

Write your answers to these questions in complete sentences on a sheet of paper.

1. An element has an atomic number of 33. How many protons does it have?

2. An element has 26 protons. What is its atomic number?

3. An element has 6 protons and a mass number of 12. How many neutrons does it have?

4. Copy the table on your paper. Then fill in the missing numbers.

Element	Atomic Number	Number of Protons	Number of Electrons
sodium	11		
aluminum			13
chlorine		17	
calcium			20

5. Copy the table on your paper. Then fill in the missing numbers. You can refer to the three relationships on page 85 for help. The first one is done for you.

Element	Atomic Number	Mass Number	Number of Protons	Number of Electrons	Number of Neutrons
carbon	6	12	6	6	6
silver		108	47		
silicon				14	14
calcium	20	40			
iodine	53	127			
chlorine	17				18
sulfur		32		16	
potassium		39	19		

Chapter 3   SUMMARY

- A molecule is the smallest particle of a substance that still has the same properties of the substance.

- An atom is the basic building block of matter.

- Scientists use models to explain things they cannot see.

- Molecules move in different ways in each of the three states of matter—solids, liquids, and gases.

- An element is matter that is made of only one kind of atom. There are 92 natural elements, which are found in nature.

- A compound is formed from two or more atoms of different elements. A compound has properties that are different from the elements that form the compound.

- An atom is made of protons, neutrons, and electrons.

- The number of protons in an atom is equal to the number of electrons.

- The atomic number of an element is equal to the number of protons in its nucleus.

- The mass number of an element is equal to the number of protons plus the number of neutrons.

Science Words

atom, 61	liquid, 62	nucleus, 76
atomic number, 82	mass number, 83	plasma, 63
compound, 70	model, 75	proton, 76
electron, 76	molecule, 60	solid, 62
element, 65	natural element, 66	state of matter, 63
gas, 63	neutron, 77	

Chapter 3   R E V I E W

Word Bank

atom

compound

element

gas

liquid

molecule

natural element

nucleus

plasma

solid

Vocabulary Review

Choose a word or words from the Word Bank that best complete each sentence. Write the answers on a sheet of paper.

1. A(n) _____ is the smallest particle of a substance that can still have the properties of the substance.

2. A form of matter with definite volume but no definite shape is a(n) _____.

3. A form of matter with no definite shape or volume is a(n) _____.

4. A form of matter with definite shape and volume is a _____.

5. A very hot gas made of particles with an electric charge is _____.

6. Matter that has only one kind of atom is a(n) _____.

7. The _____ is the building block of matter.

8. A(n) _____ is the central part of an atom.

9. A(n) _____ is found in nature.

10. A(n) _____ is a substance that is formed when atoms of two or more elements join together.

Concept Review

Choose the answer that best completes each sentence. Write the letter of the answer on your paper.

11. The states of matter are _____.
  A solid, liquid, gas, and plasma
  B elements and natural elements
  C atom, molecule, and compound
  D electrons, protons, and neutrons

12. Models of atoms help describe their _____, although they cannot be seen.
  A mass   **C** appearance and actions
  B state of matter   **D** volume

13. The particles of _____ shake violently at very high temperatures.

    A solid   **B** liquid   **C** gas   **D** plasma

14. Of the following, _____ is not a compound.

    A water   **C** sodium chloride

    B oxygen   **D** magnesium oxide

15. The particles in an atom are _____.

    A compounds   **C** molecules

    B natural elements   **D** electrons, protons, and neutrons

16. An element's atomic number is the same as the number of _____ it has.

    A electrons   **B** protons   **C** neutrons   **D** nuclei

17. If an element has 4 protons and 5 neutrons, its mass number is _____.

    A 1   **B** 4   **C** 9   **D** 20

Critical Thinking

Write the answer to each of these questions on your paper.

18. How is the movement of a molecule's particles different when it is a solid, a gas, and a liquid?

19. Does the figure at the right show a molecule or an atom? Explain your answer.

20. Look at the figure at the left. Then answer these questions. How many protons and neutrons does the atom have? How many electrons? What is the element's atomic number? What is the mass number?

Test-Taking Tip   To remember facts and definitions more easily, write them down on index cards. Practice with a partner using the flash cards.

4

Classifying Elements

Y ou might recognize the substance in the photograph as crystals of native gold. When gold is mined, it looks like these crystals. Gold has many uses. We use gold in spacecrafts and satellites, in medical research and treatment, and in electronics. We can find it in computers, telephones, and home appliances. Why is gold so useful? Gold carries heat and electricity very well. It is shiny, and its shape can be changed. These are the properties of an element that is a metal. In Chapter 4, you will learn what an element is and how elements are classified.

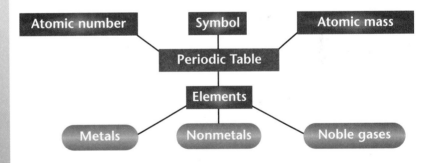

Organize Your Thoughts

Atomic number

Symbol

Atomic mass

Periodic Table

Elements

Metals

Nonmetals

Noble gases

Goals for Learning

◆ To identify the symbols used to represent different elements

◆ To explain how elements are organized in the periodic table

◆ To describe the kinds of information in the periodic table

◆ To classify elements as metals, nonmetals, or noble gases

After reading this lesson, you should be able to

◆ explain what a symbol is.

◆ explain how element symbols are alike and different.

◆ identify symbols for common elements.

Think about addressing an envelope for a letter you write to a friend. You probably use an abbreviation to indicate the state to which the letter should be delivered. What is the abbreviation for your state?

Element Symbols

Scientists also use abbreviations to represent each of the 92 natural elements. The abbreviations for elements are called **symbols.** The tables on this page and page 93 list some symbols for elements. All these symbols are alike in the following ways.

◆ All of the symbols have either one or two letters.

◆ The first letter of each symbol is a capital letter.

◆ If the symbol has a second letter, the second letter is a lowercase letter.

◆ No period appears at the end of a symbol.

Symbol
One or two letters that represent the name of an element

Table 1	
Element Name	**Element Symbol**
hydrogen	H
boron	B
carbon	C
nitrogen	N
oxygen	O
fluorine	F
phosphorus	P
sulfur	S
iodine	I
uranium	U

Table 2	
Element Name	**Element Symbol**
helium	He
lithium	Li
neon	Ne
aluminum	Al
silicon	Si
argon	Ar
calcium	Ca
cobalt	Co
bromine	Br
barium	Ba
radium	Ra

Notice that the symbols in Table 1 on page 92 use only the first letter of the element name. Look at the symbols in Table 2. This group of symbols uses the first two letters of the element name. The symbols in Table 3 also use two letters. The first letter is the first letter of the element name. The second letter is another letter from the element name.

How do the symbols in Table 4 differ from the other symbols? Most of these symbols come from the Latin names for the elements. For example, the symbol for iron is Fe, which comes from the Latin word *ferrum,* meaning "iron."

In recent years, scientists have made new elements in the laboratory. Some of these elements have symbols with three letters. You can see the symbols for these elements in the table on pages 100 and 101.

Table 3	
Element Name	Element Symbol
magnesium	Mg
chlorine	Cl
chromium	Cr
manganese	Mn
plutonium	Pu
zinc	Zn
strontium	Sr
platinum	Pt

Table 4	
Element Name	Element Symbol
sodium	Na
potassium	K
iron	Fe
silver	Ag
tin	Sn
tungsten	W
gold	Au
mercury	Hg
lead	Pb
antimony	Sb
copper	Cu

Lesson 1 REVIEW

Write your answers to these questions in complete sentences on a sheet of paper.

1. How are all of the element symbols alike?

2. Write the symbol for each of the following elements.
   A helium   **B** silver   **C** carbon   **D** chlorine   **E** calcium

3. Write the element name for each of the following symbols.
   A Hg   **B** Ne   **C** Mn   **D** O   **E** P

4. How are abbreviations and symbols alike?

5. Why is Fe the symbol for iron?

▼◀▲▼◀▲▼◀▲▼◀▲▼◀▲▼◀▲▼◀▲▼◀▲▼◀▲▼◀▲▼◀▲▼◀▲▼◀▲▼◀▲▼◀▲▼

Science at Work

Assayer

Assayers are laboratory technicians who analyze samples of precious metals. Assayers collect and analyze rocks and separate metals from them. Using chemical processes or experiments, an assayer collects information about these metals. This information includes how much and what kind of metals are in the samples.

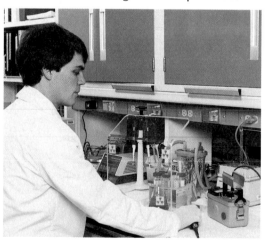

An assayer must complete a two- to three-year technical program or earn a four-year degree in science.

An assayer must be interested in precious metals and be able to keep track of details. An assayer also must be able to work in a laboratory or at a mine site. Good math, decision-making, and communication skills are very important in an assayer's work.

4-1 INVESTIGATION

Finding Iron in Your Cereal

Materials
- safety glasses
- iron-fortified cereal (flakes)
- self-sealing sandwich bag
- 250-mL beaker
- warm water
- rubber band
- bar magnet
- craft stick
- white paper
- hand lens

Purpose

Do you think that iron-fortified cereal contains real bits of iron? In this investigation, you will observe bits of iron in an iron-fortified cereal.

Procedure

1. Copy the data table on a sheet of paper.

Procedure Step	Observations
7	
8	
9	

2. Put on your safety glasses.

3. Place about a handful of iron-fortified cereal into the sandwich bag and seal the bag. Crush the cereal into a fine powder.

4. Place the cereal in the beaker. Add just enough water to cover the cereal.

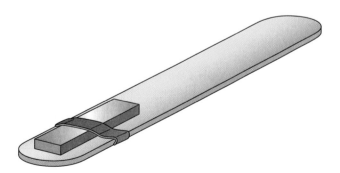

5. Use the rubber band to attach the bar magnet to the craft stick.

6. Use the magnet end of the stick to stir the cereal-water mixture for about 3 minutes. Allow the magnet to stay in the mixture for about 10 minutes. Then stir again.

7. Remove the stick and the magnet from the mixture and hold them over a sheet of white paper.

8. Use a hand lens to look at the end of the magnet. Write your observations in the data table.

9. Wipe the end of the magnet on the white paper. Use a hand lens to look at any bits that are on the paper. Write your observations in the data table.

10. Use the magnet to try to pick up bits from the paper. Record your observations.

Questions and Conclusions

1. What did you observe on the end of the magnet?

2. What did you observe on the white paper?

3. Were the bits on the white paper attracted to the magnet?

4. What element from the cereal did you see?

Explore Further

Why might iron be added to cereal? Use an encyclopedia or other reference source to find out.

Objectives

After reading this lesson, you should be able to

◆ explain how elements are arranged in the periodic table.

◆ explain the information contained in each box in the periodic table.

◆ explain what an isotope is.

◆ explain how elements in the periodic table are grouped in columns.

Periodic table

An arrangement of elements by increasing atomic number

Remember that the atomic number of an element tells you the number of protons in its nucleus.

For many years, scientists noticed that some elements were similar to others. In the mid-1800s, a Russian scientist named Dmitri Mendeleev designed the first chart that showed some of the similarities among the elements.

How Elements Are Arranged

Mendeleev began by making cards for each element known at that time. Then he organized the elements in order of increasing mass. He placed hydrogen, the lightest element, first. Mendeleev then used the cards to construct a table with rows and columns that organized the elements according to their properties. The cards formed the first **periodic table.**

Mendeleev left blank spaces in his table where he thought an element should fit—even for elements that he didn't know existed. When these elements were later discovered, his unknown elements were found to be in the correct spaces in the table.

The form of Mendeleev's table changed over the years as scientists learned more about atoms. Scientists found that an element's properties are related more closely to its atomic number than to its mass. The periodic table used today is an orderly arrangement of all known elements. The elements are arranged according to their atomic number.

Look at the periodic table shown on pages 100 and 101. Notice that elements are arranged from left to right in rows by increasing atomic number. The two separate rows at the bottom of the page are too long to fit into the drawing. Arrows show where the rows belong.

Information in the Periodic Table

You can use the periodic table on pages 100 and 101 to learn more about the elements. Each box in the periodic table contains information about one element. The figure below shows the box from the periodic table for the element hydrogen. The symbol for hydrogen, H, is shown in the center of the box. Below the symbol, you can see the name of the element hydrogen.

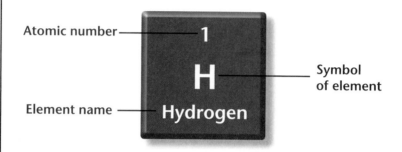

You already learned that the atomic number for hydrogen is 1. Find the atomic number in the box. You can see that the atomic number is shown above the symbol for the element.

The position of an element in the periodic table can tell you many properties of the element. The properties of elements change gradually as you move from left to right across the rows of the table. The properties change because the number of electrons that an atom of an element has increases as you move from left to right. Electrons move around the nucleus of an atom. The number of electrons that surround the nucleus of an atom determines the element's properties. Later in this chapter, you will learn how to determine some properties of an element from its position in the periodic table.

Isotopes

Remember that all atoms of one element have the same atomic number. The atomic number tells the number of protons in the nucleus. However, different atoms of one element may have different masses. The reason for this is that almost every element can be found in slightly different forms. These forms are called **isotopes.** An isotope has the same number of protons and electrons as the original element, but has a different number of neutrons in the nucleus.

The figures below show three isotopes of hydrogen. The first figure shows the most common isotope of hydrogen (H-1). This isotope has one proton and no neutrons. The second figure shows **deuterium** (H-2). Deuterium is an isotope of hydrogen that has one proton and one neutron. The third figure shows **tritium** (H-3). Tritium is an isotope of hydrogen that has one proton and two neutrons. Tritium does not occur naturally on Earth. It is made in a laboratory. Remember that each isotope of hydrogen has the same number of protons and therefore the same atomic number. The labels H-1, H-2, and H-3 refer to the atomic mass of the hydrogen isotopes.

Isotopes have many uses. Scientists use isotopes to follow the path of certain substances in living things. Radioactive isotopes emit particles or rays that can be used to find problems with organs in the human body. Another use of isotopes is to find cracks in underground plumbing pipes.

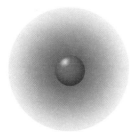

Hydrogen (H-1)
One proton

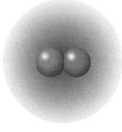

Deuterium (H-2)
One proton and
one neutron

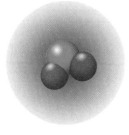

Tritium (H-3)
One proton and
two neutrons

The Periodic Table

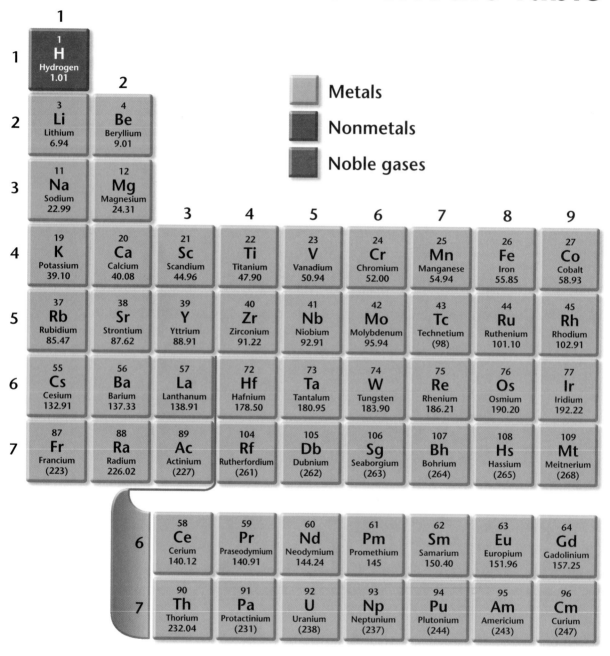

Metals

Nonmetals

Noble gases

# of Elements

								18
								2 **He** Helium 4.00

		13	**14**	**15**	**16**	**17**	
		5 **B** Boron 10.81	6 **C** Carbon 12.01	7 **N** Nitrogen 14.01	8 **O** Oxygen 16.00	9 **F** Fluorine 19.00	10 **Ne** Neon 20.18

10	**11**	**12**	13 **Al** Aluminum 26.98	14 **Si** Silicon 28.09	15 **P** Phosphorus 30.97	16 **S** Sulfur 32.07	17 **Cl** Chlorine 35.45	18 **Ar** Argon 39.95
28 **Ni** Nickel 58.70	29 **Cu** Copper 63.55	30 **Zn** Zinc 65.39	31 **Ga** Gallium 69.72	32 **Ge** Germanium 72.59	33 **As** Arsenic 74.92	34 **Se** Selenium 78.96	35 **Br** Bromine 79.90	36 **Kr** Krypton 83.80
46 **Pd** Palladium 106.42	47 **Ag** Silver 107.90	48 **Cd** Cadmium 112.41	49 **In** Indium 114.82	50 **Sn** Tin 118.69	51 **Sb** Antimony 121.75	52 **Te** Tellurium 127.60	53 **I** Iodine 126.90	54 **Xe** Xenon 131.30
78 **Pt** Platinum 195.09	79 **Au** Gold 196.97	80 **Hg** Mercury 200.59	81 **Tl** Thallium 204.40	82 **Pb** Lead 207.20	83 **Bi** Bismuth 208.98	84 **Po** Polonium 209	85 **At** Astatine (210)	86 **Rn** Radon (222)
110 **Uun** Ununnilium (269)	111 **Uuu** Unununium (272)	112 **Uub** Ununbium (277)		114 **Uuq** Ununquadium (289)		116 **Uuh** Ununhexium (289)		

65 **Tb** Terbium 158.93	66 **Dy** Dysprosium 162.50	67 **Ho** Holmium 164.93	68 **Er** Erbium 167.26	69 **Tm** Thulium 168.93	70 **Yb** Ytterbium 173.04	71 **Lu** Lutetium 174.97
97 **Bk** Berkelium (247)	98 **Cf** Californium (249)	99 **Es** Einsteinium (254)	100 **Fm** Fermium (257)	101 **Md** Mendelevium (258)	102 **No** Nobelium (259)	103 **Lr** Lawrencium (260)

Note: *The atomic masses listed in the table reflect current measurements.*
The atomic masses listed in parentheses are those of the element's most stable or most common isotope.

Sometimes an atom's nucleus is unstable. Radioactivity results from the decay of an atom with an unstable nucleus. A radioactive atom sends out small particles and gamma rays. Isotopes that are radioactive are called radioisotopes.

Atomic Mass

An element's mass number is the sum of its numbers of protons and neutrons. The sum of the numbers of protons and neutrons is different for hydrogen, deuterium, and tritium. Therefore, each isotope of hydrogen has a different mass number. What is the mass number of each isotope?

Isotopes of most elements do not have names and are identified by their atomic mass. For example, carbon has three isotopes. The most common isotope has a mass number of 12 because it has 6 protons and 6 neutrons. This isotope is called carbon-12. Another isotope of carbon is carbon-13, which has 6 protons and 7 neutrons. Carbon-14 has 6 protons and 8 neutrons.

Look at the box for hydrogen shown below. How does it differ from the box shown on page 98? An additional number appears at the bottom of the box. Notice that the number is not a whole number. This number is the element's **atomic mass,** the average mass for all the isotopes of the element. The average mass is determined by the masses of an element's isotopes and by the amount of each isotope found in nature.

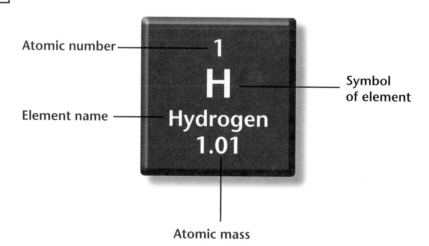

Atomic number

Symbol of element

Element name

1

H

Hydrogen

1.01

Atomic mass

Columns in the Periodic Table

Look at the periodic table shown on pages 100 and 101. The
elements in the periodic table are arranged across in order of
increasing atomic numbers. You can also read the periodic table
another way—in columns from top to bottom.

Elements that are together in a column are said to be in the
same **family.** These elements have similar properties. In other
words, elements in the same family usually react with other
kinds of matter in the same way.

Part of the first column from the periodic table is shown on this
page. It shows the elements lithium, sodium, and potassium.
Now find these three elements in the first column, or Group 1
column, of the periodic table on pages 100 and 101. The elements
in Group 1, with the exception of hydrogen, are solids at room
temperature. They are soft, shiny, and silvery. These elements react
strongly when combined with water, exploding and releasing large
amounts of heat.

Now look at the elements in Group 2, or column 2, of the periodic
table. The elements in this family are found in minerals in the
earth. Magnesium and calcium are the most common elements
in this group.

Family

*A group of elements
with similar properties,
arranged together
in a column of the
periodic table*

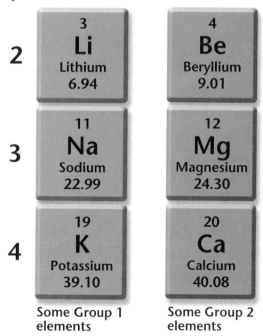

Some Group 1 elements   Some Group 2 elements

Look for other families in the periodic table. Fluorine and chlorine—both in Group 17—are poisonous gases. Helium, neon, and argon—elements in Group 18—are all gases that do not usually combine with any other kinds of matter. You will read more about this group of elements in Lesson 3.

As you read the rest of this chapter, continue to refer to the periodic table on pages 100 and 101. You will learn how the periodic table can give you even more information about different elements.

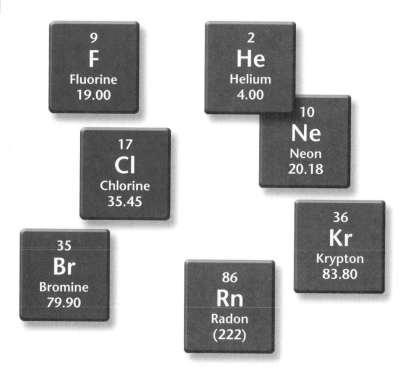

Write your answers to these questions in complete sentences on a sheet of paper.

1. How are the elements arranged in the periodic table?

2. Draw the box from the periodic table for hydrogen. Include the symbol for hydrogen as well as its atomic number and atomic mass. Write an explanation of each piece of information in the box.

3. Write a paragraph explaining how elements are grouped in columns in the periodic table.

4. How do elements in the same family usually react?

5. List one family of elements in the periodic table.

Achievements in Science

Bronze, an Ancient Alloy

Bronze is the oldest known alloy. People learned to make bronze in about 3500 B.C. The bronze that they made at that time contained copper (Cu) and arsenic (As). Gradually, tin (Sn) replaced arsenic in the alloy. Historians are not sure how people learned to smelt copper with arsenic to make bronze. Some believe that it may have been an accidental discovery.

Bronze played an important role in the lives of early people. Indeed, the period between the Stone Age and Iron Age is called the Bronze Age. People of that time used bronze to make many different items. At first, they used it mainly to make weapons and cutting tools. Later, they also made bowls, cups, and vases from bronze.

Bronze is very hard. It is harder and stronger than any other alloy except steel. It does not rust or wear away. We still use bronze today. You can find it in doorknobs and drawer handles. It is in engine parts and bearings. Many bells also are made from bronze.

You have learned about some ways the periodic table provides information about elements. An element's position in the table also indicates whether the element is a metal, a nonmetal, or a noble gas. As you read this lesson, you will find out about each of these three groups.

Metals

Look again at the periodic table on pages 100 and 101. Find the zigzag line near the right side of the chart. Find the elements shown in the green boxes to the left of the zigzag line. These elements are **metals,** a group of elements that share certain properties.

Metal

One of a group of elements that is usually solid at room temperature, often shiny, and carries heat and electricity well

Properties of Metals

◆ Most metals are solid at room temperature. Mercury is the only liquid metal.

◆ Most metals can be polished to look shiny.

◆ The shape of a metal can be changed. For example, aluminum can be pounded into a thin foil without breaking. Copper is often stretched into very thin wires.

◆ Electricity and heat travel well through metals.

Did You Know?

Mercury (Hg) is very poisonous and can cause illness and even death. Until the 1900s, hat makers used mercury when working with felt. This caused mercury poisoning, which was called "mad hatter's disease."

These items illustrate the properties of metals.

Alloy

A mixture of two or more metals

Nonmetal

One of a group of elements with properties unlike those of metals

Carbon, a nonmetal, plays a central role in the chemistry of living organisms.

Notice that hydrogen is the only element on the left side of the periodic table that is not considered a metal. As you can see, about 80 percent of all the elements are metals.

Alloys

Heat can be used to change metals into liquids. Melted metals can be combined with other metals. The mixture is cooled until it hardens. In this way an **alloy,** or mixture of metals, is formed. Alloys have a combination of the properties of the different metals. The table on this page lists some common alloys, the metals that can be combined to form them, and some of their uses.

Metal Alloys		
Alloy	**Made from**	**Used for**
alnico	aluminum (Al), nickel (Ni), cobalt (Co), iron (Fe), copper (Cu)	magnets
brass	copper (Cu), zinc (Zn)	plumbing fixtures, musical instruments, artwork
bronze	copper (Cu), tin (Sn)	coins, artwork
pewter	copper (Cu), lead (Pb), antimony (Sb), tin (Sn)	trays, pitchers, vases
solder	lead (Pb), tin (Sn)	electrical connections, plumbing connections
stainless steel	iron (Fe), chromium (Cr), nickel (Ni)	eating utensils, kitchen equipment, surgical equipment

Nonmetals

Look again at the periodic table on pages 100 and 101. Find the elements in blue boxes on the right side of the table. These elements are called **nonmetals**. They do not have the properties of metals.

Most nonmetals are solids or gases at room temperature. Sulfur and carbon are examples of solid nonmetals. You probably know about some of the nonmetal elements that are gases, such as oxygen and nitrogen.

Bromine is the only nonmetal that is a liquid at room temperature.

Notice on the pie chart below that these two gases make up most of the air. Bromine is the only nonmetal that is liquid at room temperature.

Many metals look somewhat similar. Nonmetals, however, can look very different from one another. For example, oxygen is a colorless gas, while sulfur is a yellow solid.

You can see that nonmetals do not have many properties in common. In fact, the only thing that many nonmetals have in common is that they are not metals. Nonmetals are not shiny. They cannot be pounded into thin sheets or stretched into wires. Except for some forms of carbon and silicon, nonmetals do not carry electricity or heat well. You will learn more about some nonmetals from the Science in Your Life feature on page 110.

Gases in air

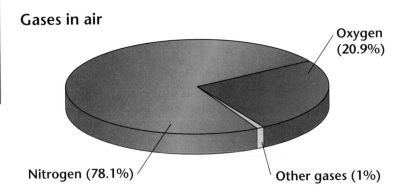

Oxygen (20.9%)

Nitrogen (78.1%)

Other gases (1%)

A few elements have some properties of both metals and nonmetals. These elements include silicon, germanium, boron, arsenic, antimony, tellurium, and polonium. You can find these elements in the periodic table next to the zigzag line that separates metals from nonmetals.

When some of these elements are combined with other materials, their ability to carry electricity is increased. This ability makes elements such as silicon useful for electronic devices like computers.

Noble Gases

The six elements listed in the last column of the periodic table are called the **noble gases**. These gases are **inert,** or inactive. They do not react or combine with any other elements under ordinary conditions. Look at Group 18 in the periodic table on pages 100 and 101 to find the names of all the noble gases.

Neon is one noble gas that may be familiar to you. Neon is a gas used for lights such as those in the sign shown in the photo. The neon is sealed in tubes. When electricity passes through the gas, neon gives off colored light.

Technology Note

Except for radon (Rn), all the noble gases are used in lighting. These gases are usually colorless. When an electrical charge passes through them, they glow.

Neon gas makes this sign glow.

Achievements in Science

Helium

Helium (He), a noble gas, is one of the most common elements in the universe. Only hydrogen (H) is more common. Stars are made mostly of helium and hydrogen. Yet helium is very rare on earth.

Helium was first discovered on the sun. Pierre Janssen of France found evidence of helium while studying a solar eclipse in 1868. Helium's name comes from the Greek word *helios,* which means sun.

Chemists discovered helium on earth in 1895. Sir William Ramsay, Nils Langlet, and Per Theodor Cleve found helium in a mineral.

In 1905, Hamilton P. Cady and David E. McFarland made an important discovery about helium. They found that it could be taken out of natural gas wells. Their discovery led to greater use of helium in industry. Helium is largely used in welding. We also use helium to fill different kinds of balloons.

Write your answers to these questions in complete sentences on a sheet of paper.

1. Describe the properties of metals.

2. Explain what a nonmetal is and give some examples of nonmetals.

3. What one thing do nonmetals have in common?

4. Explain what a noble gas is.

5. List three metal alloys and one use for each one.

Science in Your Life

Which objects contain nonmetals?

Look around your classroom. Many of the objects you see contain nonmetal elements. For example, a desk or a chair made of wood contains carbon. Now think of other objects in the world around you, such as objects in your home. You might be surprised to learn how many of them contain nonmetals. The table below lists a few nonmetal elements and some of their uses.

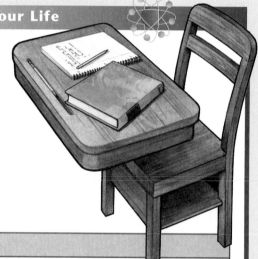

Name and Symbol	Some Uses
carbon, C	pencils, fabrics, cleaning agents, fuel, tires
chlorine, Cl	water purification, bleaching, plastics, dyes, refrigerator coolant
fluorine, Fl	etching glass, refrigerator coolant, toothpaste additive, non-stick coating for pots
iodine, I	ink pigments, disinfectants, halogen lights, ingredient in iodized salt
nitrogen, N	fertilizers, present in air
oxygen, O	present in air, needed for breathing, medical treatments, steelmaking, propellants
sulfur, S	medicines, matches, rubber, dyes, fungicides, cements

Electricity and Metals

Purpose

Do copper wire, sulfur, and aluminum all conduct electricity? In this investigation, you will identify materials that conduct electricity.

Procedure

1. Copy the data table on a sheet of paper.

Materials	Observations
copper wires	
sulfur	
aluminum	
graphite (pencil lead)	

2. Put on your safety glasses.

3. Use sandpaper to remove 3 cm of the insulated coating from each end of the copper wires. **Safety Alert: The ends of the wire can be sharp. Handle them carefully.**

4. Make a loop at the ends of each wire.

5. Using electrical tape, fasten a loop from one wire to the flat end of the battery.

6. Fasten the other loop of the wire to the lightbulb socket.

7. Tape a loop from the second wire to the other end of the battery.

Materials

- safety glasses
- sandpaper
- 3 pieces of copper wire, each 0.25 m long
- electrical tape
- 1.5-volt D-cell battery
- standard bulb in socket
- sample of sulfur
- piece of aluminum foil, about 5 cm long
- lead pencil

8. Fasten a loop of the third wire to the other side of the lightbulb socket. Your circuit should look like the one in the diagram.

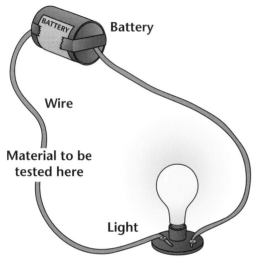

9. Hold the two unattached loops of copper wire together. Record your observations in the table.

10. Hold the sample of sulfur between the two unattached loops of wire. Record your observations.

11. Repeat step 10 with the sample of aluminum.

Questions and Conclusions

1. What happened to the lightbulb when you held the copper wires together?

2. What happened to the lightbulb when you held the samples of sulfur and aluminum between the wires?

3. What did you observe about the ability of copper, sulfur, and aluminum to conduct electricity?

4. Which materials do you think are metals? Explain your answer.

Explore Further

Pick up the pencil and hold it so the pencil lead is between the two unattached loops of wire. What happens? Can the pencil lead conduct electricity? Record your observations. Is the lead in the pencil a metal? Explain your answer.

Chapter 4 SUMMARY

- Each element has a symbol, an abbreviation for its name.

- All known elements are arranged in the periodic table in order of increasing atomic number.

- Information contained in the periodic table about an element includes its name, its symbol, its atomic number, and its atomic mass.

- Almost every element has isotopes, which are different forms of the same element.

- An isotope of an element has the same numbers of protons and electrons as the original element; however, an isotope has a different number of neutrons.

- The atomic mass of an element is an average mass of the various isotopes of the element that exist in nature.

- Elements that have similar properties and are together in a column of the periodic table are in the same family.

- Elements are classified as metals, nonmetals, or noble gases.

- Most metals are solids at room temperature and can be polished. The shape of a metal can be changed. Electricity and heat travel well through metals.

- Metals can be melted and mixed with other metals to form alloys.

- Nonmetals have properties that are different from those of metals. Most nonmetals are solids or gases at room temperature. Most nonmetals have the opposite properties of metals.

- Noble gases are called inert because they do not ordinarily react or combine with other elements.

Science Words

alloy, 107	inert, 109	nonmetal, 107
atomic mass, 102	isotope, 99	periodic table, 97
deuterium, 99	metal, 106	symbol, 92
family, 103	noble gas, 109	tritium, 99

Chapter 4 REVIEW

Word Bank

alloy

atomic mass

inert

isotope

metal

noble gas

periodic table

Vocabulary Review

Choose the word or words from the Word Bank that best complete each sentence. Write the answer on a sheet of paper.

1. The average mass of all of an element's isotopes is its _____.

2. The _____ is an arrangement of the elements by increasing atomic number.

3. Gases that are _____ do not react or combine with other elements under ordinary conditions.

4. An element that is usually solid at room temperature, often shiny, and carries heat well is a(n) _____.

5. A(n) _____ does not combine with other materials under ordinary conditions.

6. A mixture of two or more metals is a(n) _____.

7. A(n) _____ has the same number of protons and electrons but a different number of neutrons.

Concept Review

Match each element in Column A with the correct symbol in Column B. Write the symbol on your paper.

Column A	Column B
____ 8. aluminum	A K
____ 9. chlorine	B Ne
____ 10. gold	C Al
____ 11. potassium	D Na
____ 12. sodium	E Cl
____ 13. neon	F Au

Choose the answer that best completes each sentence. Write the letter of the answer on your paper.

14. _____ is an isotope of hydrogen.

    A deuterium   **C** tritium

    B uranium   **D** both A and C

15. Different atoms of one element may have a different _____.

    A atomic number   **C** electron

    B mass number   **D** symbol

16. Elements are classified in the periodic table as _____.

    A natural and synthetic

    B toxic and nontoxic

    C metals, nonmetals, and noble gases

    D isotopes and alloys

Critical Thinking

Write the answer to each of these questions. Use the figure from the periodic table to answer questions 17 to 19.

17. What is the name of the element?

18. What is the element's symbol?

19. What is the element's atomic number? What is its atomic mass?

20. Carbon's atomic number is 6. How are two carbon atoms with mass numbers of 12 and 14 different from each other? What are these atoms called?

| 20 |
| Ca |
| Calcium |
| 40.08 |

Test-Taking Tip Try to answer all questions as completely as possible. When asked to explain your answer, do so in complete sentences.

Compounds

O n April 15, 1912, the *RMS Titanic* sank to the bottom of the North Atlantic Ocean after hitting an iceberg. In the photograph, you can see the prow of the ship lying on the ocean floor. Underwater for more than 90 years, the surface of the *Titanic* has been altered by iron-oxidizing bacteria, or rust. A chemical change is taking place. Notice the "rusticles" that have formed on the prow. Rust covers the shipwreck, and it is slowly wearing away the ship's metal structure.

In Chapter 5, you will learn about chemical and physical changes, and how different elements combine to form compounds. You also will learn how compounds are classified.

Organize Your Thoughts

Formulas

Compounds — Elements — Atoms

Acids   Bases   Energy levels

Goals for Learning

◆ To describe compounds

◆ To explain how compounds are formed

◆ To tell what the information in a formula means

◆ To explain how compounds are named

◆ To classify some compounds as acids or bases

Objectives

After reading this lesson, you should be able to

◆ describe a chemical change.

◆ describe some characteristics of compounds.

Only about 90 different elements combine in various ways to form the millions of different compounds you see around you. Do these millions of compounds have any common characteristics? How do these compounds form?

Compounds and Chemical Changes

You learned in Chapter 3 that two or more elements combine to form a compound. For example, hydrogen gas combines with oxygen gas to form the liquid compound water. Water has properties that are different from the elements that form it.

Chemical change

A change that produces one or more new substances with new chemical properties

When atoms of elements combine to form a compound, a **chemical change** takes place. A chemical change produces one or more new substances with new chemical properties. A chemical change takes place when hydrogen and oxygen combine to form water.

How can you tell when a chemical change has happened? There are several possible signs. Bubbles sometimes appear. A solid may form. Temperature or color may change, or light or energy may be produced.

The photos illustrate a chemical change. As the wood burns, it changes to gases and ash. The ash is a soft, gray powder that cannot burn. Wood and ash are different substances and have different properties.

A chemical change takes place when wood burns.

Now think about taking a similar piece of wood and chopping it into tiny pieces. Does a chemical change take place when this happens? Ask yourself if the pieces of wood have properties that are different from the original piece of wood. In this case, they do not. Each small piece is still wood. The pieces just have different sizes and shapes. Changes like this are called **physical changes.** In a physical change, the appearance (physical properties) of a substance changes but its chemical properties stay the same. In a physical change, no new substances are formed.

Characteristics of Compounds

Although there are millions of compounds, they all share some basic characteristics. Any particular compound always contains the same elements. For example, the elements that make up water—hydrogen and oxygen—are always the same. The water can be from a faucet, a river, or a puddle in the road.

Another characteristic of compounds is that the atoms in a particular compound always combine in the same numbers. A molecule of water always contains two hydrogen atoms and one oxygen atom. If you change the molecule by adding another oxygen atom, the compound is no longer water. It becomes hydrogen peroxide, the clear liquid that people can use to clean cuts and other skin wounds. Water and hydrogen peroxide are different substances with different properties.

Copy the table on a sheet of paper. Identify each change as a chemical change or a physical change. Tell how you know which kind of change it is. (Remember, a chemical change produces new substances with new chemical properties.)

Change	Chemical or physical?	How do you know?
1. melting ice cream		
2. rusting a nail		
3. chopping onions		
4. baking a cake		
5. coloring hair		

Achievements in Science

Synthetic Dye

Before the 1850s, most dyes were made from vegetables or animals. It took 12,000 shellfish to make 1.5 g of a rare, expensive purple dye. First made in 1600 B.C., this dye—Tyrian purple—became the color of royalty. Because purple dyes were so expensive, only the rich had them.

In 1856, 18-year-old student William Perkin was trying to make artificial quinine, a malaria medication. He combined oxygen and aniline, a compound made from coal tar. The result was not quinine but aniline purple, an intense purple substance. Perkin mixed the substance with alcohol and found it turned silk a beautiful purple color. Named *mauveine*, this solution was the first synthetic, or manmade, dye.

Perkin and his father started a factory to make the dye commercially. Perkin developed the processes for the production and use of the new dye. This was the beginning of the synthetic dye industry. Mauveine made purple clothing available to everyone—not just royalty.

INVESTIGATION

Materials

- safety glasses
- 2 small jars with lids
- distilled water
- washing soda
- 2 plastic spoons
- Epsom salts
- clock
- soft-drink bottle
- vinegar
- baking soda
- balloon

Observing a Chemical Change

Purpose

Look at the descriptions of the three changes listed in the data table. Can you predict which will be a physical change and which will be a chemical change? In this investigation, you will observe physical and chemical changes.

Procedure

1. Copy the data table on a sheet of paper.

Change	Appearance
washing soda in water	
Epsom salts in water	
washing soda and Epsom salts in water	

2. Put on your safety glasses.

3. Fill each jar about halfway with distilled water.

4. Add a spoonful of washing soda to one jar. Place the lid on the jar and shake for about 30 seconds. Record your observations in the table.

5. Use a clean spoon to add a spoonful of Epsom salts to the second jar. Place the lid on the jar and shake for about 30 seconds. Record your observations.

6. Carefully pour the contents of one jar into the other jar. Observe for 5 minutes. Record the results.

Questions and Conclusions

1. What happened when you added the washing soda to water?

2. What happened when you added the Epsom salts to water?

3. What did you observe when you mixed the contents of the jars together in step 6?

4. Did a chemical change or a physical change take place in steps 4 and 5? Explain your answer.

5. Did a chemical change or a physical change take place in step 6? Explain your answer.

Explore Further

Place a small amount of vinegar in a soft-drink bottle. Add a small amount of baking soda. Immediately cover the mouth of the bottle with a balloon. What do you observe happening? Does a chemical change take place? Explain your answer.

Objectives

After reading this lesson, you should be able to

◆ describe how electrons in an atom are arranged.

◆ explain how electrons fill the energy levels.

◆ explain how atoms combine to form compounds.

◆ explain how ions form chemical bonds.

You now know that compounds form when chemical changes occur. But how do the atoms of elements combine to form compounds? Electrons play an important part when elements combine. Reviewing the structure of an atom can help you understand how this happens.

Arrangement of Electrons in an Atom

Electrons in an atom move around the nucleus. Each electron moves in its own space a certain distance from the nucleus. This space is called the **energy level.** Within each energy level, electrons may move in all directions.

Compare the figure of the onion with the model of the atom below. Each energy level of an atom is somewhat like a layer of an onion. Notice that each energy level is labeled with a letter. Level K is closest to the nucleus and is the smallest. Electrons in the outer energy levels have the most effect on the properties of an element.

Energy level

One of the spaces around the nucleus of an atom in which an electron moves

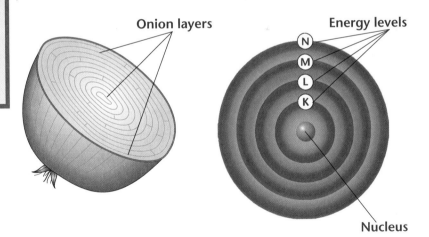

Onion layers

Energy levels

N
M
L
K

Nucleus

Each energy level can hold only a certain number of electrons. Look at the models of the hydrogen and helium atoms in the figure below. The one electron in a hydrogen atom moves around in the first level, called level K. The two electrons in helium also move at level K. Two electrons are the limit for level K.

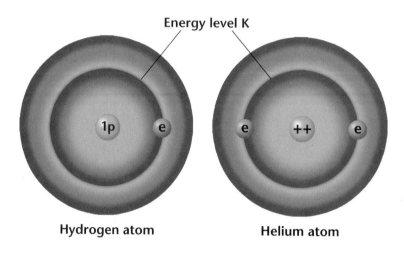

Hydrogen atom   **Helium atom**

The table shows the number of electrons each energy level can hold. Notice that the levels farther from the nucleus can hold more electrons than the levels closer to the nucleus.

An atom has seven energy levels. They are named K, L, M, N, O, P, and Q. Scientists theorize that energy level O can hold 50 electrons, level P can hold 72, and level Q can hold 98.

Energy Levels in an Atom	
Name	Number of Electrons When Filled
K	2
L	8
M	18
N	32

How Electrons Fill Energy Levels

The electrons fill the energy levels in order. Level K is the level closest to the nucleus. It is filled first. Then the second level, level L, is filled. This goes on until all the electrons are in place. For example, the element magnesium has 12 electrons. Notice in the figure that two of these electrons fill level K. Eight more electrons fill level L. The remaining two electrons are in energy level M.

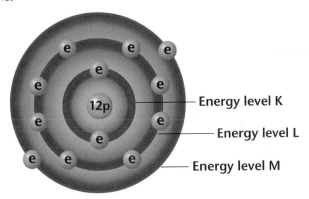

Magnesium atom

Different elements will have electrons in different numbers of levels. Helium has fewer electrons than magnesium. Helium has only two electrons. Its electrons are only in level K. But elements with more electrons fill more levels. For example, chlorine has 17 electrons. Look at the figure below.

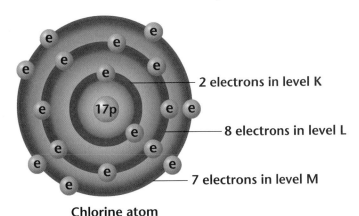

Chlorine atom

Level M will not be full because it can hold more than 7 electrons. Level M can hold as many as 18 electrons.

How Atoms Combine

You learned that compounds form when the atoms of elements combine. Exactly how do the atoms of different elements join together? When atoms form compounds, they share, lend, or borrow electrons that are in their outer energy level.

An atom has a tendency to fill its outer energy level. An atom becomes more stable when its outermost energy level is filled. An atom shares, lends, or borrows electrons to fill its outer energy level.

Look at the model of the sodium atom in the figure below. Sodium has 11 electrons. Notice that only one of its electrons is in the outer energy level. Sodium tends to lose one electron to

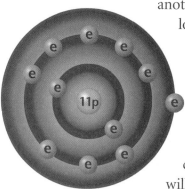

Sodium atom

another atom to become stable. By losing an electron, the outer level—level L—will have 8 electrons. It will have the most electrons it can hold. On the other hand, the chlorine atom on page 125 has 7 electrons in its outer energy level—level M. Level M can hold 18 electrons. The chlorine will become more stable if it gains or borrows one electron.

Attraction Between Atoms

Table salt is a familiar compound made from one sodium atom and one chlorine atom. The figure on page 127 shows how the sodium atom lends its electron to the chlorine atom.

Keep in mind that when sodium loses an electron, the number of protons in the nucleus remains the same. As a result, the atom has more protons than electrons. Protons have a positive charge. Electrons have a negative charge. When an atom has equal numbers of electrons and protons, the atom has no charge. But when an atom has more protons than electrons, it has a positive (+) charge.

Ion

An atom that has either a positive or a negative charge

Chemical bond

The attractive force that holds atoms together

Sodium gives an electron to chlorine to form the compound sodium chloride. The chlorine atom now has more electrons than protons. When an atom has more electrons than protons, it has a negative (−) charge.

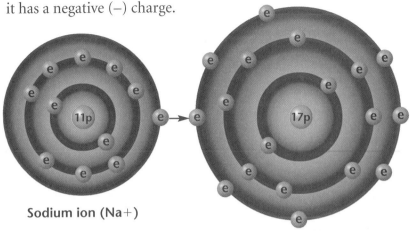

Sodium ion (Na+)

Chloride ion (Cl−)

Look at the figure shown here. How has the chlorine changed? An atom that has either a positive or a negative charge is called an **ion.** In the sodium chloride example, the chlorine becomes a negative ion. The sodium becomes a positive ion. Positive ions and negative ions strongly attract each other. The figure below shows this attraction between ions. The attractive force between atoms is called a **chemical bond.** The chemical bond between ions holds the atoms together when they form a compound. For example, a chemical bond keeps sodium and chlorine ions together when they combine to form table salt.

Ionic compounds, such as sodium chloride, form a crystal shape. The shape of the crystal is based on the arrangement of the ions that are in it. Sodium chloride forms a cube-shaped crystal.

Science Myth

All chemical bonds form in the same way.

Fact: There are two main types of chemical bonds. A covalent bond forms when two atoms share a pair of electrons. Each atom gives one electron to the electron pair. An ionic bond forms when an atom loses an electron and another atom gains the electron.

Chemical bond

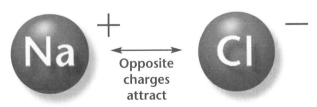

Opposite charges attract

Positive sodium ion

The sodium ion has a positive (+) charge because it lost an electron.

Negative chlorine ion

The chlorine ion has a negative (−) charge because it gained an electron.

Write your answers to these questions in complete sentences on a sheet of paper.

1. How are electrons arranged around the nucleus of an atom?

2. In what order do electrons fill energy levels?

3. Would an atom with 3 electrons in level M tend to gain or lose electrons? Explain your answer. (Hint: Use the chart on page 124.)

4. How do atoms of different elements combine?

5. How many electrons can level M hold?

▼◄▲▼◄▲▼◄▲▼◄▲▼◄▲▼◄▲▼◄▲▼◄▲▼◄▲▼◄▲▼◄▲▼◄▲▼◄▲▼

Science at Work

Textile Dye Technologist

Textile dye technologists create and test formulas for different colors of dyes for different fabrics. They have the responsibility of deciding which dye and dyeing process to use. They mix dyes, check the dyeing process at each stage, and take

samples for testing. Textile dye technologists also make sure the machinery used in dyeing fabrics works correctly.

Textile dye technologists must complete a two-year college program in textile dye or textile engineering technology. They also must have two years of on-the-job training.

Textile dye technologists have excellent color perception and a solid understanding of the principles of chemistry.

Objectives

After reading this lesson, you should be able to

◆ explain how to write a chemical formula.

◆ interpret a chemical formula.

◆ explain what a radical is.

◆ give examples of radicals.

Chemical formula

Tells the kinds of atoms and how many of each kind are in a compound

Suppose you want to describe a particular beverage such as the one in the figure. You might tell about its recipe. Notice that the recipe lists all the ingredients. It also tells the amount of each ingredient in the drink.

Recipe

Banana-Strawberry Slush

1 cup sliced bananas
1 cup fresh sliced strawberries
4 mint leaves
1 cup skim milk
1/4 cup crushed ice cubes

Mix all of the ingredients in a blender until slushy. Serve immediately.

You can describe a compound by using the same kind of information you use in a recipe. You can tell what elements form the compound. You can also tell the amount of each element in the compound.

Formulas for Compounds

Scientists use the symbols for the elements to write a **chemical formula** for each compound. A chemical formula tells what kinds of atoms are in a compound and how many atoms of each kind are present. You know that sodium and chlorine combine to form table salt. The symbol for sodium is Na. The symbol for chlorine is Cl. The chemical formula for table salt is NaCl. The formula shows that sodium and chlorine combine to form table salt.

Scientists use a number called a **subscript** to indicate the number of atoms of an element in a compound. For example, the formula for water is H_2O. The number 2 tells that a water molecule contains two atoms of hydrogen. You can see that the subscript number 2 is smaller than the H and written slightly below the letter.

Notice that no subscript is written after the O. If no subscript number is given after the symbol of an element, the compound has only one atom of that element. The formula H_2O shows that one molecule of water contains three atoms—two of hydrogen and one of oxygen.

Look at the tables to learn the chemical formulas for some other compounds. Read carefully to find out what each formula shows about the compound it represents.

CH_4			
Symbol	**Element**	**Subscript**	**Number of Atoms**
C	carbon	none	1
H	hydrogen	4	+4
			5 Total atoms

$C_{12}H_{22}O_{11}$			
Symbol	**Element**	**Subscript**	**Number of Atoms**
C	carbon	12	12
H	hydrogen	22	22
O	oxygen	11	+11
			45 Total atoms

Compounds Containing Radicals

The formulas for some compounds contain groups of two or more atoms that act as if they were one atom. These groups of atoms are called **radicals.** They form compounds by combining with other atoms. During a chemical reaction, the atoms in a radical stay together.

Household lye is one common substance with a formula that contains a radical. This strong chemical is used to clean drains. The formula for lye is NaOH. The OH is an example of a radical. It contains one atom of oxygen and one atom of hydrogen. The chemical name for this radical is the hydroxyl radical. Other examples of radicals and their names are listed in the table.

Some Common Radicals	
Radical	**Name**
SO_4	sulfate
ClO_3	chlorate
NO_3	nitrate
CO_3	carbonate
PO_4	phosphate
OH	hydroxide

Compounds containing more than one radical are written with the radical in parentheses. A subscript outside of the parentheses tells how many units of the radical are in one molecule of the compound. For example, in the formula $Ba(OH)_2$, the Ba atom combines with two OH radicals as shown in the figure.

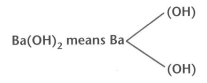

Here is another example. In $Al(OH)_3$, the Al atom combines with three OH radicals.

When formulas contain radicals with subscripts, the subscripts multiply the number of atoms inside the parentheses. Study the table below. The compound $Ba(NO_3)_2$ is barium nitrate. The nitrate radical is made up of one nitrogen atom and three oxygen atoms. But in barium nitrate, the barium atom combines with *two* nitrate radicals. You can see from the table that the compound has a total of two nitrogen atoms and six oxygen atoms.

$Ba(NO_3)_2$				
Symbol	Element	Subscript	Radical Subscript	Number of Atoms
Ba	barium	none	not in a radical	1
N	nitrogen	none	2	2 (2 × 1)
O	oxygen	3	2	+6 (2 × 3)
				9 Total atoms

Fireworks contain the compound barium nitrate.

Copy the table on a sheet of paper. Fill in the missing information. Use the periodic table on pages 100 and 101 if you need help naming the elements. The first one is done for you.

Compound	Symbols	Elements	Subscripts	Number of Each Kind of Atom
1. $NaHCO_3$	Na	sodium	none	1
	H	hydrogen	none	1
	C	carbon	none	1
	O	oxygen	3	3
2. $K_2Cr_2O_7$				
3. H_2SO_4				
4. $KClO_3$				
5. HCl				

Write the answers to these questions in complete sentences on your paper. Use the periodic table on pages 100 and 101 if you need help.

6. What does a formula tell about a compound?

7. Write a formula for a compound that contains one atom of aluminum and three atoms of chlorine.

Complete the table for the compound $Al_2(SO_4)_3$. Copy the table on your paper.

$Al_2(SO_4)_3$				
Symbol	Element	Subscript	Radical Subscript	Number of Atoms
8. Al				
9. S				
10. O				$+$ _____ Total atoms

Objectives

After reading this lesson, you should be able to

◆ explain how compounds containing two elements are named.

◆ explain how compounds containing more than two elements are named.

Binary compound

A compound that contains two elements

How would you identify yourself to a new acquaintance? You most likely would give your complete name, your first name and your last name. A compound also has a complete name, including a first and last name.

Compounds Containing Two Elements

A compound that contains two elements is called a **binary compound.** The name of a binary compound is a combination of the names of the two elements that form the compound. The number of atoms in the compound is not considered when naming a compound. The following two rules are used to name compounds containing two elements.

◆ The first name of a compound is the same as the name of the first element in the compound's formula.

◆ The second name of a compound is the name of the second element in the compound's formula with the ending changed to *-ide*. The table shows how names of some elements are written when they are the second elements in a formula.

Naming Binary Compounds	
Element	**Element's Name in a Compound**
chlorine (Cl)	chlor**ide**
iodine (I)	iod**ide**
fluorine (Fl)	fluor**ide**
bromine (Br)	brom**ide**
oxygen (O)	ox**ide**
sulfur (S)	sulf**ide**

You can see how looking at the formula for a compound can help you determine the compound's name. The formula NaCl contains symbols for the elements sodium and chlorine. The first name of the compound is the name of the first element, sodium. We change chlorine to chloride to form the second name of the compound. NaCl is sodium chloride.

| Sodium | Chlorine | Sodium chloride |

Another example is the formula BaO. The first part of the compound's name is the name of the first element, barium. The second element is oxygen. We change its name to oxide. The compound name is barium oxide.

| Barium | Oxygen | Barium oxide |

Compounds with More Than Two Elements

A compound that contains more than two elements usually has a radical in its formula. The first name of such a compound is the name of the first element in the formula. The second name of the compound varies according to the radical the formula contains. Review the names for some common radicals in the table on page 131. The subscript numbers in a formula with radicals do not affect the name of the compound.

To find the name of the compound with the formula $Al(OH)_3$, use the name of the first element—aluminum. Then add the name of the OH radical—hydroxide. The name of the compound is aluminum hydroxide.

Identifying radicals accurately is important. The seashells shown on this page contain the compound $CaCO_3$, calcium carbonate. The radical carbonate, CO_3, is listed in the table on page 131. The formula for the compound CO_2 looks similar. However, note that CO_2 has a different subscript—a 2 instead of a 3. In fact, it is the formula for a completely different compound. CO_2 is carbon dioxide, a gas in the air.

Seashells contain calcium carbonate, a compound with the formula $CaCO_3$.

Write the names of these binary compounds on a sheet of paper. Use the periodic table on pages 100 and 101 to find the element name for each symbol.

1. $CaBr_2$

2. $AlCl_3$

3. AgI

4. MgO

5. $CaCl_2$

6. BaI_2

7. CaF_2

8. HCl

9. MgS

10. $NaBr$

Write the names of these compounds on your paper. Refer to the periodic table if you need help.

11. $Al_2(SO_4)_3$

12. $Ba(OH)_2$

13. $Al(NO_3)_3$

14. K_2CO_3

15. $ZnSO_4$

Objectives

After reading this lesson, you should be able to

◆ describe the properties of acids.

◆ describe the properties of bases.

◆ explain how to test for acids and bases.

Acid

A compound that reacts with metals to produce hydrogen

Imagine biting into a lemon. How would it taste? You probably would describe its taste as sour. Then think about a time when you accidentally got soap in your mouth while washing. How did it taste? Soap has a bitter taste. These contrasting tastes, sour and bitter, help illustrate the differences between two groups of substances—acids and bases.

Properties of Acids

What gives a lemon its sour taste? A lemon contains a substance called an **acid.** All acids have the following characteristics.

◆ They taste sour.

◆ They contain hydrogen.

◆ They react with metals to produce hydrogen.

Weak acids, such as the citric acid in a lemon, give food a sour, sharp flavor. Vinegar is another familiar substance that contains an acid called acetic acid. The table lists some common acids and tells where they are found.

You can see from the table that you can eat some acids. But other acids are poisonous. Some acids can burn your skin. In fact, even touching a strong acid for a moment can cause a severe burn. That is why it is wise to never taste or touch an unknown substance.

Common Acids		
Name of Acid	**Formula**	**Where It Is Found**
acetic acid	$HC_2H_3O_2$	vinegar
boric acid	H_3BO_3	eyewashes
carbonic acid	H_2CO_3	rain water, soft drinks
hydrochloric acid	HCl	gastric juice in stomach
citric acid	$H_3C_6H_5O_7$	citrus fruits (oranges, lemons, etc.)
sulfuric acid	H_2SO_4	batteries, acid rain, volcanic smoke

Properties of Bases

Why does soap have such a bitter taste? Soap belongs to a group of compounds called **bases.** All bases have the following characteristics.

◆ They taste bitter.
◆ They contain the OH radical.
◆ They feel slippery.

Many common bases are weak, so weak that you can eat them! For example, magnesium hydroxide is a weak base that is used in some medicines. However, strong bases, such as sodium hydroxide, or lye, can cause severe burns. Many bases can be poisonous. The table below lists some common bases and tells where they are found.

Common Bases		
Name of Base	Formula	Where It Is Found
aluminum hydroxide	$Al(OH)_3$	deodorants, antacids, water purification
magnesium hydroxide	$Mg(OH)_2$	laxatives, antacids
potassium hydroxide	KOH	soap, glass
sodium hydroxide	NaOH	drain cleaner, soap making
calcium hydroxide	$Ca(OH)_2$	mortar

Testing Acids and Bases

Tasting or feeling a substance to determine if it is an acid or a base usually is not safe. But there is a way to make this determination by using another characteristic of both acids and bases. You can find out how they react to **indicators.** Indicators change color to identify acids or bases. Litmus is a common indicator used in the laboratory. Litmus turns from blue to red in acids. It turns from red to blue in bases. You will use an indicator in Investigation 5-2.

Some indicators tell you the **pH** of a substance. The pH is a number that tells whether the substance is an acid or a base. Acids have a pH from 0 to 7. Bases have a pH from 7 to 14. Some substances are neither acids nor bases. These substances are said to be neutral. They have a pH of 7. You can see the pH of some common substances in the chart on this page.

You can use indicators to tell how strong an acid or a base is. The lower the pH number of an acid, the stronger the acid is. For example, your stomach produces acid that is very strong. Its pH is 1. Milk is only slightly acidic. Its pH is 6.9. The higher the pH of a base, the stronger the base. Lye has a pH around 13. It is a strong base. Liquid soaps are much weaker bases.

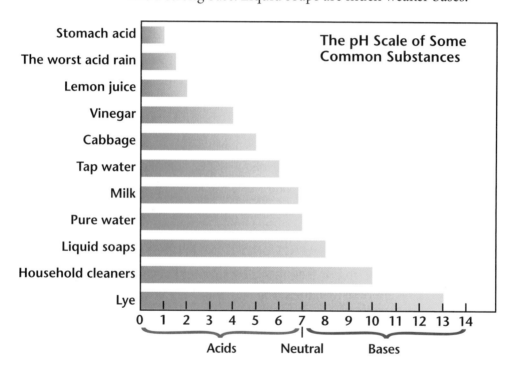

The pH Scale of Some Common Substances

Technology Note

A pH meter is an instrument that shows the strength of an acid or base. A pH meter measures and compares the electric charge of the ions in a sample. Then the meter changes this information into a pH number. Scientists use a pH meter to test water.

What is acid rain?

Imagine visiting a beautiful lake such as the one in the photo. You can't wait to get in the water to swim. Maybe you have been thinking about the fish you will catch there. But suppose the water is not safe for swimming. Suppose no fish or plants live in the lake. You wonder what has happened. Perhaps the water is polluted.

One cause of water pollution is acid rain, which is also called acid deposition. Acid deposition does not harm only water. It harms plants and animals, and affects buildings, bridges, and statues. Acid rain also damages human health.

Acid deposition starts when cars, factories, or power plants burn coal, gas, or oil. This produces gases in the air. The gases combine with water, oxygen, and other substances to form harmful acids.

There are two ways these acids reach the earth. When rain, snow, or cloud water carries acids to the earth, wet deposition occurs. When acidic gases or particles fall on plants, land, water, or buildings, dry deposition occurs. Rain can wash dry deposits off trees and plants, making the rain even more acidic. When the wind blows, acids in the air can travel long distances.

People first noticed the effects of acid rain in the 1960s. They noticed that fish in some lakes in Europe and North America were dying. Next, they noticed that some forests showed signs of damage.

Reducing acid deposition starts with reducing pollutants given off by cars, factories, and power plants. Since 1990, the levels of these pollutants in the air have decreased, but not enough. Governments, industries, scientists, and individuals continue to work to solve the problem of acid rain.

Write on your paper whether each of the following is a property of an acid or a base.

1. Tastes sour

2. Is slippery

3. Has a pH of 3

4. Has a pH of 11

5. Contains the OH radical

6. Tastes bitter

7. Turns litmus from red to blue

8. Contains hydrogen

9. Turns litmus from blue to red

10. Reacts with a metal to produce hydrogen

Achievements in Science

Nylon

In the late 1920s, Wallace H. Carothers began experimenting with polymers. Polymers are giant molecules made of thousands of smaller molecules. The small molecules are identical to each other and are chemically bonded to each other. The chemically bonded molecules form a chain. Carothers had studied silk, a natural polymer. He understood that the new fiber needed to have the same properties as silk. Carothers began making polymers that were longer than any that had ever been made before.

In 1935, Carothers combined hexamethylenediamine and adipic acid to make a new fiber. This fiber, which chemists called Fiber 66, was stronger and more elastic than silk. Fiber 66 became known as nylon. Nylon is a synthetic, or manmade, polymer. Each molecule has a polymer chain of repeating molecules made of carbon, hydrogen, and oxygen atoms.

The production of nylon began in 1938. The first products made from nylon— toothbrushes—were introduced in 1939. Nylon stockings also appeared on the market in 1939. Today carpets, clothes, parachutes, tires, and thread are among the many products made of nylon.

Materials

- safety glasses
- marker
- 8 small paper cups
- spoon
- aspirin tablet
- baking soda
- white vinegar
- lemon juice
- weak ammonia solution
- soap
- soft drink
- milk of magnesia
- red-cabbage juice
- graduated cylinder
- litmus paper

Identifying Acids and Bases

Purpose

Read the substances listed in the data table. Can you identify which substances are acids and which are bases? In this investigation, you will use an indicator to test for acids and bases.

Procedure

1. Copy the data table on a sheet of paper.

Substance	Color After Cabbage Juice Is Added	Acid or Base
baking soda		base
vinegar		acid
lemon juice		
weak ammonia		
aspirin		
soap		
soft drink		
milk of magnesia		

2. Put on your safety glasses.

3. Use a marker to label each cup with the name of one substance from the table. Use these labels: baking soda (base), vinegar (acid), lemon juice, weak ammonia solution, aspirin, soap, soft drink, and milk of magnesia.

4. Add a small amount of each substance to the cup labeled with its name. Use a spoon to crush the aspirin tablet before adding it to the cup.

5. The cabbage juice will be the acid-base indicator. Record the color of the cabbage juice in the data table.

6. Use the graduated cylinder to measure 20 mL of cabbage juice. Add the cabbage juice to the cup labeled baking soda (base). Stir. Notice the color of the liquid in the cup. Record this color in the data table. Baking soda is a base. Any substance that changes to a color similar to the liquid in the baking soda cup after you add cabbage juice is a base.

7. Add 20 mL of cabbage juice to the vinegar (acid) cup. Record the results in the data table. Vinegar is an acid. Any substance that changes to a color similar to the liquid in the vinegar cup after you add cabbage juice is an acid.

8. Add 20 mL of cabbage juice to each of the remaining cups and stir. Determine whether each cup contains an acid or a base. Record your results.

Questions and Conclusions

1. Which of the substances are acids?

2. Which of the substances are bases?

3. Are some bases stronger than others? Explain your answer.

Explore Further

Use a piece of long-range litmus paper to test each substance. Record your results. How do your results compare with your previous results for each substance?

- A compound forms when two or more elements combine. A chemical change takes place when elements combine to form a compound. In a chemical change, new substances with new chemical properties are formed.

- A physical change is a change in which the appearance (physical properties) of a substance changes but its chemical properties stay the same.

- Molecules of the same compound always contain the same elements. The atoms in the molecules of the same compound always combine in the same numbers.

- An electron moves in a certain energy level around the nucleus of an atom. Each energy level can hold only a certain number of electrons. Electrons fill the energy levels in order.

- Different elements have electrons in different numbers of levels. Atoms share, borrow, or lend electrons to other atoms in order to form compounds.

- An atom that has a charge is called an ion. Ions with opposite charges attract each other.

- A chemical formula is used to show what kinds of atoms and how many atoms of each kind are in a compound.

- A radical is a group of elements that behaves as if it were one element.

- In naming a compound, use the name of the first element and the name of the second element with the ending changed to -ide.

- Acids are compounds that contain hydrogen, react with metals to form hydrogen, and have a sour taste.

- Bases are slippery compounds that contain the hydroxyl radical, and have a bitter taste.

- Indicators can be used to identify acids and bases.

Science Words

acid, 138	chemical formula, 129	pH, 140
base, 139	energy level, 123	physical change, 119
binary compound, 134	indicator, 139	radicals, 131
chemical bond, 127	ion, 127	subscript, 130
chemical change, 118		

Word Bank

acid

base

chemical bond

chemical change

chemical formula

indicator

ion

pH

physical change

radicals

subscript

Vocabulary Review

Choose the word or words from the Word Bank that best complete each sentence. Write the answers on a sheet of paper.

1. A(n) _____ changes color in an acid or a base.

2. In a(n) _____, a substance's appearance changes but its chemical properties do not.

3. A(n) _____ tells whether a substance is an acid or a base.

4. A(n) _____ reacts with metals to produce hydrogen.

5. A compound that contains the hydroxyl (OH) radical is a _____.

6. A(n) _____ is an atom that has either a positive or a negative charge.

7. A(n) _____ tells the kinds of atoms and how many are in a compound.

8. A(n) _____ produces one or more new substances with new chemical properties.

9. A(n) _____ tells the number of atoms of an element in a compound.

10. A(n) _____ is the attractive force that holds atoms together.

11. A group of two or more atoms that act like one atom are _____.

Concept Review

Choose the best answer to each question. Write the letter of the answer on your paper.

12. Which of the following is *not* a physical change?
  A painting a wall   **C** boiling water
  B developing film   **D** shredding cheese

Test-Taking Tip

If you have to choose the correct word to complete a sentence, read the sentence using each of the words. Then choose the word that best fits the sentence.

13. Where do compounds with more than one radical appear in a chemical formula?

A in parentheses   **C** at the beginning

B at the end   **D** as a subscript

14. Which of the following does not describe an acid?

A tastes sour   **C** feels slippery

B contains hydrogen   **D** turns litmus from blue to red

15. Which of the following substances is not a base?

A household cleaner, which has a pH of 10

B lye, which has a pH of 13

C liquid soap, which has a pH of 8

D lemon juice, which has a pH of 2

Critical Thinking

Write the answer to each of these questions on your paper.

16. Describe the characteristics of compounds and explain how compounds are named.

17. Explain the difference between a chemical change and a physical change.

18. Describe the energy levels in an atom. Explain how electrons fill energy levels and what happens to electrons when atoms form compounds.

19. Look at the figure of the compound calcium fluoride. Explain what the figure shows.

20. When you digest food, your body changes the food into nutrients. The nutrients are carried through your bloodstream to your body cells. What type(s) of changes happen to the food in your mouth and your stomach?

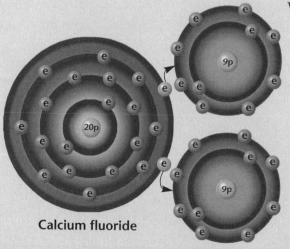

Calcium fluoride

How Matter Changes

When cool, autumn weather arrives, the leaves on many trees change color. Leaves, like the ones in the photograph, turn from green to brilliant red, yellow, and orange. What is happening in the leaves to cause this dramatic change? Different types of chemical reactions are taking place. Some compounds are breaking down. New compounds are forming. In Chapter 6, you will learn about different types of chemical reactions. You also will learn how to read the equations scientists use to describe chemical reactions.

Organize Your Thoughts

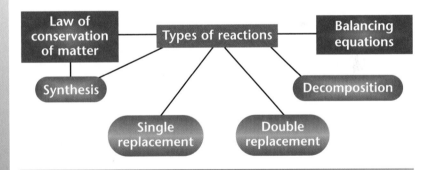

Goals for Learning

- ◆ To explain what a reaction is
- ◆ To describe what occurs when something dissolves
- ◆ To state the law of conservation of matter
- ◆ To interpret and write balanced chemical equations
- ◆ To name and explain the four main types of chemical reactions

Chemical reaction

A chemical change in which elements are combined or rearranged

Mixture

A combination of substances in which no reaction takes place

Science Myth

Air and oxygen are the same thing.

Fact: Air is a mixture of a number of substances. Oxygen makes up only 21 percent of air. Air contains mostly nitrogen. Water vapor and a very small amount of other gases are also part of air.

Hundreds of years ago, early scientists known as alchemists tried to change different materials into gold. Imagine being able to change iron or lead into solid gold!

Alchemists were early scientists who tried to turn other materials into gold.

Unfortunately for the alchemists, they never succeeded. Today, scientists know that chemically changing one element into another is not possible. But during a chemical change, elements can be combined to form compounds. The elements in compounds can be rearranged to form new compounds. When elements combine or rearrange, they are said to react. The process is called a **chemical reaction.** For some reactions, it is necessary to heat the substances. And some substances must be mixed with water for a chemical reaction to take place.

Substances do not always react when combined. Many elements and compounds can be mixed together and nothing at all happens. A **mixture** is formed when substances are combined and no reaction takes place. When you stir sugar and cinnamon together, you form a mixture.

Dissolving

Dissolve

To break apart

Solute

The substance that is dissolved in a solution

Solution

A mixture in which one substance is dissolved in another

Solvent

A substance capable of dissolving one or more other substances

Many reactions take place only when the substances have been dissolved in other liquids. To **dissolve** means to break up substances into individual atoms or molecules. An example of dissolving occurs when sugar is placed in water. The sugar mixes with the water and seems to disappear. But the sugar is still there. The pieces of the sugar have been broken down into tiny particles—molecules.

When a substance is thoroughly dissolved in another, the result is a mixture called a **solution.** The substance that dissolves is called the **solute.** When you dissolve sugar in water, the solute is sugar. A substance that is capable of dissolving one or more other substances is a **solvent.** In the sugar-water solution, water is the solvent. Can you think of other examples of solutions, solutes, and solvents?

Types of Solutions		
Substance (solute)	Dissolved in (solvent)	Examples
liquid	liquid	alcohol in water
	gas	water vapor in air
	solid	ether in rubber
gas	liquid	club soda in water (CO_2 in water)
	gas	air (nitrogen, oxygen, other gases)
	solid	hydrogen in palladium
solid	liquid	salt in water
	gas	iodine vapor in air
	solid	brass (copper and zinc)

A solution does not always have to be a solid dissolved in a liquid. Solutions can also be formed by dissolving substances in solids and gases. The table above gives some examples of solutions.

Write your answers to these questions in complete sentences on a sheet of paper.

1. What metal were the alchemists trying to produce? Did they succeed?

2. What are two things a scientist can do to cause some substances that are mixed together to react?

3. Suppose you dissolve salt in water. Name the solvent and the solute.

4. What is a chemical reaction?

5. How is a mixture different from a chemical reaction?

Science in Your Life

How does a permanent wave work?

To understand how a permanent wave works, you need to understand something about hair's biochemistry. Like almost everything in your body, hair is mostly protein. The proteins in hair—called keratin—are long chains of the amino acid cystine. Cystine is made of carbon, hydrogen, oxygen, nitrogen, and sulfur atoms.

In cystine, sulfur atoms can form a disulfide bond. Wherever this bond occurs in the protein chain, hair bends. All hair has some disulfide bonds. Many disulfide bonds in a protein chain make hair curly.

Permanent waves can be added to hair that doesn't have many disulfide bonds. Two chemical reactions take place to make straight hair curly. First, we need to break the existing disulfide bonds in hair. A chemical called a reducing agent breaks the disulfide bonds. This is the first chemical reaction. Next, we use curlers to give the hair a new

shape. Then another chemical —a neutralizer—uses oxidation to make new disulfide bonds. This is the second chemical reaction. The longer the neutralizer is left on the hair, the curlier the hair will be when the curlers are removed, and the neutralizer is rinsed away. Now the protein in the hair has many new disulfide bonds—and lots of curls.

Materials

- safety glasses
- spoon
- 2 g sand
- 2 g table salt (sodium chloride, NaCl)
- sheet of paper
- stirring rod
- graduated cylinder
- 200 mL water
- 2 beakers
- circular piece of filter paper or paper towel
- funnel

Separating a Mixture

Purpose

Look at the materials listed in the data table. Can you predict which material will be the solvent? Which material will be the solute? In this investigation, you will separate a mixture through dissolving.

Procedure

1. Copy the data table on a sheet of paper.

Materials	Observations
salt	
sand	
mixture of salt and sand	
solution of salt, sand, and water	
filter paper	
sides of beaker	

2. Put on your safety glasses. Place about one spoonful of sand and one spoonful of salt in separate piles on a sheet of paper. Observe the appearance of the salt and the sand. Record your observations in the data table.

3. Use the stirring rod to thoroughly mix the salt with the sand. Describe the resulting mixture.

4. Using a graduated cylinder, measure 200 mL of water. Pour the water into a beaker.

5. Put the salt-sand mixture in the beaker with the water.

6. Stir the solution with the stirring rod. Observe the liquid in the beaker. Record your observations.

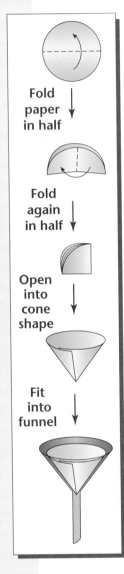

Fold paper in half

Fold again in half

Open into cone shape

Fit into funnel

7. Follow the steps shown in the figure. Fold the filter paper and put it in the funnel.

8. Hold the funnel over a second beaker. Slowly pour the solution from the first beaker into the funnel. Allow the second beaker to catch the liquid as it passes through the funnel.

9. Observe the filter paper. Record your observations.

10. Let the second beaker and its contents sit in a warm place for several days.

11. After all the liquid has evaporated, observe the sides of the beaker. Record your observations.

Questions and Conclusions

1. In steps 5 and 6, what happened to the salt when you added water to the mixture?

2. In step 6, did the sand dissolve? How do you know?

3. In step 9, where was the salt after you poured the solution into the second beaker? How do you know?

4. In step 9, which material remained on the filter paper?

5. In step 11, what substance formed in the beaker?

6. What is the solvent in this investigation? What is the solute?

Explore Further

Suppose you had a mixture of iron filings and sugar. How would you separate it? Write the procedure you would use.

Objectives

After reading this lesson, you should be able to

◆ explain how a chemical equation describes a chemical reaction.

◆ balance chemical equations.

You know that chemical symbols and formulas can be used to represent substances. You can also use these symbols to describe reactions. A **chemical equation** is a statement that uses symbols, chemical formulas, and numbers to stand for a chemical reaction. Look at the simple chemical equation below. The symbols and formulas describe the chemicals that are involved. Below the equation, you can see the description in words.

Reactants   Products

HCl + NaOH   ⟶   **NaCl + H$_2$O**

hydrogen chloride plus sodium hydroxide yields sodium chloride plus water

Chemical equation

A statement that uses symbols, formulas, and numbers to stand for a chemical reaction

Reactant

A substance that is altered in a chemical reaction

Product

A substance that is formed in a chemical reaction

Notice that the arrow symbol (⟶) stands for "yields" or "makes." The chemicals on the left side of the arrow are called **reactants.** They are the substances that are reacting together. A reactant is a substance that is altered in a chemical reaction. The chemicals on the right side of the arrow are called **products.** A product is a substance that is formed in a chemical reaction. The product forms from the reactants. In the above example, HCl and NaOH are the reactants. The products are NaCl and H$_2$O.

Technology Note

Rubber used for most purposes is vulcanized. Before vulcanization, rubber products became soft in hot weather. In cold weather, they were brittle. Even at room temperature, rubber stuck to everything it touched and could not hold its shape. Vulcanized rubber is treated with sulfur and then heated. This chemical reaction produces rubber that is hard, strong, and elastic.

Law of Conservation of Matter

The reactants present *before* a reaction can be quite different from the products present after the reaction. But the kinds of atoms do not change during the reaction. Different substances are formed, but the same atoms are there. The atoms are just rearranged. In the reaction below, magnesium and fluorine (the reactants) combine to form a new compound called magnesium fluoride. Notice how the atoms rearrange themselves.

A chemical equation shows the rearrangement of atoms that happens after a chemical change.

Mg	+	F$_2$	→	MgF$_2$
magnesium		fluorine		magnesium fluoride

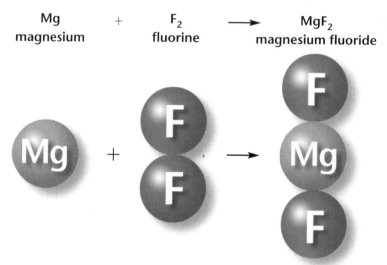

The same numbers and kinds of atoms are present before and after a reaction. Mass does not change during the reaction. The mass of the reactants equals the mass of the products. This fact illustrates the **law of conservation of matter.** The law states that matter cannot be created or destroyed in chemical and common physical changes. This law is sometimes called the law of conservation of mass.

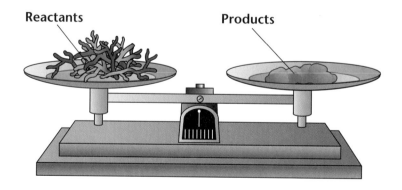

Reactants   Products

In a balanced equation, a coefficient of 1 usually is not written.

Balancing Equations

To satisfy the law of conservation of matter, a chemical equation must show the same number of each kind of atom on both sides of the equation. Scientists say that the equation must be **balanced.** To balance an equation means to keep the same number of each kind of atom on both sides of the equation.

Look at the following equation. It shows that hydrogen plus oxygen makes water.

$$H_2 + O_2 \longrightarrow H_2O$$

This equation is not balanced. Two oxygen atoms are shown on the left side of the equation. Only 1 oxygen atom is shown on the right. The left side of the equation has a total of 4 atoms, but the right side has only 3 atoms.

$$H_2 + O_2 \longrightarrow H_2O$$

H 2 atoms	H 2 atoms
O 2 atoms	O 1 atom
Total of 4 atoms	Total of 3 atoms

You can see that there are 4 atoms in the reactants and only 3 in the products. The law of conservation of matter says that atoms do not disappear in chemical reactions. You cannot change the formulas for the reactants or products.

To balance the equation, you can place numbers before the formulas. A number that is placed before a formula in a chemical equation is called a **coefficient.** A coefficient shows how many molecules or atoms are involved in the chemical reaction. For example, look at $2H_2O$. The 2 before H_2O means 2 water molecules.

You can change coefficients by changing the numbers of atoms. By writing $2H_2O$, you are saying that 4 atoms of hydrogen and 2 atoms of oxygen are in the products. If you write $3H_2O$, you are saying that 6 atoms of hydrogen and 3 atoms of oxygen are in the products.

By placing a 2 in front of the H_2O, you have made the number of oxygen atoms equal on both sides of the equation. But the number of hydrogen atoms is not equal.

$H_2 + O_2$	$\longrightarrow$	$2H_2O$
H 2 atoms		H 4 atoms (2×2)
O 2 atoms		O 2 atoms (1×2)
Total of 4 atoms		Total of 6 atoms

You can see that there are 2 hydrogen atoms in the reactants. There are 4 hydrogen atoms in the product. Therefore, you need 2 more hydrogen atoms in the reactants. Again you can change the number of atoms by using a coefficient. You can balance the equation like this.

$2H_2 + O_2$	$\longrightarrow$	$2H_2O$
H 4 atoms		H 4 atoms
O 2 atoms		O 2 atoms
Total of 6 atoms		Total of 6 atoms

The equation is now balanced. Look at the figure below. The coefficients show that there are 2 molecules each of hydrogen and water. Since the oxygen has no coefficient, it means that there is 1 molecule. The equation tells you that whenever hydrogen and oxygen combine to form water, 2 molecules of hydrogen will combine with 1 molecule of oxygen to produce 2 molecules of water. The number of each kind of atom is the same before and after the reaction.

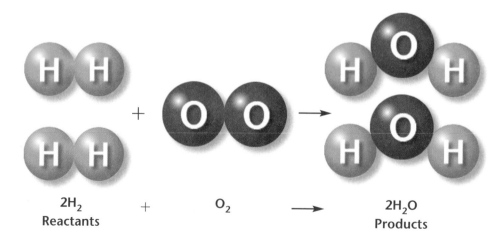

$2H_2$
Reactants
$+$
O_2
$\longrightarrow$
$2H_2O$
Products

Lesson 2 R E V I E W

1. Copy the table on a sheet of paper. Then complete the table. The first one is done for you.

Reaction	Reactants	Products
A $Fe + S \longrightarrow FeS$	Fe, S	FeS
B $H_2SO_4 + Zn \longrightarrow ZnSO_4 + H_2$		
C $Mg + S \longrightarrow MgS$		
D $AgNO_3 + NaCl \longrightarrow NaNO_3 + AgCl$		

2. Write the following chemical equations in words.

   A $Mg + S \longrightarrow MgS$ **B** $Ba + S \longrightarrow BaS$

Study the following equation. Then write your answers to the questions.

$$2Na + Cl_2 \longrightarrow 2NaCl$$

3. What are the reactants?

4. What is the product?

5. Is the equation balanced? Explain your answer.

Achievements in Science

Inexpensive Aluminum Processing

Aluminum is a light metal that carries electricity well and does not rust. It is the third most common element in the earth's crust. However, we cannot find aluminum in its pure form in nature. We must mine aluminum oxide from rocks, and that can be costly.

Scientists discovered a way to get larger amounts of aluminum oxide from rocks in the mid-1800s. The cost of aluminum dropped from $1,200 per kilogram in 1852 to $40 in 1859. Still, aluminum was too costly to be used a lot. It was so costly that, until the late1800s, aluminum was a semiprecious metal.

In 1885, chemists Charles Hall and Paul Heroult were 22 years old. The two chemists separately discovered an inexpensive way to process aluminum. The Hall-Heroult process involves dissolving aluminum oxide. It uses electricity to create a decomposition reaction that leaves pure aluminum precipitates. By 1909, the price of aluminum was $0.60 per kilogram. The Hall-Heroult process is still the only method for processing aluminum.

Millions of different chemical reactions are possible. Even chemists cannot learn all of them. How can you make sense out of all those possibilities? It turns out that most reactions can be grouped into four major types. You will learn about two of these types of reactions in this lesson.

Synthesis Reactions

The first type of reaction is called a **synthesis reaction.** The word *synthesis* means "to combine parts." In a synthesis reaction, two or more elements combine to form a compound. An example of a synthesis reaction is combining iron and sulfur. Iron is a metal used in making steel. Sulfur is a yellow nonmetal that is used in making some medicines. You can see these two elements in the figures below.

Iron

Sulfur

Suppose you mix iron (in the form of slivers called filings) with sulfur powder. No reaction takes place. The combination of iron and sulfur is an example of a mixture. A mixture is formed when substances are simply stirred together and no new substance is formed.

In a mixture, the properties of the substances remain separate. In fact, you could separate the iron and sulfur in the mixture by using a magnet. The iron is attracted to a magnet, but the sulfur is not. The mixture is separated quite easily. The magnet pulls the iron away from the sulfur.

Now suppose you heat the iron and sulfur mixture. A reaction will occur. A new compound called iron sulfide (FeS) will form. The two elements have formed a compound. Therefore, the reaction is a synthesis. Iron sulfide has properties different from those of either iron or sulfur. When a magnet is placed near the iron sulfide, the compound will not be attracted to it.

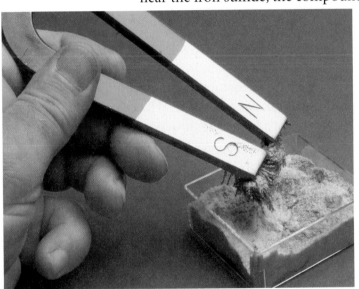

Notice in the photo that the color of iron sulfide is gray-black. The yellow color of sulfur and the silvery color of iron are gone. The properties have changed because a new substance has formed.

The balanced chemical equation for this synthesis reaction appears below the three photos.

You can use a magnet to separate an iron and sulfur mixture.

Fe	+	S	→	FeS
Iron	plus	sulfur	yields	iron sulfide
(grey solid)		(yellow solid)		(grey-black solid)

Decomposition Reactions

Sometimes in a chemical reaction a compound breaks down into two or more simple substances. This type of reaction is called a **decomposition reaction.** For example, sugar is a compound you are familiar with. Its formula is $C_6H_{12}O_6$. When you heat sugar, it breaks down into carbon (C) and water (H_2O). Carbon is a black solid. Water is a compound made of hydrogen and oxygen. The carbon and the water contain the same atoms that were in the sugar. The equation for the reaction is shown here.

$$C_6H_{12}O_6 \longrightarrow 6C + 6H_2O$$

sugar	carbon	water
(white solid)	(black solid)	(colorless liquid)

Another example of a decomposition reaction occurs when the compound mercuric oxide is heated. The chemical equation for the reaction is shown here. The upward arrow ($\uparrow$) after the O_2 indicates that oxygen is a gas that is given off.

$$2HgO \longrightarrow 2Hg + O_2\uparrow$$

mercuric oxide	mercury	oxygen

Technology Note

Stainless steel is an alloy whose mass contains at least 12 percent chromium. Chromium gives stainless steel its resistance to rust and other types of corrosive chemical reactions. Knives, pots and pans, tableware, and sinks are among the household items that use stainless steel. Many automobile, airplane, and train parts also are made of stainless steel.

Copy the following equations on a sheet of paper. Then tell if each is a synthesis reaction or a decomposition reaction.

1. $2MgO \longrightarrow 2Mg + O_2\uparrow$

2. $2Hg + O_2 \longrightarrow 2HgO$

3. $C + O_2 \longrightarrow CO_2$

4. $BaCl_2 \longrightarrow Ba + Cl_2$

5. $2H_2O \longrightarrow 2H_2 + O_2$

Write the products of the following synthesis reactions.

6. $2Na + Cl_2 \longrightarrow$ _____

7. $Mg + Cl_2 \longrightarrow$ _____

8. $CO + O_2 \longrightarrow$ _____

Complete the following decomposition reactions.

9. $CaCO_3 \longrightarrow$ _____ $+ CO_2$

10. $2FeO \longrightarrow$ _____ $+ O_2$

Science at Work

Food Technologist

Food technologists study the nature of foods. They experiment with new ingredients and new ways to use ingredients. Food technologists develop ways to process and to improve the quality of foods. They also test samples to make sure foods meet food laws and standards. Most often, food technologists work in a laboratory, often set up like a kitchen.

Most food technologists have a four-year degree in food science, biochemistry, or chemistry. To do research, an advanced degree is required.

Food technologists are creative. They have curiosity and good instincts about food. They also must be able to carry out tests and to work well under pressure.

After reading this lesson, you should be able to

◆ identify single-replacement reactions.

◆ identify double-replacement reactions.

You now know about two kinds of reactions—synthesis reactions and decomposition reactions. Two other kinds of reactions are common.

Single-Replacement Reactions

Look at the photo below. It shows a container of a silver nitrate solution and a copper wire. Notice what happens when the copper wire is placed in the solution of silver nitrate. Silver metal forms on the wire. A chemical reaction has taken place. The equation for the reaction is shown here.

$$Cu + 2AgNO_3 \longrightarrow 2Ag + Cu(NO_3)_2$$

Single-replacement reaction

A reaction in which one element replaces another in a compound

Notice that copper (Cu) has replaced the silver (Ag) in the silver nitrate. A new compound, copper nitrate—$Cu(NO_3)_2$—is formed. The silver is set free. That is the kind of change that occurs in a **single-replacement reaction.** A single-replacement reaction is a reaction in which one element replaces another in a compound.

Did You Know?

The same chemical reaction that causes rust also creates fireworks. Oxidation produces both, but it occurs at a different rate in each reaction. When an item rusts, oxidation moves very slowly. In fireworks, oxidation occurs almost instantly.

In this single-replacement reaction, the copper replaces the silver.

Double-Replacement Reactions

The fourth kind of chemical reaction is the **double-replacement reaction.** In this kind of reaction, the elements in two compounds are exchanged.

An example of a double-replacement reaction is the reaction between sodium chloride ($NaCl$) and silver nitrate ($AgNO_3$). Look at the equation for the reaction shown here.

$$NaCl + AgNO_3 \longrightarrow NaNO_3 + AgCl\downarrow$$

Sodium chloride plus silver nitrate has formed two new compounds—sodium nitrate ($NaNO_3$) and silver chloride ($AgCl$). The elements in the two compounds have exchanged places. That is what makes the reaction a double replacement.

The downward-pointing arrow ($\downarrow$) after the AgCl means that this substance is a solid that forms and settles out of the solution. A solid formed in this way is called a **precipitate.** A precipitate usually sinks to the bottom of a solution.

The table below summarizes the four kinds of chemical reactions.

Four Kinds of Reactions	
Type	**General Form**
Synthesis	A + B ⟶ AB
Decomposition	AB ⟶ A + B
Single replacement	A + BC ⟶ B + AC
Double replacement	AB + CD ⟶ AD + CB

Identify each of these reactions as either synthesis, decomposition, single replacement, or double replacement.

1. $Pb(NO_3)_2 + 2KI \longrightarrow 2KNO_3 + PbI_2$

2. $S + O_2 \longrightarrow SO_2$

3. $BaCl_2 \longrightarrow Ba + Cl_2$

4. $Cl_2 + 2NaBr \longrightarrow 2NaCl + Br_2$

5. $2Fe_2O_3 + 3C \longrightarrow 4Fe + 3CO_2$

Complete each of these reactions. Then identify the kind of reaction (single replacement or double replacement).

6. $2NaBr + Cl_2 \longrightarrow$ _____ + _____

7. $Zn + 2HCl \longrightarrow$ _____ + _____

8. $KOH + HBr \longrightarrow$ _____ + HOH

9. $BaCl_2 + Na_2SO_4 \longrightarrow$ _____ + _____

10. $AgNO_3 + NaBr \longrightarrow$ _____ + _____

Achievements in Science

Chlorination

In 1774, Carl Wilhelm Scheele first made chlorine by combining an acid with a compound. English chemist Sir Humphry Davy determined that chlorine was an element in 1810. Chlorine gas reacts with water to break down and kill harmful bacteria-carrying diseases. The process of using chlorine to disinfect water is chlorination.

In the mid-1800s, cities began using chlorination to disinfect water. One of the first known uses was in 1850. A water supply pump in London was disinfected with chlorine after an outbreak of cholera. Later in the century, chlorine was used to sterilize water after a typhoid fever outbreak. In 1908, chlorination began in New Jersey, and it quickly spread throughout the United States. From 1900 to 1960, chlorination cut cases of typhoid fever dramatically in the United States.

Chlorination also is used to kill bacteria in swimming pools. There is debate about the safety of some of the other products of chlorination. But chlorination continues to be the main way water is disinfected throughout the world.

INVESTIGATION

Materials

- safety glasses
- small piece of steel wool
- tongs
- Bunsen burner
- test-tube rack
- 4 test tubes
- hydrogen peroxide solution (H_2O_2)
- manganese dioxide (MnO_2)
- match
- wooden splint
- copper sulfate solution ($CuSO_4$)
- iron nail
- sodium carbonate solution (Na_2CO_3)
- calcium chloride solution ($CaCl_2$)

Observing Different Kinds of Reactions

Purpose

Can you predict the outcome of each reaction described on pages 167 and 168? In this investigation, you will study the four main types of chemical reactions.

Procedure

1. Copy the data table on a sheet of paper.

Reaction	Observations
1	
2	
3	
4	

2. Put on your safety glasses.

Reaction 1

3. Pick up a small piece of steel wool with a pair of tongs. Use the tongs to touch the steel wool to the flame of the Bunsen burner. **Safety alert: Be careful not to burn yourself. If you have long hair, be sure it is pulled back.** Record what happens.

Reaction 2

4. Fill a test tube to the halfway point with hydrogen peroxide (H_2O_2) solution. Add a tiny piece of manganese dioxide (MnO_2). The manganese dioxide will simply speed up the reaction. It is a catalyst. It is not a reactant itself. Observe what happens over the next few minutes.

5. Once the reaction is occurring quickly, use a match to light a wooden splint. **Safety alert: Be careful not to burn yourself. Pull back long hair.** Blow out the splint and immediately insert it into the test tube so that the glowing end is slightly above the liquid level. Record what happens.

Reaction 3

6. Fill a test tube to the halfway point with copper sulfate ($CuSO_4$) solution. Gently place an iron nail into the test tube. Record what happens.

Reaction 4

7. Add sodium carbonate (Na_2CO_3) solution to a test tube until it is one-third full.

8. Add calcium chloride ($CaCl_2$) solution to another test tube until it is one-third full.

9. Pour the contents of the second test tube into the first. Record what happens.

Questions and Conclusions

Copy the data table on your paper and complete it.

Reaction	Equation	Type of Reaction
1	$4Fe + 3O_2 \longrightarrow 2Fe_2O_3$	
2	$2H_2O_2 \longrightarrow 2H_2O + O_2$	
3	$Fe + CuSO_4 \longrightarrow FeSO_4 + Cu$	
4	$Na_2CO_3 + CaCl_2 \longrightarrow 2NaCl + CaCO_3$	

Explore Further

Remember, the chemicals on the right side of the arrow are the products. In which of the above equations on the product (right) side, would you put an upward arrow? In which would you put a downward arrow?

Chapter 6 S U M M A R Y

- A chemical reaction involves a change of substances into other substances.

- Reactions can be represented by chemical equations, which should be balanced for atoms.

- The law of conservation of matter states that matter cannot be created or destroyed in chemical and common physical changes.

- A combination of materials in which no reaction takes place is called a mixture.

- The four main types of chemical reactions are synthesis (A + B → AB), decomposition (AB → A + B), single replacement (A + BC → B + AC), and double replacement (AB + CD → AD + CB).

- In a synthesis reaction, elements combine to form a compound.

- In a decomposition reaction, a compound breaks down into simpler substances.

- In a single-replacement reaction, one element replaces another in a compound.

- In a double-replacement reaction, elements in two compounds are exchanged.

Science Words

balance, 157	double-replacement reaction, 165	reactant, 155
chemical equation, 155	law of conservation of matter, 156	single-replacement reaction, 164
chemical reaction, 150		solute, 151
coefficient, 157	mixture, 150	solution, 151
decomposition reaction, 162	precipitate, 165	solvent, 151
dissolve, 151	product, 155	synthesis reaction, 160

Chapter 6 REVIEW

Vocabulary Review

Word Bank

chemical equation

chemical reaction

coefficient

law of
   conservation
   of matter

mixture

precipitate

product

reactant

solute

solution

solvent

Choose the word or words from the Word Bank that best complete each sentence. Write the answer on a sheet of paper.

1. A chemical change in which elements are combined or rearranged is a _____.

2. A mixture in which one substance is dissolved in another is a _____.

3. A number placed before a formula in a chemical equation is a _____.

4. A statement that uses symbols, formulas, and numbers to stand for a chemical reaction is a _____.

5. A substance that is altered in a chemical reaction is a _____.

6. A substance that is formed in a chemical reaction is a _____.

7. A _____ is a solid that is formed in a chemical reaction; it usually sinks to the bottom of the solution.

8. A _____ dissolves one or more other substances.

9. A _____ is dissolved in a solution.

10. When substances are combined and no reaction occurs, a _____ is formed.

11. The _____ states that matter cannot be created or destroyed in chemical and common physical changes.

Concept Review

Match the equation in Column A with the kind of reaction it represents in Column B. Write the name of the reaction on your paper. You will use one answer twice.

Column A

12. $2SO_3 \rightarrow 2SO_2 + O_2$

13. $AgNO_3 + NaI \rightarrow AgI + NaNO_3$

14. $Zn + SnCl_2 \rightarrow ZnCl_2 + Sn$

15. $C + O_2 \rightarrow CO_2$

16. $C + H_2O \rightarrow CO + H_2$

Column B

A decomposition

B double replacement

C single replacement

D synthesis

Critical Thinking

Write the answer to each of these questions on your paper.

17. Explain what happens in a chemical reaction and what can cause it.

18. Describe what happens when a solute and a solvent are combined.

19. Balance the following equation by adding coefficients: $Al + O_2 \rightarrow Al_2O_3$. Then identify the reactant(s) and the product(s).

20. Explain what is happening in the photo.

Test-Taking Tip   When you review your notes to prepare for a test, use a marker to highlight key words and example problems.

7 Motion

Do you recognize the animal in the photograph? Have you ever seen a cheetah run? Cheetahs are the fastest land mammals in the world. How fast can a cheetah run? It can cover approximately 200 meters in 7 seconds. It can accelerate from 0 to 29 meters per second in 3 seconds. But what do these numbers actually tell us about the speed of a cheetah? In Chapter 7, you will find out about the laws of motion. You will learn what motion is, how to measure it, and how scientists describe it.

Organize Your Thoughts

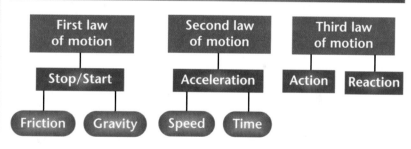

Goals for Learning

◆ To define and explain motion and speed

◆ To calculate speed, distance, and time

◆ To use a graph to describe motion and make predictions

◆ To calculate acceleration and deceleration

◆ To define and explain force

◆ To explain and apply Newton's three laws of motion

◆ To define and explain gravity

◆ To explain the law of universal gravitation

Objectives

After reading this lesson, you should be able to

◆ define and explain motion.

◆ calculate elapsed time.

◆ explain speed and average speed.

◆ perform calculations involving speed.

The earth travels in space. A car carries you from place to place. You walk to the store. An amusement park ride spins you around. What do all these actions have in common? In each case, objects are changing position in space. We say they are moving. **Motion** is simply a change of position.

All change, including change in position, takes place over time. To help you understand motion, you will begin by learning how the passage of time is measured.

Elapsed Time

Suppose you have just taken an airplane trip from Miami to New York in the same time zone. Your flight began at 8:00 P.M. It ended at 11:00 P.M. How long did this trip take?

To answer this question, you calculate the **elapsed time.** Elapsed time is the amount of time that passes from one event to another. To calculate elapsed time, just subtract the time of the earlier event from the time of the later event.

In the case of the flight, subtract the departure time from the arrival time.

Motion

A change in position

Elapsed time

The length of time that passes from one event to another

The motion of an object is always judged with respect to another object or point.

```
  11:00   arrival time
-  8:00   departure time
   3      hours travel time = elapsed time
```

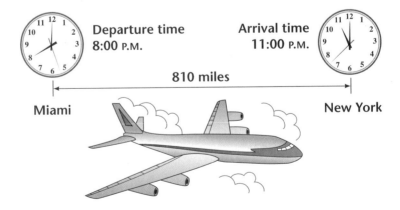

Departure time 8:00 P.M. Arrival time 11:00 P.M.

Miami   810 miles   New York

Speed

When something is moving, it is natural to wonder how fast it is going, or what its **speed** is. Speed tells how fast an object is moving. The more distance a moving object covers in a given time, the greater its speed. For example, a cheetah can travel at a speed of 100 kilometers per hour. But an ant can cover only 36 meters in an hour. The cheetah has greater speed than the ant.

Notice that speed uses two units—**distance** and time. Distance is the length of the path between two points. It is the length of the path traveled by the object in motion. You can use the following formula to find the speed of an object.

$$\text{average speed} = \frac{\text{distance}}{\text{time}}$$

Suppose the airplane mentioned on page 174 traveled 810 miles between the two cities. The elapsed time for the trip was 3 hours. You can use the formula to calculate the speed of the airplane. Look at the example.

EXAMPLE

$$\text{average speed} = \frac{810 \text{ miles}}{3 \text{ hours}}$$

$$\text{average speed} = \frac{270 \text{ miles}}{1 \text{ hour}}$$

The speed of the airplane is 270 miles per hour. This means that each hour the plane traveled 270 miles.

In the example, it is unlikely that the airplane traveled at a constant speed of 270 miles per hour during the entire flight. A plane starts and stops very slowly. Between the beginning and the end of the trip, the speed varies during the flight. The speed calculated is actually the average speed. The actual speed at any particular moment could be more or less than the average speed. The speed at a particular moment is called the instantaneous speed.

Speed does not have to be measured in miles per hour.

Think about a race at a track meet where the distance around the track is 400 meters. Suppose a runner completes the race in 40 seconds. What was the runner's speed? Look at the example.

EXAMPLE

$$\text{average speed} = \frac{\text{distance}}{\text{time}}$$

$$\text{average speed} = \frac{400 \text{ meters}}{40 \text{ seconds}}$$

$$\text{average speed} = \frac{10 \text{ meters}}{1 \text{ second}}$$

The average speed of the runner is 10 meters per second. The runner covers an average distance of 10 meters each second.

Calculating Distance

Suppose you are taking a trip by car. You know you can travel about 50 miles an hour on the roads you will be using. You also know you can travel about 6 hours a day. You would like to know how far you can go in one day. In other words, you would like to calculate distance. Since you already know your speed and your time, you can use the formula for finding speed to calculate distance. Study the example. Notice how the hours cancel out of the equation.

EXAMPLE

$$\text{average speed} = \frac{\text{distance}}{\text{time}}$$

$$\text{distance} = \text{speed} \times \text{time}$$

$$\text{distance} = \frac{50 \text{ miles}}{1 \text{ hour}} \times 6 \text{ hours}$$

$$\text{distance} = 300 \text{ miles}$$

Calculating Time

Sometimes you might want to figure out how long it will take to cover a certain distance. Suppose you have a job marking the lines on a sports field. The distance to be marked is 80 meters. You mark at a speed of 50 meters per minute. How much time will it take you to mark the whole line? The formula for speed also can be rearranged to solve for the time. Look at the example.

The answer in the first example on this page—50 meters/minute—has a slash mark. The slash mark stands for the word *per*. The answer in this example is read as *50 meters per minute.*

EXAMPLE

$$speed = \frac{distance}{time}$$

$$time = \frac{distance}{speed}$$

$$time = \frac{80 \text{ meters}}{50 \text{ meters/1 minute}}$$

When you divide by a fraction, you invert the fraction and multiply.

EXAMPLE

$$time = \frac{80 \text{ meters}}{1} \times \frac{1 \text{ minute}}{50 \text{ meters}}$$

$$time = \frac{80 \text{ minutes}}{50}$$

$$time = 1.6 \text{ minutes}$$

It would take you 1.6 minutes to mark the whole line.

Copy this table on a sheet of paper. Calculate the average speed for each of the items. The first one is done for you.

	Distance Traveled	Time	Average Speed
1.	30 miles	5 hours	6 miles/hour
2.	100 yards	13 seconds	
3.	10 centimeters	5 seconds	
4.	380 kilometers	2 hours	
5.	3,825 feet	30 minutes	

Find the answer to each word problem. Write the answers on your paper. Use one of these formulas and show your work.

$$\text{distance} = \text{speed} \times \text{time}$$

$$\text{time} = \frac{\text{distance}}{\text{speed}}$$

6. A train's average speed is 120 kilometers per hour. Its elapsed time is 2 hours. How far did it travel?

7. A student rides her bike to school. Her school is 5 miles from her home. She travels at an average rate of 16 miles per hour. How much time does she need for this trip?

8. Suppose it takes a plane 5 hours to travel from Philadelphia to San Francisco. It travels at an average speed of 500 miles per hour. What is the approximate distance between the two cities?

9. A rocket can travel at an average rate of 18,000 miles per hour. How far will the rocket travel in 4.5 hours?

10. A man rode on a motorcycle for 2 hours. His average speed was 45 miles per hour. How far did he travel?

Sometimes it is useful to use a graph to show motion. Suppose
that a car traveled for 5 hours. The following table shows the
elapsed time and the distance traveled by the car.

Time and Distance	
Elapsed Time (hours)	**Distance Traveled (kilometers)**
0	0
1	50
2	100
3	150
4	200
5	250

The information in the table above appears on the line graph
below. The graph shows distance and time. Points have been
plotted for the car. For example, the first point is the one that
shows a distance of 50 km at a time of 1 hour.

Notice that the line on the graph is straight, not curved. That
means that the car is traveling at a **constant speed.** Constant
speed is speed that does not change. For example, observe the
first point for the car on the graph. It shows that 50 kilometers
are covered in 1 hour. What is the car's speed?

Constant speed

*Speed that does
not change*

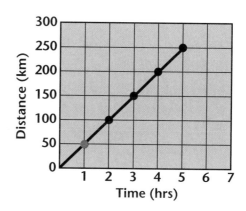

$$\text{speed} = \frac{\text{distance}}{\text{time}}$$

$$\text{speed} = \frac{50 \text{ kilometers}}{1 \text{ hour}}$$

speed = 50 kilometers/hr

The car's speed during the first hour is 50 kilometers per hour. Likewise, the second hour, the car's speed would be 50 kilometers per hour.

EXAMPLE

$$\text{speed} = \frac{\text{distance}}{\text{time}}$$

$$\text{speed} = \frac{100 \text{ kilometers}}{2 \text{ hours}}$$

speed = 50 kilometers/hr

If you continue to calculate the speed at each of the times, you will find that the car travels at a speed of 50 kilometers per hour each hour. The car is traveling at a constant speed.

Finding Unknown Distances

Suppose you want to know the distance traveled by the car at the end of 4.5 hours. You can use a graph to find the distances at times that are not shown. Use the method below.

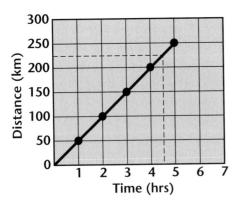

1. Copy the graph onto a sheet of paper.

2. Find the time of 4.5 hours along the time axis. This is halfway between 4 hours and 5 hours.

3. Draw a vertical (up-and-down) line from this point on the time axis up to the plotted line.

4. From the point where the vertical line touches the plotted line, draw a horizontal (side-to-side) line to the distance axis.

5. Estimate the distance on the scale. It is the point where the horizontal line touches the distance axis. The distance is about 225 kilometers.

Predicting Distances

You know from the graph how far the car travels in 5 hours. But what if you need to predict where the car will be at some later time? You can use the graph to make this kind of prediction.

For example, suppose you would like to know how far the car will travel in 6 hours. Follow these steps.

1. Copy the graph onto a sheet of paper.

2. Extend the plotted graph line as shown.

3. Draw a vertical line from the 6-hour line to the plotted line.

4. From the point where the vertical line and the extended graph line touch, draw a horizontal line to the distance axis. Then read the approximate distance. It is about 300 kilometers.

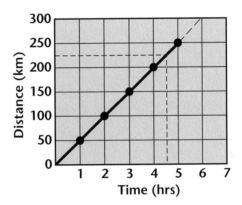

You know quantities are velocities, not speeds, when they include information about speed and direction. These types of quantities are called vector quantities. Vector quantities have size, such as speed, and direction.

Velocity

So far we have talked only about the speed of motion. But what about the direction of motion? That can be important, too. For example, you might tell someone that you drove your car north at 90 kilometers per hour. You are telling about the **velocity** of the car. Speed tells how fast an object moves. Velocity tells the speed and direction in which an object is moving.

Look at the figure below. Suppose you walk 5 kilometers in an hour in an eastward direction. Your velocity would be 5 kilometers per hour eastward.

As you walk, you pass another person traveling westward at 5 kilometers per hour. Both you and the other person have the same speed—5 kilometers per hour. However, your velocities are different because you are going in different directions.

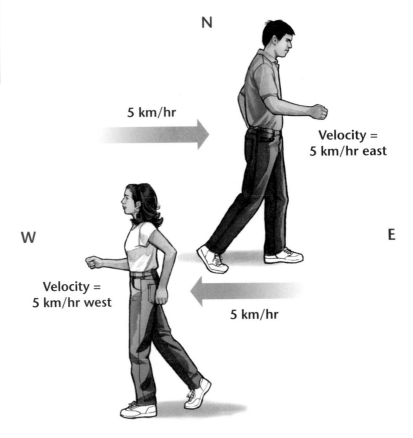

N

5 km/hr

Velocity = 5 km/hr east

W   E

Velocity = 5 km/hr west

5 km/hr

S

Varying Speed

Few objects move at constant velocity or speed. Look at the following graph. It shows the changes in speed as a family drove a car along a road. Notice that the plotted line in this graph is not straight. This tells you that the car's speed was not constant. But you can still use the information in the graph to find the average speed of the car. You can see that at the end of 6 hours, the car had traveled 300 kilometers. The average speed is shown in the example below.

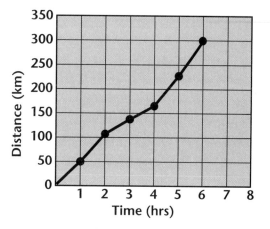

EXAMPLE

$$\text{speed} = \frac{\text{distance}}{\text{time}}$$

$$\text{speed} = \frac{300 \text{ kilometers}}{6 \text{ hours}}$$

$$\text{speed} = 50 \text{ kilometers/hr}$$

Technology Note

Speed skaters wear speed suits to help them move faster in competition. A speed suit covers a skater's body like a second skin. Speed suits are made of different fabrics so different body parts have less air resistance. By reducing air resistance, skaters subtract critical fractions of seconds from their race times. The time saved can be the difference between winning and losing.

Lesson 2   R E V I E W

1. Use the data in the table to make a line graph.

Elapsed Time (hours)	Distance Traveled (kilometers)
0	0
1	100
2	200
3	300
4	400
5	500

2. What does the line graph you drew tell about the data?

3. Use your graph to find the distance traveled for each of these times.

   A 3 hours   **B** 4.5 hours   **C** 7 hours   **D** 10 hours

4. How you can tell whether speed is constant or varying by looking at a graph of distance versus time? Explain your answer.

5. Use the data in the table to make a line graph of distance versus time.

Elapsed Time (minutes)	Distance Traveled (meters)
0	0
1	200
2	340
3	580
4	760
5	900

Finding Speed

Purpose

What formula would you use to calculate speed using distance and time? In this investigation, you will calculate speed by measuring distance and time and use a graph to show motion.

Procedure

1. Copy the data table on a sheet of paper.

Length (meters)	Time (seconds)	Speed (distance/time)

2. Put on your safety glasses.

3. Work on a large table, as directed by your teacher. At one end of the table, place one end of the meterstick on the edge of a book. The ruler's groove should be on top. Refer to the figure on page 186.

4. Set a book at the other end of the table. Measure the length from the book to the edge of the ruler on the table. Record the length in your data table.

5. Set the marble at the top of the ruler's groove. Release the marble. Let it roll down the groove. Do not push it. Start the stopwatch when the marble leaves the ruler. Stop timing when the marble reaches the book at the end of the table. Record the time in your data table.

6. Use your data to calculate the average speed of the marble, in meters per second. Use this formula.

$$\text{speed} = \frac{\text{distance}}{\text{time}}$$

Questions and Conclusions

1. Make a graph with distance in meters on the vertical (up-and-down) axis. Place time in seconds on the horizontal (left-to-right) axis. Extend the axes twice as far as you need to in order to graph your data. Plot one point where 0 seconds crosses 0 meters, to show the beginning of the roll. Plot a second point, using the distance and time values you recorded. Connect the two points with a straight line.

2. Use the graph you made to estimate the distance the marble traveled after it had been moving for half the recorded time.

3. Extend the graph. Estimate the distance the marble would have gone if it had traveled for twice the recorded time.

Explore Further

What do you think would happen if you stacked another book on top of the book that is under the ruler? How would the graph for this setup look? How would this graph be different from the graph you made?

After reading this lesson, you should be able to

◆ define and explain acceleration.

◆ perform calculations involving acceleration.

◆ define and explain deceleration.

◆ perform calculations involving deceleration.

Acceleration

The rate of change in velocity

A car stopped at a traffic light is not moving. But when the light turns green, the driver steps on the gas pedal. The car moves forward. Its speed increases. If the car moves away quickly, its velocity changes quickly. Some people might say that it has good "pickup."

Cars stopped at a stoplight accelerate as they begin to move forward.

In science, the word **acceleration**—rather than pickup—is used to describe a change in velocity. Acceleration also tells the rate at which velocity is changing. You can find the acceleration of an object by using this formula.

$$\text{acceleration} = \frac{\text{change in velocity}}{\text{change in time}}$$

A car starts from a stopped position. At the end of 5 seconds, it has a speed of 40 km/hr. Follow this method to find the car's acceleration.

1. Find the change in speed. To do so, subtract the beginning speed from the final speed.

40 km/hr	final speed
−0 km/hr	original speed
40 km/hr	change in speed

2. Divide the change in speed by the time required to make the change, 5 seconds. The result is the acceleration.

$$\text{acceleration} = \frac{\text{change in speed}}{\text{change in time}}$$

$$\text{acceleration} = \frac{40 \text{ km}/1 \text{ hr}}{5 \text{ sec}/1}$$

$$\text{acceleration} = \frac{40 \text{ km}}{1 \text{ hr}} \times \frac{1}{5 \text{ sec}}$$

$$\text{acceleration} = 8 \text{ km/hr per sec}$$

The answer is read *8 kilometers per hour per second.* This means that the car's speed increases by 8 km per hour during every second of the acceleration.

Acceleration can also refer to a change in direction. For example, suppose a car moves at a constant speed around a curve. The car is accelerating because the direction in which it is traveling is changing.

The sky diver decelerates to land.

Deceleration

Acceleration is the rate of change in velocity. The examples of acceleration you have read about involved increases in speed. Objects can also slow down. When they slow down, they are said to decelerate. **Deceleration** is the rate of slowdown. The sky diver in the photo accelerates until the parachute opens. Then the sky diver decelerates.

Because deceleration is a form of acceleration, you can use the formula for acceleration to find deceleration. The result is a negative number instead of a positive number. A negative number is a number that is less than zero.

To understand deceleration, think about this example. A car is traveling at 20 km/hr. The driver suddenly puts on the brakes. The car comes to a complete stop 4 seconds later. You can follow this method to calculate the acceleration.

1. The original speed was 20 km/hr. The final speed is 0 km/hr. Therefore, the change in speed is calculated as follows.

$$
\begin{array}{ll}
0 \text{ km/hr} & \text{final speed} \\
-20 \text{ km/hr} & \text{original speed} \\
\hline
-20 \text{ km/hr} & \text{change in speed}
\end{array}
$$

2. Divide the change in speed by the change in time to obtain the acceleration.

$$
\text{acceleration} = \frac{-20 \text{ km/1 hr}}{4 \text{ sec/1}}
$$

$$
\text{acceleration} = \frac{-20 \text{ km}}{1 \text{ hr}} \times \frac{1}{4 \text{ sec}}
$$

$$
\text{acceleration} = -5 \text{ km/hr per sec}
$$

The acceleration is –5 km/hour for each second. The minus (–) sign to the left of the 5 means that the number is less than zero. Therefore, this can also be expressed as a deceleration of 5 km per hour per second. The word *decelerating* already expresses the idea of negative acceleration. So, the negative sign does not have to be used if the answer is given as deceleration rather than acceleration.

Science in Your Life

When is a baseball moving fastest?

Pitchers have found ways to increase the velocity of their pitches—curveballs, fastballs, and sliders. But whatever the pitch, the ball starts slowing down when it leaves the pitcher's hand.

The pitcher puts the first force on the ball. The greatest acceleration occurs between the pitcher's windup and the release of the ball. While the ball is still in the pitcher's hand, it moves forward with increasing velocity. Once the ball is thrown, its forward velocity cannot increase. There is no longer a force acting on the ball in the direction of home plate.

Other forces are acting on the ball. Gravity pulls it toward the ground. Air resistance pushes the ball in the opposite direction of the motion. This causes the ball to decelerate. After it leaves

the pitcher's hand, a baseball loses forward velocity. This loss occurs at the rate of about one kilometer per hour every 1.3 meters. By the time the ball reaches home plate, it has slowed down about 14 kilometers per hour.

Hitters depend on Newton's Laws to give them a fighting chance against a sizzling fastball.

Lesson 3   REVIEW

Complete the table by finding the acceleration for each item. Some of your answers might be negative numbers. They express deceleration in terms of negative acceleration. The first one is done for you.

	Beginning Speed	Ending Speed	Elapsed Time	Acceleration
1.	40 km/hr	50 km/hr	5 sec	2 km/hr per sec
2.	20 km/sec	109 km/sec	4 sec	
3.	20 km/hr	55 km/hr	7 sec	
4.	0 m/sec	10 m/sec	10 sec	
5.	30 mm/sec	22 mm/sec	0.2 sec	
6.	20 mm/sec	22 mm/sec	0.2 sec	
7.	25 cm/sec	10 cm/sec	0.5 sec	
8.	60 km/hr	70 km/hr	2 sec	
9.	30 m/min	60 m/min	10 sec	
10.	5 cm/sec	10 cm/sec	0.5 sec	

Achievements in Science

Special Theory of Relativity

In 1905, Albert Einstein proposed his special theory of relativity. A main idea in Einstein's theory involves the speed of light. Einstein said that light always travels at the same speed and that nothing travels faster than light. The measurement of the speed of light never changes.

Einstein showed that time and space could not be considered separately. He concluded that space and time change when things move near the speed of light. Metersticks measure space; clocks measure time. At very high speeds, clocks slow down and metersticks get shorter. Measuring length and time depends on the object's speed relative to the measurer's speed. This is because measurement of the speed of light remains constant.

Einstein's conclusions shocked other physicists and still are challenging to understand. In daily life, we do not see length and time change with speed. But we also do not move at speeds close to the speed of light. Einstein's ideas have been proven mathematically and in the real world. They have changed the way scientists view the universe.

Objectives

After reading this lesson, you should be able to

◆ explain what is meant by a force.

◆ define and explain friction.

◆ explain and apply the three laws of motion.

Force

A push or a pull

Friction

A force that opposes motion and that occurs when things slide or roll over each other

Did You Know?

Automobile designers try to reduce air resistance from friction to make cars more efficient.

Sir Isaac Newton was a scientist who lived about 350 years ago. He studied changes in the motion of objects. From his studies, he was able to propose three laws to explain motion.

The First Law of Motion

If you wanted to move a large box that is resting on the floor, you would have to push or pull it. We call this push or pull a **force.** Whenever any object changes its velocity or accelerates, a force causes the change in motion.

> Newton's first law of motion states that if no force acts on an object at rest, it will remain at rest. The law also says that if the object is moving, it will continue moving at the same speed and in the same direction if no force acts on it.

Let's use an example to explain the second part of the law. A car on flat ground will roll to a stop if you take your foot off the gas pedal. The car slows down because an invisible force is at work. This invisible force is called **friction.** Friction is a force that opposes motion and occurs when things slide or roll over each other. Friction resists the movement of one surface past another. The rougher the surfaces are, the greater the friction.

The figure illustrates how friction helps stop a moving car. Notice the air resistance. Air resistance is a form of friction. It occurs when molecules of air touch the surface of the car.

Air resistance

Friction between road and moving tires

Inertia

The tendency of an object to resist changes in its motion

Technology Note

Cars need friction to turn without skidding. The usual way to increase friction is to add weight. But adding weight to a car slows it down. Having a spoiler lets air push a car against the road, which increases friction. A spoiler keeps the car's tires from spinning so it moves faster.

Science Myth

If an object is not moving, that means there is no force acting upon it.

Fact: Even when an object is not moving, forces are acting upon it. When a book is sitting on a table, gravity is pulling the book downward. At the same time, the table is pushing upward on the book.

An object tends to resist changes in its motion. This tendency to resist changes in motion is called **inertia.** Inertia causes objects at rest to stay at rest. It also causes moving objects to continue moving.

The inertia of an object depends on its mass. The greater the mass of an object, the greater the force needed to cause a given change in its motion. For example, suppose you tried to push two rocks—a large one and a small one—across the ground. You would notice that if you apply the same push (force) to both rocks, the smaller rock will move faster after a certain amount of time. To make both rocks move at the same speed, you would have to push the large rock harder. The large rock has more mass than the small rock. Therefore, it has more inertia.

The Second Law of Motion

Newton's second law of motion says that the amount of force needed to produce a given change in the motion of an object depends on the mass of the object. The larger the mass, the more force is needed to give it a certain acceleration.

Suppose you drive a truck to a brickyard to pick up some bricks. After you load the bricks into the truck, you leave the brickyard. On the drive home, you notice that it takes longer to reach the same speed than it did when the truck was empty. What causes the difference? The truck full of bricks has more mass than the empty truck. So if you apply the same force to the truck both times (push the gas pedal the same amount), the truck with the bricks (more mass) will take longer to reach a given velocity.

Newton's second law can be written as follows.

$$\text{force} = \text{mass} \times \text{acceleration}, \text{ or } F = ma$$

A small force acting on a large mass will cause very little change in motion. A large force acting on a small mass will cause a much larger change in motion, that is, a greater acceleration.

The Third Law of Motion

Newton's third law of motion says that if an object exerts a force on a second object, the second object will always exert a force on the first object. This force will be equal to the force exerted by the first object. But the force will be in the opposite direction. This law is sometimes stated: For every action, there is an equal and opposite reaction.

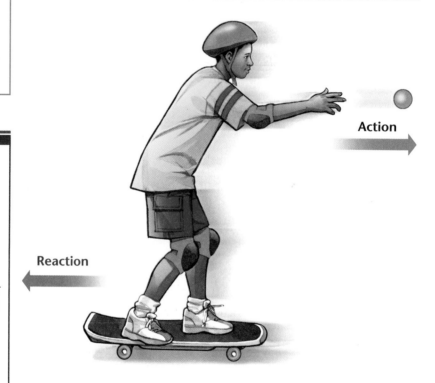

Action

Reaction

In the figure, the boy is standing on a skateboard, holding a ball in his hand. When he throws the ball forward, the boy and the skateboard move in the opposite direction from the ball. They move backward. This is an example of action and reaction. The action is throwing the ball. The reaction is the force of the ball on the boy. The boy is standing on the skateboard. Therefore, the skateboard moves backward. The action of throwing the ball causes the equal and opposite reaction of the skateboard moving backward.

Write your answers to these questions in complete sentences on a sheet of paper.

1. What are Newton's three laws of motion?

2. When a marble is rolled along a floor, what force or forces cause it to slow down and stop?

3. If an object is at rest, what must happen for it to begin moving?

4. What is the reaction force when a hammer hits a nail?

5. Car A has twice the mass of car B. If the same force is used to push each car separately, how will their acceleration differ?

▼◄▲▼◄▲▼◄▲▼◄▲▼◄▲▼◄▲▼◄▲▼◄▲▼◄▲▼◄▲▼◄▲▼◄▲▼◄▲▼◄▲▼◄▲▼◄▲▼

Science at Work

Wind Tunnel Technician

Wind tunnel technicians help study the effects of wind on airplanes and other objects. In a wind tunnel, air is blown at an object and instruments record the effects. Wind tunnel technicians operate the tunnels and run the computers that collect data.

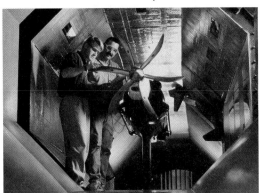

They also watch tests to be sure that they run smoothly and nothing breaks down.

Wind tunnel technicians usually have a two-year degree in a technical or engineering field. They also have engineering work experience. They often get on-the-job training as well.

Wind tunnel technicians must be observant and good with details. They must also have strong computer skills.

Objectives

After reading this lesson, you should be able to

◆ define and explain gravity.

◆ state the law of universal gravitation.

◆ explain how air resistance and gravity affect acceleration.

Gravity

The force of attraction between any two objects that have mass

Law of universal gravitation

Gravitational force depends on the mass of the two objects involved and on the distance between them

One force with which you are probably familiar is the force of **gravity.** You might know that gravity keeps you from flying off the earth. If you are like many people, you might think of gravity as the pull exerted by Earth on other objects. But gravity is a force of attraction between any two objects that have mass.

The Law of Universal Gravitation

The gravitational force between two objects depends on the product of the masses of the two objects. Earth and the moon are two objects that have large masses. The gravitational force between them is large. Smaller objects, such as people, trees, and buildings, have much smaller gravitational forces because they have less mass. These forces are so small that they are very difficult to observe.

Mass is not the only thing that affects the pull of gravity. The distance between objects also determines how strong the force is due to gravity. The greater the distance between objects, the smaller the gravitational force is between them.

Think about an astronaut. When the astronaut is on Earth, gravity keeps him or her on the surface. The earth pulls on the astronaut. But the astronaut also pulls on the earth. The earth's gravity is strongest near the earth's surface. As the astronaut travels away from the earth in a spaceship, the pull of Earth's gravity gets weaker. But no matter how far from the earth the astronaut travels, the earth still exerts a force. In fact, Earth's gravity extends millions of kilometers into space.

The gravitational force of the sun, acting on the earth, keeps the earth in its orbit. The gravitational force prevents Earth from traveling away into space. Gravity also keeps the planets in space. And each planet exerts a gravitational force on nearby objects.

Science Myth

Raindrops keep falling faster and faster until they reach the ground.

Fact: A falling object's velocity increases but only up to terminal velocity. As velocity increases, air resistance increases. When the force of the air resistance equals the object's weight, the object's velocity no longer increases. This is called terminal velocity. If raindrops did not reach terminal velocity, they would crash through buildings.

Sir Isaac Newton, who stated the three laws of motion, put these ideas about gravity together in the **law of universal gravitation.** That law says two things. First, gravitational force depends on the product of the masses of the two objects involved. Second, the gravitational force depends on the distance between the objects.

Gravity and Acceleration

Have you ever jumped off a low diving board and then a high one? If so, you might have noticed that when you jumped from the higher board, you were moving faster when you struck the water. And you hit the water harder. That is because the force of gravity causes an object to speed up as it falls.

Gravity causes all objects to have the same acceleration as they fall. But another force—air resistance—also acts on a falling object. (Recall that air resistance is a form of friction. It is caused by molecules of air rubbing against a moving object.) Air resistance causes objects to fall at different speeds. The amount of air resistance acting on a moving object depends on the shape of the object. You can see in the figure that a sheet of paper will fall more slowly than a small stone. The reason is because the mass of the paper is spread out over a wider, thinner area than that of the stone. More molecules of air hit the surface of the paper.

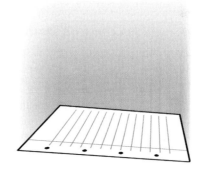

Write your answers to these questions in complete sentences on a sheet of paper.

1. What is gravity?

2. What three factors affect the pull of gravity?

3. Weight is a measure of the pull of gravity on an object. Use this information to explain why an astronaut weighs less on the moon than on Earth.

4. How does gravity affect acceleration?

5. How does gravity affect deceleration?

Achievements in Science

Law of Uniformly Accelerated Motion

Aristotle believed that heavier objects fall faster than lighter ones. He believed that objects that weigh twice as much as others fall twice as fast. For about 1,000 years, scientists generally agreed with Aristotle's thinking.

In the early 1600s, Galileo conducted the first experiment that showed that Aristotle was wrong. Galileo faced challenges in constructing his experiment. He could not simply drop objects from a tall building for two reasons. First, the clocks of his time were not accurate. Second, he had no way to measure the speed when each object hit the earth.

Instead, Galileo tested Aristotle's theory by rolling objects on a slanted ramp. He determined their positions at equal time periods, using his own pulse as a clock.

Galileo's experiments showed that all objects experience constant acceleration when air resistance is not considered. No matter how much they weigh, all objects fall at a steady rate of acceleration. This type of acceleration is known as free fall. Free fall acceleration has its own symbol, g. At sea level, g equals 9.8 m/sec^2.

7-2

INVESTIGATION

Materials

- ◆ safety glasses
- ◆ string, 3 meters long
- ◆ 2 straws
- ◆ 2 chairs
- ◆ 2 long balloons
- ◆ masking tape

Newton's Third Law of Motion

Purpose

What happens when you release a balloon that is filled with air? This investigation will demonstrate action and reaction using balloons filled with air.

Procedure

Part A

1. Copy the data table on a sheet of paper.

Part A Observations	Part B Observations

2. Put on your safety glasses.

3. Thread the string through the two straws.

4. Tie the ends of the string to the backs of two chairs.

5. Blow up a balloon. Hold the end closed. Have a classmate use masking tape to attach the balloon to one of the straws, as shown in Figure A. Position the balloon near the end of the string.

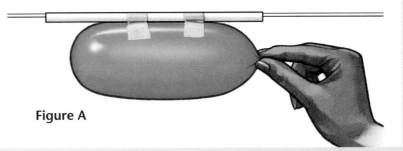

Figure A

6. Release the balloon. Record your observations.

Part B

7. Tape the ends of the two straws together. Blow up the balloon again. Hold the end closed. Ask a classmate to attach the balloon to one of the straws.

8. Blow up another balloon so it has about as much air as the first balloon. Ask a classmate to attach the balloon to the other straw as shown in Figure B.

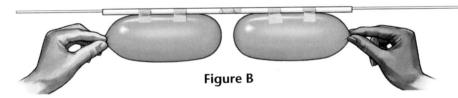

Figure B

9. Release both balloons at the same time. Record your observations.

Questions and Conclusions

1. In Part A, in what direction does the escaping air move?

2. In Part A, in what direction does the balloon move?

3. How does Part A demonstrate Newton's third law of motion?

4. In Part B, in what direction do the balloons move?

5. In Part B, describe the directions of the forces to explain what the balloons do.

Explore Further

In Part A, if you attached a weight to the balloon, how would that affect its motion?

Chapter 7 SUMMARY

- Motion is a change in position.

- Elapsed time is the time between events. It is calculated by subtracting the time of the earlier event from the time of the later event.

- Speed is the rate at which the position of an object changes. It is equal to distance divided by time.

- The formula for speed can be rearranged for calculation of distance or time.

- Graphs of distance versus time can be used to describe motion and to make predictions about distances.

- Velocity tells about the speed and direction of a moving object.

- Objects may travel at varying speed rather than constant speed.

- Acceleration is the rate of change in velocity. Acceleration equals the change in velocity divided by the change in time.

- Deceleration is the rate of slowdown. Deceleration occurs whenever acceleration is negative. It is usually calculated as negative acceleration.

- A force is a push or a pull.

- Newton's first law of motion states that an object remains at rest or keeps moving at constant speed unless an outside force acts on it.

- Newton's second law of motion states that the amount of force needed to change the motion of an object depends on the mass of the object.

- Newton's third law of motion states that for every action there is an equal and opposite reaction.

- Gravity is a force of attraction between any two objects that have mass. According to the law of universal gravitation, the greater the masses are, the greater the force is. The greater the distance is, the less the force is.

- Gravity causes all falling objects to have the same acceleration. Air resistance acts on falling objects to slow them down.

Science Words

acceleration, 187	force, 192	law of universal
constant speed, 179	friction, 192	gravitation, 196
deceleration, 188	gravity, 196	motion, 174
distance, 175	inertia, 193	speed, 175
elapsed time, 174		velocity, 182

Chapter 7 REVIEW

Word Bank

force

friction

inertia

law of universal gravitation

motion

Vocabulary Review

Choose a word or words from the Word Bank that best complete each sentence. Write the answer on a sheet of paper.

1. Newton put ideas about gravity together in the _____.

2. A change in position is called _____.

3. A push or pull is called _____.

4. When things slide or roll over each other, _____ occurs.

5. The tendency to resist changes in motion is called _____.

Concept Review

Choose the answer that best completes each sentence. Write the letter of the answer on your paper.

6. To find the speed of an object, you need to know _____ and time.
   A motion   B distance   C acceleration   D elapsed time

7. The length of time that passes from one event to another is _____.
   A average speed   C elapsed time
   B constant speed   D inertia

8. You can calculate acceleration by _____.
   A adding change in velocity and change in time
   B subtracting change in time from change in velocity
   C multiplying change in velocity and change in time
   D dividing change in velocity by change in time

9. If the result of calculating acceleration is a negative number, an object is _____.
   A speeding up   C decelerating
   B moving at a constant speed   D moving uphill

10. The formula for calculating force is _____.
    A mass + acceleration   C mass × acceleration
    B acceleration − mass   D mass ÷ acceleration

11. The law that states that if no force acts on an object at rest, it will remain at rest is _____.

A Newton's first law of motion

B Newton's second law of motion

C Newton's third law of motion

D the law of universal gravitation

Critical Thinking

Write the answer to each of these questions on your paper.

12. The figure below shows the motion of a bike. Calculate the speed of the bike.

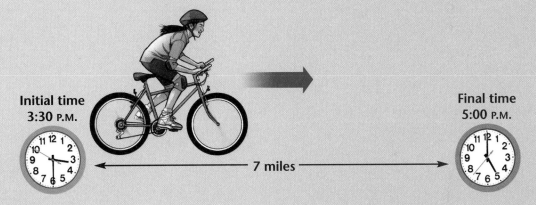

Initial time 3:30 P.M. 7 miles Final time 5:00 P.M.

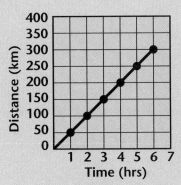

13. The graph shows distance and time for 6 hours for a train moving at a constant speed. Use the graph to predict how far the train will have traveled at the end of 7 hours. Explain how you used the graph to make your prediction.

14. Why does it take an empty bus less time than a bus filled with people to reach the same speed?

15. How does mass affect gravity?

Test-Taking Tip When studying for a test, review any tests or quizzes you took earlier that cover the same information.

8

Work and Machines

The falling water in a dam has a lot of mechanical energy. We can harness that mechanical energy and turn it into electrical energy. We do this through a machine called a turbine. A turbine converts the mechanical energy of the water into electrical energy. In Chapter 8, you will learn about six main forms of stored energy—mechanical, electrical, chemical, heat, nuclear, and radiant. You also will explore the nature of work and how scientists measure work. And you will learn how machines make work easier.

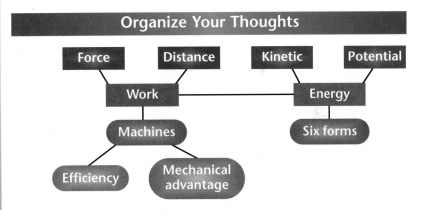

Organize Your Thoughts

Force — Distance — Kinetic — Potential

Work — Energy

Machines — Six forms

Efficiency — Mechanical advantage

Goals for Learning

◆ To define and explain work and power

◆ To define and explain energy

◆ To name six forms of energy

◆ To describe the classes of levers

◆ To calculate efficiency and mechanical advantage

◆ To describe six types of simple machines

You probably do some "work" around your home. What things do you consider work? You might think of ironing clothes, washing dishes, taking out the garbage, and sweeping the floors. In everyday language, we use the word *work* as another word for *labor*.

Scientific Meaning of Work

To scientists, however, **work** is what happens when an object changes its position by moving in the direction of the force that is being applied. Remember, a force is a push or a pull.

Suppose you struggled for an hour to lift a very heavy box, but you could not budge it. No work was done in the scientific sense, because the box did not move. If you rolled a ball down a ramp, however, work was done. The reason is the ball changed its direction due to the force of gravity.

Work

What happens when an object changes its position by moving in the direction of the force that is being applied

Measuring Work

How can you measure work? You can start by measuring how much force is used to do the work. Spring scales, like the one shown on page 207, are used to measure force. In the metric system, force is measured in newtons. The spring scale shows that the apple is exerting a force of 1 newton.

To measure work, you must also measure the distance (in meters) through which the force acted. To find out how much work was done, use this formula.

$$\text{work} = \text{force} \times \text{distance}$$

When Sarah lifts the box, she is doing work.

Your answer will be in newton-meters. Scientists have a simpler name for a newton-meter. It is called a **joule**. A joule is the metric unit of work. When calculating work, your answer will be in joules.

Suppose a woman is pushing a bike. She uses a force of 2 newtons and pushes the bike a distance of 10 meters. How much work did she do?

EXAMPLE

work = force × distance
work = 2 newtons × 10 meters
work = 20 newton-meters
work = 20 joules

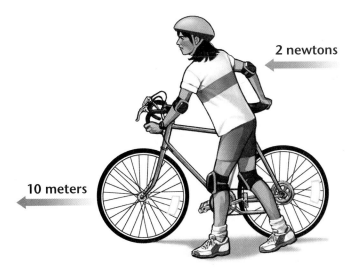

2 newtons

10 meters

Because force, distance, and work are always related, you can calculate any one of them if you know the other two. For example, if you know how much work was done and you know the distance, you can calculate how much force was used. Take the amount of work done and divide it by the distance.

$$\text{force} = \frac{\text{work}}{\text{distance}}$$

If you know how much work was done and how much force was needed, you can calculate the distance. Take the amount of work done and divide it by the amount of force that was used.

$$\text{distance} = \frac{\text{work}}{\text{force}}$$

Write your answers to these questions in complete sentences on a sheet of paper.

1. What is the scientific meaning of work?

2. What must you know to find the amount of work done on an object?

3. What is the metric unit of work?

4. A man pushed a table, using a force of 8 newtons. He moved the table 13 meters. How much work did he do?

5. One person solved 40 math problems in her head. Another person picked up a kitten. Which person did more work, in the scientific sense?

▼◀▲▼◀▲▼◀▲▼◀▲▼◀▲▼◀▲▼◀▲▼◀▲▼◀▲▼◀▲▼◀▲▼◀▲▼◀▲▼◀▲▼◀▲▼◀▲▼

Science at Work

Machine Designer

Machine designers work in teams with engineers to design and build machinery. They use computer systems to make designs, drawings, and specifications for machines and their parts. Machine designers make cost and parts estimates and project schedules. As part of their work, they also test and analyze machines and their parts.

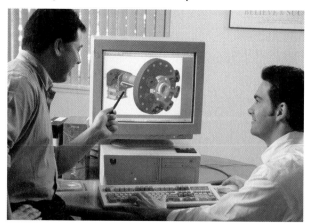

Machine designers usually have completed a two- or three-year technical program in mechanical engineering.

Machine designers are natural inventors. They are good at sketching, drawing, mathematics, and mechanical problem solving. Machine designers must know about materials and equipment involved in designing, constructing, and operating machines.

Objectives

After reading this lesson, you should be able to

◆ define and explain power.

◆ measure and calculate power.

Power

The amount of work a person does within a given period of time

Watt

The unit used to measure power

The watt was named for James Watt who developed the steam engine. Since a watt is a small amount of power, the kilowatt (1,000 watts) is often more convenient to use.

Imagine pushing a box 3 meters across a floor using 50 newtons of force. You would do 150 joules of work on the box. Notice that work does not take into account the amount of time it takes for you to move the box. The amount of work you do within a given period of time is called **power.** Power is the rate at which you do work. To calculate power, take the amount of work done and divide it by the amount of time it took to do the work.

$$\text{power} = \frac{\text{work}}{\text{time}}$$

Suppose you did 150 joules of work in 5 seconds. The power would be equal to 30 joules per second.

EXAMPLE

$$\text{power} = \frac{150 \text{ joules}}{5 \text{ seconds}}$$

$$\text{power} = 30 \text{ joules per second}$$

The unit for measuring power is the **watt.** A watt is 1 joule of work done in 1 second. In the example above, 30 joules of work were done in one second, so 30 watts of power were used. You will learn more about the watt in Chapter 11.

Imagine someone else pushing the box with the same force but taking 10 seconds to move it. In that case, the work that was done would still be the same—150 joules. But, the power would be different.

EXAMPLE

$$\text{power} = \frac{\text{work}}{\text{time}}$$

$$\text{power} = \frac{150 \text{ joules}}{10 \text{ seconds}}$$

$$\text{power} = 15 \text{ joules per second or 15 watts}$$

Here is another way to look at this example. If you do the same amount of work as someone else, but do it in half the time, then you have used twice as much power.

Write your answers to these questions in complete sentences on a sheet of paper.

1. What is power?

2. Power depends on two quantities. What are they?

3. How much power would a person use to move a piano 10 meters in 10 seconds using a force of 100 newtons?

4. How much power would a person use to move the same piano in 5 seconds?

5. What happens to the power used when the time is shorter?

Have you ever tried to play a radio with a "dead" battery? The radio would not play because the battery had no more energy stored inside. In science, **energy** is defined as "the ability to do work." Without energy, no work can be done.

Kinetic and Potential Energy

A moving object has the energy of motion, called **kinetic energy.** When a car is moving, it can do work. It can overcome road friction and air resistance and keep going forward. The amount of kinetic energy a moving object has depends on the object's mass and speed. The greater the mass or speed, the greater the kinetic energy.

Some objects are not moving, but they have the potential to move because of their position. These objects have stored energy. This stored energy is called potential energy. A book sitting on the floor has no **potential energy.** It cannot do work. But if you set the book so that it hangs over the edge of a table, the book has stored energy. It can do work by falling to the floor. The book's potential energy changes to kinetic energy as it falls. If you place the book over the edge of a higher table, the book has more potential energy because it can fall farther. The spring of a mousetrap is another example of potential energy. It can do work as it snaps shut.

Energy

The ability to do work

Kinetic energy

Energy of motion

Potential energy

Stored energy

You can see several examples of kinetic energy around you, such as geologic faults and water falls. Can you think of other examples?

Joules measure both work and energy, which shows the close relationship between the two. You cannot have work without energy, or vice versa. Doing work on something adds energy to it; releasing energy is work.

The Forms of Energy

The energy you use to do work exists in six main forms. These six forms of energy can be stored. They can also produce motion. That is, each form of energy can be potential or kinetic.

Chemical energy is stored in the bonds between atoms. When substances react, they can release some of the chemical energy in the substances and warm the surroundings. For example, burning coal produces heat.

Heat energy is associated with the moving particles that make up matter. The faster the particles move, the more heat energy is present. All matter has some heat energy. You will learn more about heat in Chapter 9.

Mechanical energy is the energy in moving objects. Objects, such as a moving bicycle, wind, and a falling rock, have mechanical energy in kinetic form. Sound is a form of mechanical energy that you will learn about in Chapter 10.

Nuclear energy is energy that is stored in the nucleus, or center, of an atom. It can be released in devices such as nuclear power plants and atomic weapons.

Radiant energy is associated with light. Some energy that Earth receives from the sun is in the form of light energy. You will learn more about light in Chapter 10.

Which forms of energy can you find in this photo?

Generator

A device used to convert mechanical energy to electrical energy

Electrical energy is energy that causes electrons to move. Electrons are the negatively charged particles in atoms. Appliances, such as refrigerators and vacuum cleaners, use electrical energy. You will learn about electricity in Chapter 11.

Energy can be changed from one form to another. For example, at an electric power plant, chemical energy is converted to heat energy when fuel is burned. The heat energy is used to make steam. The steam turns a turbine and produces mechanical energy inside a **generator.** The generator converts mechanical energy to electrical energy by moving coils through a magnetic field. Perhaps you have a generator in your home. Or maybe you have seen one at a friend's house, or a business. Generators are commonly used as backup electrical systems in homes. They are also used to supply power to small tools and machinery.

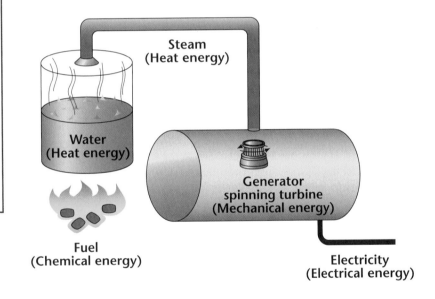

Steam
(Heat energy)

Water
(Heat energy)

Generator
spinning turbine
(Mechanical energy)

Fuel
(Chemical energy)

Electricity
(Electrical energy)

The Law of Conservation of Energy

Energy might change its form, but it does not disappear. You can add energy to an object or take energy away from it, but the total amount of the energy does not change. The **law of conservation of energy** states that energy cannot be created or destroyed. A book falling from a table illustrates the law of conservation of energy.

As the book falls, its potential energy decreases. The kinetic energy increases by the same amount. The total amount of energy (potential plus kinetic) stays the same. Just before the book hits the ground, its potential energy is approaching zero and all the energy has become kinetic. After the book hits the ground, the kinetic energy is changed into heat energy which causes a temperature change in the book and the ground. In this example, the energy has changed form, but the total energy remains the same.

Science in Your Life

How can energy change forms?

Have you ever ridden a roller coaster? A roller coaster is a good example of how energy can change from one form to another. When you first climb into the car at the bottom of the hill, the car has no potential energy. A chain must pull you up the first big hill.

That chain changes electrical energy into potential energy. When the cars are at the top, they can fall downward. Potential energy changes to kinetic energy as the cars plunge down one hill. Kinetic energy is converted back into potential energy as the cars go up the next hill. The cars slow as they reach the top of the hill. The kinetic energy that pushed them up the hill has changed back to potential energy. That stored energy converts to kinetic energy as the cars zoom down again.

You might notice that the hills get smaller and smaller during the ride. Although energy is not actually lost, friction converts some of it to other forms of energy, such as heat energy. The heat energy warms the tracks and the air but is not useful for propelling the cars forward.

Write your answers to these questions in complete sentences on a sheet of paper.

1. What is energy?

2. What is the difference between kinetic and potential energy?

3. Explain the law of conservation of energy.

4. Name the six forms of energy.

5. Each figure shows an example of energy changing form. List the energy changes that take place in each example.

A

B

C

Mass, Height, and Energy

Materials

- safety glasses
- paper cup
- grooved ruler
- textbook
- safety scissors
- small marble
- large marble

Purpose

Does an object's mass have an effect on its potential and kinetic energy? This investigation will demonstrate how mass affects potential and kinetic energy.

Procedure

1. Copy the data table on a sheet of paper.

Object	Distance Cup Moved
small marble	
large marble	

2. Put on your safety glasses.

3. Cut a 2.5-cm square window from the lip of the cup, as shown in Figure A.

4. Place one end of the ruler on the edge of the textbook to form a ramp, as shown in Figure B. The ruler's groove should be on top.

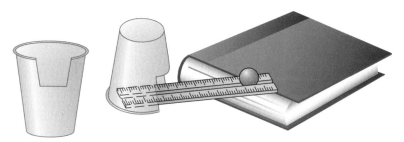

Figure A   Figure B

5. Place the cup upside down over the other end of the ruler. The ruler should touch the back of the cup.

6. Measure the distance from the edge of the book to the back edge of the cup. Mark the base line at the back edge of the cup.

7. Set the small marble at the top of the ruler's groove. Let it roll down by itself. Do not push it.

8. Observe what happens to the cup. Measure the distance from the edge of the book to the back edge of the cup. Record this distance in the data table.

9. Reset the cup at the base line. Repeat steps 6 and 7, using the large marble. Measure and record the distance.

Questions and Conclusions

1. Which marble pushed the cup farther from the ramp?

2. What conclusion can you draw about the effect of mass on kinetic energy?

Explore Further

How does the height of the ramp affect potential energy? Repeat the investigation using ramps of different heights. Record the results in the data table.

Have you ever tried to open a paint can, using only your fingers? It is hard, if not impossible, to do. With a screwdriver, you can easily pry the lid from the can. A screwdriver, used in this way, is an example of a **simple machine.** A simple machine is a tool with few parts that makes it easier or possible to do work. Simple machines change the direction or size of the force you apply. Or, they change the distance through which the force acts.

The Lever

A **lever** is a simple machine. Levers can have many shapes. In its most basic form, the lever is a bar that is free to turn around a fixed point. The fixed point is called a **fulcrum.**

In the figure below, the woman is using a lever to move a boulder. Notice that the lever changes the direction of the force the woman applies. She pushes down, but the boulder moves up. The force the woman applies to the machine is called the **effort force** (F_e).

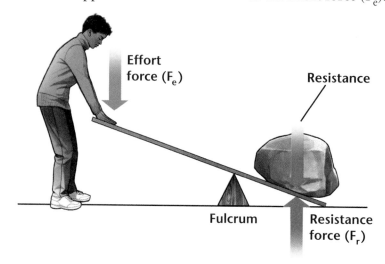

Effort force (F_e)

Resistance

Fulcrum

Resistance force (F_r)

The object to be lifted is called the resistance. In this example, the boulder is the resistance. Gravity is pulling down on the boulder, so the machine must exert a force upward to lift it. The force the machine uses to move the resistance is called the **resistance force** (F_r).

The force the machine exerts is greater than the force the woman exerts. In other words, using the lever makes the woman's job easier. The lever takes the amount of force she exerts and increases that force.

The Three Classes of Levers

Levers can be grouped into three classes. The classes of levers are based on the position of the resistance force, the fulcrum, and the effort force. The figure below illustrates a first-class lever.

In a first-class lever, the fulcrum is positioned between the effort and the resistance. A first-class lever changes the direction of a force and can also increase the force.

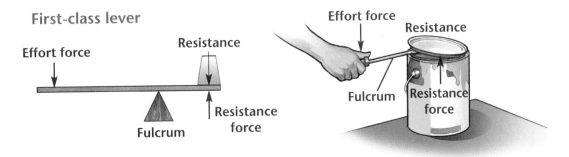

First-class lever

In a second-class lever, shown below, the resistance is positioned between the effort and the fulcrum. Second-class levers always increase the force applied to them. They do not change the direction of the force. Wheelbarrows, paper cutters, and most nutcrackers are examples of second-class levers.

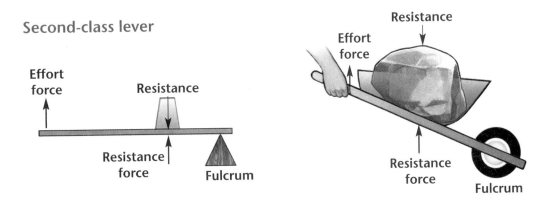

Second-class lever

Look at the third-class lever in the figure below. Notice that the effort is between the fulcrum and the resistance. Third-class levers increase the distance through which the force moves, which causes the resistance to move farther or faster. A broom is an example of a third-class lever. You use effort force on the handle between the fulcrum and the resistance force. When you move the handle of the broom a short distance, the brush end moves a greater distance.

Third-class lever

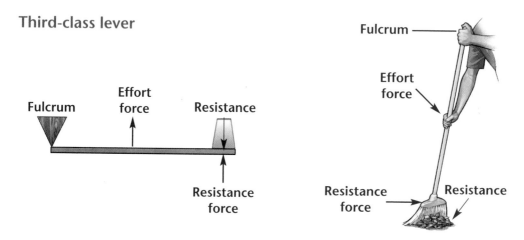

Work and Efficiency for a Lever

Energy cannot be created or destroyed. Because energy is the ability to do work, work cannot be created either. No simple machine can do more work than the person using it supplies. What machines can do is increase or change the direction of the force a person exerts. Lesson 1 explained that work = force × distance. Some machines allow a person to use less force to do the same amount of work. But in return, that person must exert the force over a greater distance.

Science Myth

A machine is something that has been manufactured.

Fact: Our bodies are machines. They contain all three classes of levers. When you lift your head forward or back, you use a first-class lever. When you stand on your toes, you use a second-class lever. When you hold a weight in your hand with your arm extended, you are using a third-class lever.

In the figure below, a woman is using a lever to move a boulder. The distance the effort moves is called the effort distance (d_e). The distance the resistance moves is called the resistance distance (d_r). Notice that the effort distance is much greater than the resistance distance.

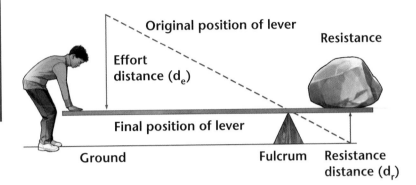

Original position of lever

Resistance

Effort distance (d_e)

Final position of lever

Ground

Fulcrum

Resistance distance (d_r)

Technology Note

Most appliances sold in the United States must display their energy efficiency. The label with this information is bright yellow with black lettering. It shows how much it costs to operate the appliance. Its efficiency is compared to the highest and lowest efficiency of similar appliances.

The amount of work a person puts into a machine is called the **work input.** The work input equals the person's effort force multiplied by the distance of that effort.

$$\text{work input} = F_e \times d_e$$

The amount of work actually done by the machine against the resistance is called the **work output.** The work output equals the resistance force multiplied by the distance the resistance moved.

$$\text{work output} = F_r \times d_r$$

Work output can never be greater than work input because energy cannot be created. But in reality, work output is always less than work input. No machine can do quite as much work as a person puts into it. Machines cannot destroy energy, but they change some of it to heat and other forms of energy that cannot do useful work.

The **efficiency** of a machine measures how much useful work it can do compared with how much work was put into it. You can find the efficiency of a machine by using this formula.

$$\text{efficiency} = \frac{\text{work output}}{\text{work input}} \times 100\%$$

Efficiency is written as a percent. Multiplying by 100 tells you what percent of the work input is converted to work output. All machines have efficiencies that are less than 100 percent.

Suppose a woman uses a lever to lift a crate. She applies 120 newtons of effort force. She pushes her end of the lever 1.0 meter. The machine exerts 400 newtons of resistance force. It lifts the crate 0.2 meter. What is the work input, the work output, and the efficiency of the lever?

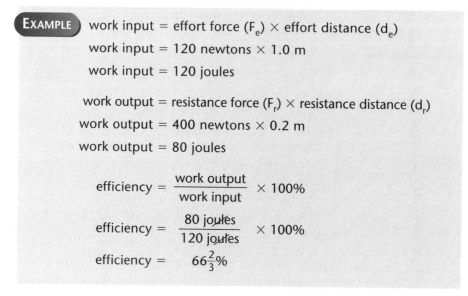

EXAMPLE

work input = effort force (F_e) × effort distance (d_e)

work input = 120 newtons × 1.0 m

work input = 120 joules

work output = resistance force (F_r) × resistance distance (d_r)

work output = 400 newtons × 0.2 m

work output = 80 joules

$$\text{efficiency} = \frac{\text{work output}}{\text{work input}} \times 100\%$$

$$\text{efficiency} = \frac{80 \text{ joules}}{120 \text{ joules}} \times 100\%$$

$$\text{efficiency} = 66\frac{2}{3}\%$$

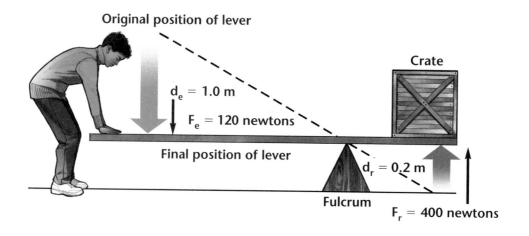

Original position of lever

Crate

d_e = 1.0 m

F_e = 120 newtons

Final position of lever

d_r = 0.2 m

Fulcrum

F_r = 400 newtons

Lesson 4   R E V I E W

Write your answers to these questions in complete sentences on a sheet of paper.

1. Draw a first-class lever. Show the fulcrum, effort force, and resistance.

2. Draw a second-class lever. Show the fulcrum, effort force, and resistance.

3. Draw a third-class lever. Show the fulcrum, effort force, and resistance.

4. What is work input? What is work output?

5. What does efficiency tell you about a machine?

Achievements in Science

The Law of the Lever

Levers probably were used in prehistoric times. In 260 B.C., Archimedes was the first to prove mathematically how levers work. His proof is known as the law of the lever.

The law of the lever is based on three principles. The first is that equal weights at equal distances from a fulcrum balance. The second is that two weights no longer balance if something is added to one. The side with the increased weight goes down. The third principle is that two weights do not balance if something is taken from one. The side holding the weight that did not change goes down.

Here is the formula for the law of the levers: $F_1 \times l_1 = F_2 \times l_2$. F_1 is the weight of an object on one side of a fulcrum. The length from that object to the fulcrum is l_1. F_2 is the weight on the other side. The length of that object to the fulcrum is l_2.

Archimedes's proof shows that anything, no matter how heavy it is, can be lifted using a lever.

After reading this lesson, you should be able to

◆ explain and calculate mechanical advantage.

◆ use effort arm and resistance arm to determine the mechanical advantage of a lever.

People often use simple machines to make tasks easier. A simple machine makes a task easier because it multiplies the force a person applies.

The number of times a machine multiplies your effort force is called the **mechanical advantage** of the machine. You can find a machine's mechanical advantage (MA) with this formula.

$$\text{mechanical advantage} = \frac{\text{resistance force}}{\text{effort force}} \quad \text{or} \quad MA = \frac{F_r}{F_e}$$

Look at the figure below. Suppose a machine lifts a resistance that weighs 30 newtons when the woman applies an effort force of only 10 newtons. What is the machine's mechanical advantage?

EXAMPLE

$$MA = \frac{F_r}{F_e}$$

$$MA = \frac{30 \text{ newtons}}{10 \text{ newtons}}$$

$$MA = 3$$

Mechanical advantage, MA

Factor by which a machine multiplies the effort force

The mechanical advantage is 3. The machine has multiplied the woman's effort force by 3. This makes the object easier for her to lift.

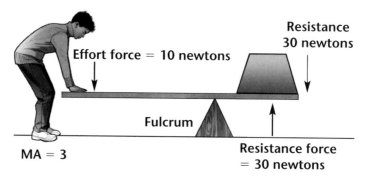

Effort force = 10 newtons

Resistance 30 newtons

Fulcrum

MA = 3

Resistance force = 30 newtons

Some machines are not used to multiply effort force. Instead, people use them to increase the distance or speed the resistance will move, or to change the direction of a force. Rather than increasing a person's effort force, the machine may even reduce it.

Effort Arm and Resistance Arm

Effort arm

The distance between the fulcrum and the effort force of a lever

Resistance arm

The distance between the fulcrum and resistance force of a lever

You can increase the mechanical advantage of a lever simply by moving the fulcrum closer to the resistance and farther from the effort force. Another way to find the mechanical advantage of a lever is to measure the **effort arm.** The effort arm is the distance between the fulcrum and the effort force of a lever. Measure the resistance force and the **resistance arm.** The resistance arm is the distance between the fulcrum and the resistance force of a lever. Now divide the effort arm by the resistance arm.

$$MA = \frac{\text{effort arm}}{\text{resistance arm}}$$

What is the mechanical advantage of the lever shown in the figure?

EXAMPLE

$$MA = \frac{\text{effort arm}}{\text{resistance arm}}$$

$$MA = \frac{2.4 \text{ m}}{0.6 \text{ m}}$$

$$MA = 4$$

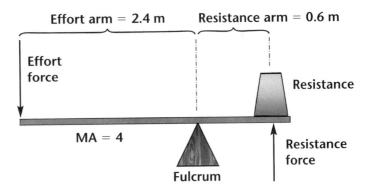

Effort arm = 2.4 m   Resistance arm = 0.6 m

Effort force

Resistance

MA = 4

Fulcrum

Resistance force

Write your answers to these questions in complete sentences on a sheet of paper.

1. What is mechanical advantage?

2. How do you find the mechanical advantage of most simple machines?

3. How can you find the mechanical advantage of levers?

4. What is the mechanical advantage of a lever with an effort arm of 16 cm and a resistance arm of 2 cm?

5. A machine has a mechanical advantage of 4. Your effort force is 10 newtons. What is the resistance force?

Achievements in Science

Mechanical Calculator

Blaise Pascal was 19 when he invented his calculating machine, the Pascaline, in 1642. Others before Pascal, including Leonardo DaVinci, had put forth ideas about mechanical calculators. But Pascal's machine was the first to be built and used.

The Pascaline could add numbers automatically. It used a set of wheels linked to gears to make calculations. The wheels were arranged in a row. The first wheel represented ones, the second represented tens, the third hundreds, and so forth. Each wheel had 10 teeth. Each of the gears had one tooth. When a wheel moved 10 notches, a gear moved the next wheel one notch. The wheels and gears were in a box with windows. The windows showed the numbers on the wheels. Later inventors added keys and a crank.

People used mechanical calculators until the 1970s, when electronic calculators became available. The principles of mechanical calculators remain in use in odometers and electric and water meters. The mechanical calculator was the first in a series of inventions leading to modern computers.

INVESTIGATION

8-2

Materials

- safety glasses
- spring scale
- 200-g weight
- rubber band
- stiff meterstick
- triangular wooden wedge or other fulcrum

Finding the Mechanical Advantage of a Lever

Purpose

Which fulcrum position would have a greater mechanical advantage—one at 20 cm or one at 80 cm? In this investigation, you will find the mechanical advantage of a lever.

Procedure

1. Copy the data table on a sheet of paper.

Fulcrum Position	Resistance Force	Effort Force	Resistance Arm	Effort Arm
50 cm				
80 cm				
20 cm				

2. Put on your safety glasses.

3. Use a spring scale to hold up a 200-g weight. Record the weight (the resistance force) in newtons.

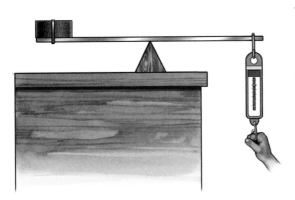

4. Using a rubber band, attach the 200-g weight to the top side of a stiff meterstick, at the 0-cm end.

5. Work at a table or desk. Place the weighted meterstick on a fulcrum so that it is positioned under the stick's 50-cm mark. The end of the stick without the weight should extend beyond the edge of the table, as shown in the diagram.

6. Use a spring scale to gently pull down on the 100-cm end of the stick until it is level at both ends. On the spring scale, read the effort force you apply to make the stick level. Record that force, in newtons, on the 50-cm line of the data table.

7. Record the length of the resistance arm (the distance from the weight to the fulcrum). Then record the effort arm (the distance from the fulcrum to the spring scale).

8. Follow the basic procedure used in steps 4 to 6 except position the fulcrum under the 80-cm mark. Record the values in the data table. Then place the fulcrum under the 20-cm mark. Repeat the basic procedure in steps 4 to 6. Record the values.

Questions and Conclusions

1. Where was the fulcrum placed when you had to apply the most force? Where was it placed when you had to apply the least force?

$$MA = \frac{\text{effort arm}}{\text{resistance arm}}$$

2. Calculate the mechanical advantage of the three levers using the formula at the left.

3. Which setup showed the greatest mechanical advantage? Which setup showed the least?

4. How do the mechanical advantages you calculated in step 3 compare to your answers to question 1?

5. Explain how the position of the fulcrum affects a lever's mechanical advantage.

Explore Further

Repeat the investigation steps, but use a weight with a different mass. Record your observations. Explain how a weight's mass affects mechanical advantage.

Objectives

After reading this lesson, you should be able to

◆ explain how pulleys work and how to estimate their mechanical advantage.

◆ explain how inclined planes work and how to estimate their mechanical advantage.

◆ explain how screws work and relate them to inclined planes.

◆ explain how wedges work and relate them to inclined planes.

◆ explain how wheels and axles work.

There are six types of simple machines, including the lever. In this lesson, you will learn about the other five types.

The Pulley

A **pulley** is a wheel with a rope, chain, or belt around it. The figure shows a single fixed pulley.

A single fixed pulley changes the direction of the force you apply, but it does not multiply that force. The mechanical advantage equals 1. You can use this type of pulley to lift a heavy object by pulling down instead of lifting up.

The pulley in Figure A is called a fixed pulley because it is fixed or attached at the top. The wheel is free to spin, but it cannot move up and down.

The pulley in Figure B is a movable pulley. As effort is applied to a movable pulley, the entire pulley and the object attached to it will rise. You can use this type of pulley to make a lifting job easier. Because the rope supports the pulley from two directions, you need to apply only half as much force to lift the object. Therefore, the pulley has a mechanical advantage of 2.

Pulley

A simple machine made up of a rope, chain, or belt wrapped around a wheel

Figure A

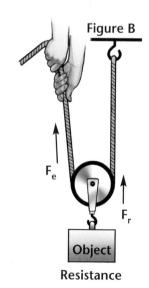

Figure B

There is a price to pay for making the object easier to lift. You must pull twice as far on the rope as the object actually moves. For example, to lift the object 1 meter, you must pull up a distance of 2 meters on the rope. The direction of the force is not reversed. To lift the object, you must pull up on the rope, not down.

Pulleys can be combined in different ways. Look at the figures below. Note the number of supporting ropes pulling up on each object. Note the mechanical advantage (MA) of each pulley system. The MA of a pulley system is usually about equal to the number of ropes that pull upward. In Figure C, two ropes pull up on the object. Mechanical advantage equals 2. In Figure D, three ropes pull up on the object. The MA of this system equals 3.

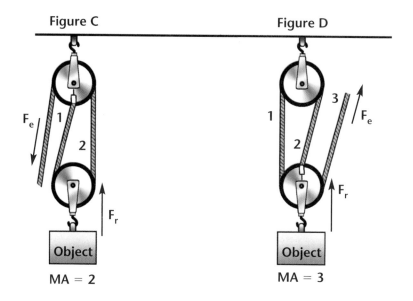

The Inclined Plane

An **inclined plane** is a simple machine made of a ramp. It has no moving parts. You use an inclined plane to lift an object.

Inclined planes, such as the one shown here in Figure E, decrease the force you need to move an object. Once again, you pay for this decrease in effort force by an increase in the distance the object has to be moved.

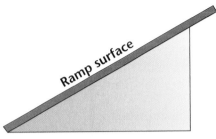

Figure E

For example, if a delivery person needs to put a box on a truck that is 1 meter from the ground, he might use an inclined plane, or ramp, to make his job easier. Rather than lifting the box 1 meter, he can push it up the ramp. It takes less force to push an object than to pick it up. However, he must move the object farther, as shown in Figure F below.

Did You Know?

Mountain roads that zigzag are examples of inclined planes. Although they are longer, roads that zigzag have mechanical advantage. It takes more force to reach a mountaintop on a road that goes straight up the mountain.

The friction between a ramp and a box could be reduced by placing the box on a dolly.

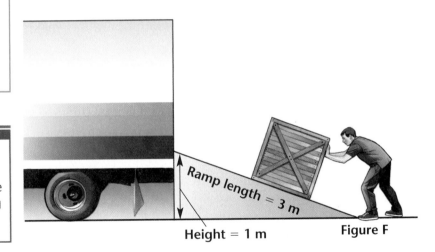

Ramp length = 3 m

Height = 1 m

Figure F

In Figure F, the mechanical advantage is 3. You divide the ramp length, 3 m, by the height, 1 m. The mechanical advantage of an inclined plane is the length of the slanted surface, divided by the vertical (up and down) height. The more gradual the slant, the greater the mechanical advantage, but the farther the object must go.

The Screw

Screw

A simple machine made up of an inclined plane wrapped around a straight piece of metal

Wedge

A simple machine made up of an inclined plane or pair of inclined planes that are moved

Another kind of simple machine, the **screw,** is a form of inclined plane. Think of a screw as a straight piece of metal with an inclined plane wrapped in a spiral around it. The ridges formed by this spiral are called threads.

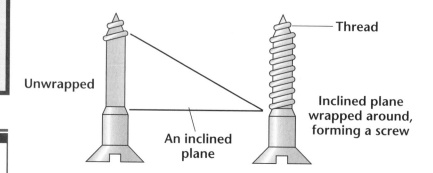

Unwrapped

An inclined plane

Thread

Inclined plane wrapped around, forming a screw

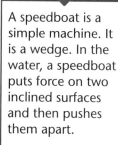

A speedboat is a simple machine. It is a wedge. In the water, a speedboat puts force on two inclined surfaces and then pushes them apart.

Screws make it easier to fasten objects together. The mechanical advantage of a screw depends on the distance between the threads. The smaller the distance, the more times the inclined plane is wrapped around, making the mechanical advantage greater.

The Wedge

A **wedge** is an inclined plane that moves when it is used. It is thick at one end and thinner at the other. A wedge is often made up of two inclined planes joined together. Both edges are slanted. You can use a wedge for a job like splitting wood. A force applied to the thick end is multiplied and acts at the thin end, piercing the wood. The thinner and more gradual the wedge, the greater the mechanical advantage.

A wedge is useful for splitting wood.

The Wheel and Axle

An automobile steering wheel and a doorknob are examples of a simple machine called a **wheel and axle.** In this simple machine, a wheel is attached to a shaft called an axle, as shown in the figure.

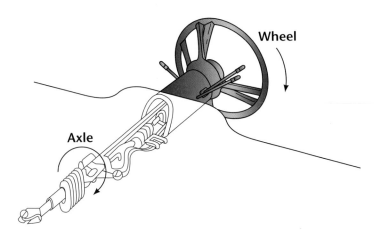

A wheel and axle increases the twisting force you apply to the wheel. The multiplied force can then turn something else attached to the axle. The mechanical advantage of a wheel and axle depends on the size of the wheel compared to the thickness of the axle. The bigger the wheel is in comparison to the thickness of the axle, the greater the mechanical advantage.

Write your answers to these questions in complete sentences on a sheet of paper.

1. What is a fixed pulley?

2. What is the difference between a fixed pulley and a movable pulley?

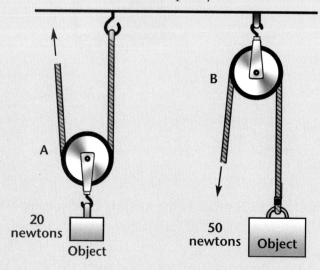

20 newtons
Object

50 newtons   Object

3. What is the mechanical advantage of each of the pulleys in the figure?

4. Explain the mechancial advantage of a movable pulley system that has two ropes that pull upward.

5. What is an inclined plane?

6. How can you find the mechanical advantage of an inclined plane?

7. Screws and wedges are variations of what simple machine?

8. Which will have a greater mechanical advantage: a screw with closely spaced threads or one with widely spaced threads? Explain your answer.

9. Which will have a greater mechanical advantage: a thin, gradual wedge or a thick, greatly sloping one? Explain your answer.

10. Why does a bus usually have a steering wheel that is larger than the one in a car?

- Work is what happens when a force makes something move in the direction of the force.

- Power is the amount of work a person does within a given period of time.

- Energy is the ability to do work.

- Kinetic energy is energy of motion. Potential energy is stored energy.

- The six main forms of energy are chemical, heat, mechanical, nuclear, radiant, and electrical. Energy can change from one form to another.

- Energy cannot be created or destroyed.

- Simple machines make doing work easier by changing the direction or size of a force and the distance through which it acts.

- Resistance force is the force applied by a machine against a resistance. Effort force is the force applied to a machine by the person using it.

- A lever is a bar that turns around a fulcrum.

- Levers are divided into three classes, according to the relationship between the effort, fulcrum, and resistance.

- The mechanical advantage of a machine is the number of times by which the machine multiplies effort force.

- A pulley is made up of a rope, chain, or belt wrapped around a wheel.

- An inclined plane is a ramp.

- A screw and a wedge are special forms of inclined planes.

- A wheel and axle is a wheel attached to a shaft.

Science Words

effort force

energy

joule

kinetic energy

law of
conservation
of energy

potential energy

Vocabulary Review

Choose a word or words from the Word Bank that best complete each sentence. Write the answer on a sheet of paper.

1. Stored energy is _____, and energy of motion is _____.

2. The ability to do work is _____.

3. The force applied to a machine by the user is _____.

4. The _____ states that energy cannot be created or destroyed.

5. The metric unit of work is a(n) _____.

Concept Review

Choose the answer that best completes each sentence. Write the letter of the answer on your paper.

6. Work = _____.

   A force + distance   **C** force × distance

   B force − distance   **D** force ÷ distance

7. Machines can be used to _____.

   A multiply effort force

   B increase the distance or speed the resistance will move

   C change the direction of a force

   D all of the above

8. A simple machine containing a bar that can turn about a fixed point is a(n) _____.

   A wheel and axle   **C** inclined plane

   B lever   **D** wedge

9. Work input = _____.

   A $F_e \times d_e$ **B** $F_e \times d_r$ **C** $F_e \times F_r$ **D** $F_r \times d_r$

10. Work output = _____.

   A $F_e \times d_e$ **B** $F_e \times d_r$ **C** $F_e \times F_r$ **D** $F_r \times d_r$

11. To calculate the mechanical advantage of a lever you
_____.

    A divide F_r by F_e
    B multiply F_r and F_e
    C divide the effort arm by the resistance arm
    D either A or C

12. Power = _____.

    A force × distance   **C** work output ÷ work input

    B work ÷ time   **D** $F_e × d_e$

Critical Thinking

Write the answer to each of these questions on your paper.

13. What class of lever is shown in the diagram below?
How can you tell?

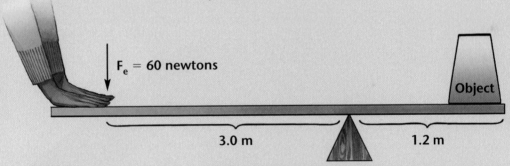

F_e = 60 newtons

Object

3.0 m   1.2 m

14. Give examples of three simple machines. Explain how
simple machines make it possible or easier to do work.

15. List six main forms of energy and write a brief explanation
of each one.

Test-Taking Tip Before you begin an exam, skim through the whole test
to find out what is expected of you.

9 Heat

Look at the flame in the photograph. What words would you use to describe the flame? You might say *fire, bright, hot, glowing,* or *heat.* In this photo, the flame is from a match. The flame is a hot gas that will burn if you touch it. It is so hot that it glows. The flame produces heat. But is fire the only way to produce heat? Are there other sources of heat? In Chapter 9, you will learn about heat energy and its sources. You also will learn ways to measure heat, how heat affects matter, and how heat travels.

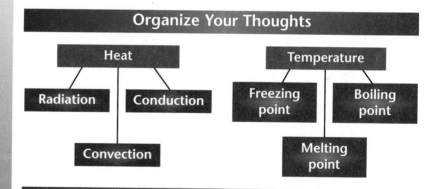

Organize Your Thoughts

Heat

Radiation   Conduction

Convection

Temperature

Freezing point   Boiling point

Melting point

Goals for Learning

◆ To explain how heat energy can be produced

◆ To tell how heat changes matter

◆ To explain how temperature is measured

◆ To identify the difference between temperature and heat

◆ To calculate heat gained or lost

◆ To explain how matter is heated by conduction, convection, and radiation

Objectives

After reading this lesson, you should be able to

◆ define heat.

◆ explain how heat energy can do work.

◆ explain how heat is produced.

◆ describe some sources of heat.

What happens when you hold an ice cube in your hand? Your hand is warmer than the ice cube. The warmth from your hand causes the ice cube to melt. **Heat** causes the ice to melt. Heat is a form of energy that results from the motion of particles in matter. Heat energy flows from a warmer object to a cooler object.

Heat

A form of energy resulting from the motion of particles in matter

Heat from your hand will cause an ice cube to melt.

You learned in Chapter 8 that heat is a form of energy. Energy can do work. Therefore, heat can do work. Machines can change heat energy into useful mechanical energy. For example, a steam engine uses the heat energy contained in steam to move the parts of the engine. An automobile engine also uses heat energy. Burning fuel produces hot gases that make the engine work.

Sources of Heat

What produces heat energy? Remember that all matter is made up of atoms and molecules. These tiny particles are always moving. The random motion and vibrations of particles in matter is a measure of the heat energy. The faster the particles move, the more heat energy they have.

Imagine going outside on a summer day. You feel heat from the sun. The sun is the earth's most important **heat source.** A heat source is a place from which heat energy comes. Nuclear reactions in the sun are the source of the heat energy that warms you.

You might recall from Chapter 8 that energy comes in different forms. Other forms of energy can be changed into heat energy. For example, hold your hands together and rub them rapidly. Your hands will begin to feel warm. Friction between your hands is a form of mechanical energy—the energy of motion—that produces heat.

Rubbing your hands together produces heat.

Fusion is the process responsible for the energy of the sun and other stars.

Sometimes the heat produced by mechanical energy can cause harmful effects. For example, the oil well drills used to drill through rock produce a lot of heat. Workers must cool the drills with water to keep them from melting.

Another source of heat is chemical energy. When substances react chemically with each other, they sometimes release heat. For example, when natural gas and other fuels burn, they produce heat.

Electricity is also a heat source. Look at the toaster below. When energy from an electric current passes through the wires of the toaster, the wires become hot. This energy can toast bread. What other appliances can you name that change electricty into heat energy?

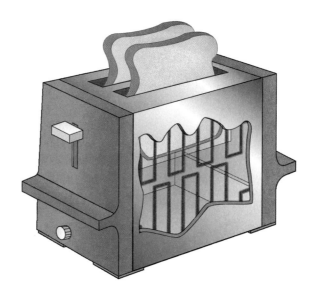

Nuclear energy is another form of energy. It is energy stored in the nucleus of an atom. When the nucleus of an atom is split, the nucleus becomes smaller nuclei. Energy is released as heat and light. This reaction is called **nuclear fission.** Nuclear energy is also released when atoms are joined together. When two nuclei are combined, they form a larger nucleus. This reaction is called **nuclear fusion.** Stars shine because their atoms release nuclear energy. Nuclear energy produces the sun's heat and light.

Lesson 1   R E V I E W

Write your answers to these questions in complete sentences on a sheet of paper.

1. What is heat?

2. What produces heat energy?

3. Give an example of how another form of energy can be changed into heat energy.

4. Does heat energy flow from a warm object to a cooler object or from a cool object to a warmer one?

5. What form of energy produces the sun's heat?

Achievements in Science

Steam Engine

The first steam engine, invented by the Greeks before 300 A.D., was used as a toy. Later steam engines had more practical uses. In 1698, Thomas Savery invented a steam-powered pump to drain water from mines. In 1765, Thomas Newcomen designed a more efficient steam engine pump. James Watt's steam engine, invented in 1763, was the first to do more than pumping. Watt's steam engine could make something turn. Watt's improvements led to machines that could do work that had once been done by hand.

Steam engines use heated water to operate. Most steam engines have a furnace that burns fuel, which produces heat energy. All have a boiler in which heat energy changes water to steam. The pressure from the expanding steam pushes on the engine parts to make them move.

Some early uses of steam engines were in steam locomotives and steamships. Today we continue to use steam engines to convert heat into mechanical work. Steam engines are at work in most electric power plants and all nuclear power plants.

Evaporate

To change from a liquid to a gas

Condensation

To change from a gas to a liquid

Did You Know?

There is no air inside the bubbles of boiling water. The bubbles of boiling water are made up of water vapor, also called steam.

Matter exists in different states. In a gas, the particles (molecules) are generally very far apart. They move freely. In a liquid, the particles are close together, but are still able to move freely. In a solid, the particles are close together and are not able to move past each other. They are constrained to specific positions in the solid. Heat can cause particles to move faster and move farther apart. Heat can change matter from one state to another.

Changing from a Liquid to a Gas

You might have noticed that if you boil water for a period of time, the amount of water gradually decreases. What happens to the water? Heat makes the water molecules move faster. As the molecules move faster, they bump into each other more often and push each other apart. As a result, the water **evaporates,** or changes from a liquid to a gas.

Heat rises

Changing from a Gas to a Liquid

If you have ever seen frost form on a window inside your home, you have seen an example of **condensation.** The temperature outside is cooler than the temperature inside your home. Condensation occurs when water vapor in the air returns to its original liquid state. This happens when the air cools and the temperature of the air drops. The molecules in the air move at a slower speed. Cold air cannot hold as much water vapor as warm air. Some of the water vapor condenses to form tiny drops of liquid water. Water drops that appear on a mirror after you have taken a hot shower are another example of condensation.

Changing from a Solid to a Liquid

What happens to an ice cube (a solid) when it is left in a warm room? It melts. But why does it melt? Heat speeds up the vibrational motion of the molecules in the ice cube. This motion disrupts the structure of the ice crystal. The molecules are free to move around relative to each other. The solid ice cube changes to liquid water.

Expanding and Contracting Matter

Heat causes particles in matter to push farther apart. Then the matter **expands,** or becomes larger in size. It fills up more space. The figure shows a joint in a metal bridge. Summer heat makes the material in the bridge expand. What might happen if the bridge did not have an expansion joint?

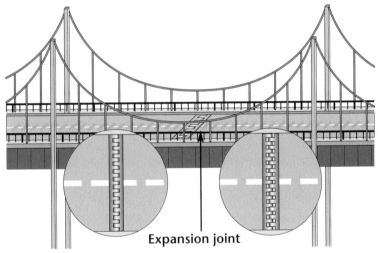

Expansion joint

Bridge in summer   **Bridge in winter**

Solids, liquids, and gases do not expand equally. In most cases, liquids expand more than solids. Gases usually expand the most.

Sometimes, matter loses heat. Particles in matter move more slowly and stay closer together as they lose heat. The matter **contracts,** or becomes smaller. It takes up less space. In the figure, notice the joint in the bridge in winter. The material in the bridge contracts in cold weather. Water is a material that behaves differently. Cooled water contracts until it reaches 4°C. Below this temperature, water expands until it freezes at 0°C.

Write your answers to these questions in complete sentences on a sheet of paper.

1. What happens to an ice cube when it is heated?

2. What happens when water in a puddle evaporates?

3. How does heat affect the amount of space matter fills?

4. Why does the amount of water decrease when it boils?

5. Is fog an example of condensation? Explain your answer.

▼◄▲▼◄▲▼◄▲▼◄▲▼◄▲▼◄▲▼◄▲▼◄▲▼◄▲▼◄▲▼◄▲▼◄▲▼◄▲▼◄▲▼◄▲▼◄▲▼

Science at Work

Heating, Ventilation, and Air Conditioning (HVAC)) Technician

HVAC technicians install, maintain, and repair heating, ventilation, and air conditioning systems. They work in both homes and businesses. They also recharge systems with refrigerants or cooling gases, such as Freon. Their other responsibilities include testing, troubleshooting, and adjusting systems to make sure they work properly.

HVAC technicians receive on-the-job training or they complete an apprenticeship program.

HVAC technicians must work well with their hands and have good vision and hand-eye coordination. They also must be patient and be able to work effectively under stressful conditions.

INVESTIGATION

9-1

Materials

- safety glasses
- balloon
- flask
- masking tape or electrical tape
- 2 buckets
- cold water
- warm water
- paper towels

Observing and Comparing Expansion and Contraction

Purpose

What happens when a gas expands and contracts? In this investigation, you will observe and compare expansion and contraction of gases.

Procedure

1. Copy the data table on a sheet of paper.

Environment	Changes in balloon
In warm water	
In cold water	
At room temperature	

2. Put on your safety glasses.

3. Carefully stretch the opening of the balloon over the opening of the flask. Use tape to seal the balloon to the flask.

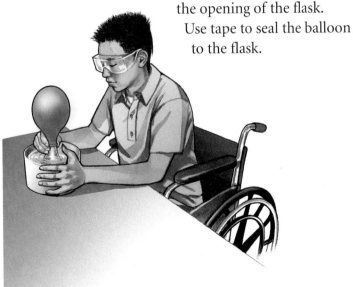

4. Fill one bucket with cold water.

5. Fill the other bucket with hot water. **Safety Alert: Do not use water hot enough to cause a burn.** Place the flask in the bucket of hot water. Keep the flask in the water until the flask becomes hot.

6. Observe the balloon. Record any changes you see in the data table.

7. Remove the flask from the bucket of hot water. Place the flask in the bucket of cold water. Keep the flask in the cold water until the flask becomes cold. Record any changes to the balloon.

8. Take the flask out of the water and dry it. Watch the balloon as the flask returns to room temperature. Record any changes to the balloon.

Questions and Conclusions

1. What happened to the balloon when the flask was heated?

2. What happened to the balloon as the flask cooled?

3. What caused the changes you observed in the balloon?

Explore Further

Explain what would happen to a helium-filled balloon if it was moved to a colder room. Explain what would happen to the balloon if it was moved to a warmer room.

Objectives

After reading this lesson, you should be able to

◆ explain how temperature is measured.

◆ compare and contrast temperature scales.

◆ describe freezing point, melting point, and boiling point.

Temperature

A measure of how fast an object's particles are moving

Heat energy from Maria's hand heats the water and melts the ice cubes.

What happens when you put your hand in a bowl of cool water? Heat energy from your hand flows into the water and makes the water warmer.

The more your hand heats the water, the faster the water particles move. **Temperature** is a measure of how fast an object's particles are moving. The higher the temperature, the faster an object's particles move.

Touching an object does not always give an accurate measurement of the object's temperature. For example, suppose you place your hand in cold water. Heat energy from your hand moves to the water and your hand becomes cooler. Now move that same hand out of the cold water and into a container of lukewarm water. The water will feel hotter than it actually is because your hand is cool.

Thermometers

You often cannot rely on your sense of touch to accurately tell temperature. So how can you measure temperature accurately? A **thermometer** is a device we use to measure temperature. Two different kinds of thermometers are shown below.

The thermometer in the figure at the right is a glass tube with a small amount of liquid inside. The liquid is usually mercury or alcohol. As the thermometer measures higher temperatures, heat causes the particles of liquid to expand, or move farther apart. As the liquid expands, it moves up the tube. The more heat that passes to the liquid, the more the liquid will expand and the higher it moves in the tube. When the liquid stops expanding, it stops beside a number on the tube. This number tells the temperature of the substance touching the bulb of the thermometer.

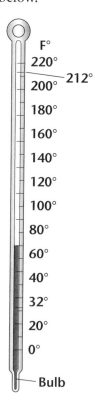

Look at the electronic thermometer in the photo below. Many doctors and medical workers use this kind of thermometer to take people's temperatures. It measures temperatures very quickly.

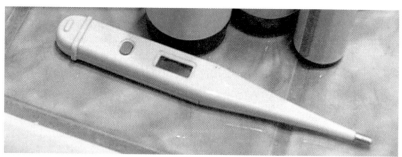

Digital (electronic) thermometers measure temperatures quickly.

Temperature Scales

Two common scales are used to measure temperature. People in the United States usually use the **Fahrenheit scale.** Fahrenheit is abbreviated as *F.* People in many other countries use the **Celsius scale.** The abbreviation for Celsius is *C.* Scientists use the Celsius scale.

Look at the thermometers on this page to compare the Fahrenheit scale with the Celsius scale. Find the equally spaced units on each scale. For both temperature scales, temperature is measured in units called **degrees.** The symbol for degree is °. The temperature shown on the Fahrenheit scale is 68 degrees Fahrenheit. It is written as 68°F. The same temperature in the Celsius scale is 20 degrees Celsius. It is written as 20°C.

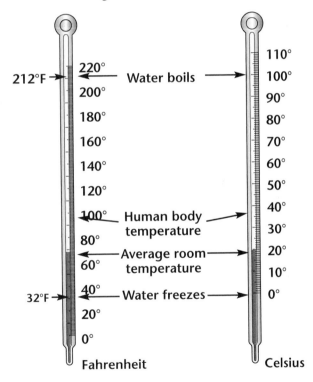

We write any temperature below zero degrees with a minus (−) sign. For example, a temperature of 10 degrees below zero on the Celsius scale is written as −10°C. The table on the next page shows how we write temperatures on the Fahrenheit scale and the Celsius scale.

Temperature Conversion

If you know the temperature of a substance on one scale, you can convert to an equal temperature on the other scale. The table shows how temperatures convert from one scale to the other.

Temperature Conversion Table			
°C	°F	°C	°F
100	212	45	113
95	203	40	104
90	194	35	95
85	185	30	86
80	176	25	77
75	167	20	68
70	158	15	59
65	149	10	50
60	140	5	41
55	131	0	32
50	122		

If you need a conversion that is not listed in the table, you can use a formula to figure it out. You can use this formula to convert a Celsius temperature to Fahrenheit.

$$F = \frac{9}{5} \times C + 32 \text{ or } F = 1.8 \times C + 32 \text{ (the fraction } \frac{9}{5} \text{ is equal to 1.8)}$$

Suppose you want to convert 22° Celsius to Fahrenheit.

EXAMPLE
$$F = 1.8 \times C + 32$$
$$F = 1.8 \times 22 + 32$$
$$F = 1.8 \times 22 = 39.6 + 32$$
$$F = 71.6° \text{ or } F = 72°$$

We usually round the decimal portion of the number to the nearest whole number. So, you would round 71.6 to 72.

Use this formula to convert a Fahrenheit temperature to Celsius.

$$C = \frac{5}{9} \times (F - 32)$$

Suppose you want to convert 48° Fahrenheit to Celsius.

Freezing point

The temperature at which a liquid changes to a solid

Melting point

The temperature at which a solid changes to a liquid

EXAMPLE

$$C = \frac{5}{9} \times (F - 32)$$

$$C = \frac{5}{9} \times (48 - 32)$$

$$C = \frac{5 \times 16}{9} = \frac{80}{9}$$

$$C = 8.8° \; or \; C = 9°$$

Notice that $\frac{80}{9}$ is 80 ÷ 9 or 8.8888. Round the decimal portion of the number to the nearest whole number to get 9.

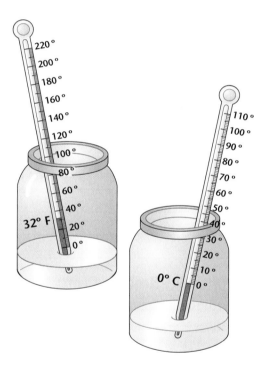

Freezing Point

What happens when you place a container of water in the freezer? The water gradually changes to ice. Suppose you recorded the temperature of the water every five minutes. You would notice that as time passed, the temperature would decrease. As the temperature of the water decreases, the water loses heat. Eventually the liquid water becomes solid.

The temperature at which a liquid changes to a solid is called its **freezing point.** The figure shows the freezing point of water. On the Celsius scale, the temperature at which water freezes is 0°. On the Fahrenheit scale, the temperature at which water freezes is 32°.

Melting Point

The temperature at which a solid changes to a liquid is called its **melting point.** The melting point of a substance is the same as its freezing point. The term *melting point* is used when a substance is being heated. When ice is heated, it changes to a liquid at a temperature of 0°C. Therefore, the melting point of ice is 0°C.

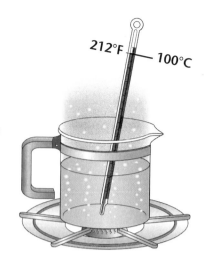

212°F — 100°C

Boiling point

The temperature at which a substance changes from a liquid to a gas under normal atmospheric pressure

Did You Know?

You cannot make an egg boil faster by increasing the heat. Under normal conditions, water cannot be hotter than 100°C. Because the water cannot be hotter, the egg cannot cook faster.

Boiling Point

The **boiling point** of a substance is the temperature at which it changes from a liquid to a gas under normal atmospheric pressure. You can see in the figure that the temperature at which water boils is 100° on the Celsius scale. On the Fahrenheit scale, the boiling point is read as 212°.

Every substance has its own freezing and boiling points. Scientists use the freezing and boiling points of substances to help identify unknown substances. You can see the freezing and boiling points of a few substances in the table.

The Freezing and Boiling Points of Some Substances				
	Freezing/Melting Point		Boiling Point	
Substance	°F	°C	°F	°C
water	32	0	212	100
aluminum	1,220	660	4,473	2,467
iron	1,762	961	4,014	2,212
alcohol	−202	−130	173	78

Changing Freezing Point and Boiling Point

You can change the freezing point and the boiling point of a substance by mixing substances together. For example, if you add alcohol to water, the freezing point of the mixture will be lower than the freezing point of water alone. Antifreeze contains alcohol. Adding antifreeze to an automobile radiator lowers the freezing point of the water in the radiator. This keeps the water from freezing and prevents engine damage. The antifreeze also has a higher boiling point than water. Antifreeze boils more slowly than water in hot weather.

Certain compounds of sodium and calcium are used on icy roads and walkways in winter. These compounds lower the freezing point of water and change the ice back to a liquid.

Write your answers to these questions in complete sentences on a sheet of paper.

1. How does the motion of molecules affect temperature?

2. Explain how a liquid thermometer works.

3. Write the following temperatures:

   A thirty-four degrees Fahrenheit

   B sixty-six degrees Celsius

   C four degrees below zero on the Fahrenheit scale

   D one hundred ten degrees on the Celsius scale

4. What is meant by the freezing point of a substance?

5. What is meant by the melting point of a substance?

6. What is meant by the boiling point of a substance?

7. How can the freezing point of a substance be changed?

8. Change 35° Fahrenheit to Celsius.

9. Change 18° Celsius to Fahrenheit.

10. Which temperature is hotter, 23° Celsius or 65° Fahrenheit?

Technology Note

A pop-up timer shows when a turkey is cooked. The timer has an outer case. This case contains a plastic stem within a piece of soft metal and a spring. The soft metal is solid at room temperature. When it reaches its melting point, the metal releases the stem. The spring makes the stem pop up.

Objectives

After reading this lesson, you should be able to

◆ explain how temperature and heat differ.

◆ explain how heat is measured.

◆ calculate heat gain and loss.

Did You Know?

When temperatures fall, bridges become covered with ice before roads do. Bridges have more surface exposed to the air than roads. Because of this, they lose heat energy more quickly. This makes them freeze faster.

Suppose you fill a tub with warm water. Then you fill a cup with water from the tub. The temperature of the water in each container would be the same. However, the water in the tub would give off more heat than the water in the cup. The amount of heat given off depends on the mass of the water, the surface area, and the temperature of the air.

Temperature and Heat

Temperature and heat are different. Temperature is a measure of how fast the molecules in a substance are moving. The higher the temperature, the greater the atomic or molecular motion. Heat depends on the temperature of a substance and the amount of matter, or mass, the substance has.

As the temperature of an object increases, the amount of heat in the object also increases. If two objects of different mass are at the same temperature, the object with the greater mass will give off more heat. The temperature of the lighted candle in the figure is the same as the temperature of the bonfire. The bonfire contains more mass than the candle. Therefore, the bonfire gives off more heat.

Measuring Heat

Calorie

A unit of heat; the amount of heat needed to raise the temperature of 1 g of water by 1°C

You know that temperature is measured in units called degrees. Scientists measure heat in units of energy called **calories.** A calorie is the amount of heat needed to raise the temperature of 1 gram of water by 1 degree Celsius.

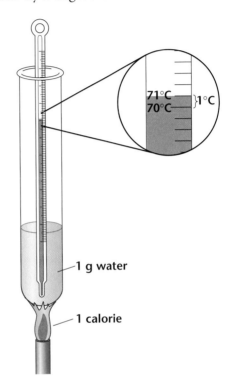

Specific heat is the amount of heat needed to raise the temperature of 1 g of any substance by 1°C. Different things have different specific heat. Only 0.1 calorie makes 1g of iron 1°C warmer.

Other units that measure heat energy are joules and British thermal units (BTUs). One joule equals 0.239 calories. One BTU equals 251.996 calories. Calories also measure food energy. One food calorie equals 1,000 heat energy calories.

You can use a formula to find out the amount of heat (calories) you would need to change the temperature of a substance.

Heat (calories) = change in temperature (°C) × mass (grams)

How many calories of heat are needed to raise the temperature of 1 gram of water by 3 degrees C?

EXAMPLE

Heat = change in temperature × mass
Heat = 3°C × 1 g
Heat = 3 calories

When matter changes from one state to another, the temperature remains the same. What changes is the distance between the particles that compose the matter. The temperature may change only after a change in state.

You can use the same formula to calculate the following problem.

How many calories of heat are needed to raise the temperature of 6 grams of water from 5°C to 15°C?

EXAMPLE First, calculate the temperature change.
Change in temperature = 15°C − 5°C
Change in temperature = 10°C

Then calculate the heat.
Heat = change in temperature × mass
Heat = 10°C × 6 g
Heat = 60 calories

Cooling

Heat can also be lost or given off by a substance when it is cooling. We place a minus sign (−) in front of the answer to indicate that the water is being cooled.

Suppose 20 grams of water are cooled from 20°C to 8°C. How much heat is given off?

EXAMPLE First, calculate the change in temperature.
Change in temperature = 20°C − 8°C
Change in temperature = 12°C

Then, calculate the calories.
Heat = change in temperature × mass
Heat = 12°C × 20 g
Heat = 240 calories

The answer is expressed as −240 calories to show that heat is given off.

The above examples are for water. In order to calculate heat lost or gained by other substances, you would use the same formula. However, different substances require different amounts of heat to raise their temperatures by 1°. That amount is called the specific heat.

Write your answers to these questions in complete sentences on a sheet of paper.

1. If two objects that have the same temperature have a different mass, which object gives off the most heat?

2. Suppose 25 grams of water are heated to from 0°C to 5°C. How many calories are needed?

3. Suppose 15 grams of water are heated from 12°C to 22°C. How many calories are needed?

4. If 20 grams of water are heated to from 0°C to 1°C, how much heat is added?

5. Suppose 35 grams of water are cooled from 15°C to 10°C. How much heat is given off?

6. Suppose 88 grams of water are cooled from 22°C to 16°C. How much heat is given off?

7. Suppose 16 grams of water are cooled from 13°C to 1°C. How much heat is given off?

8. Suppose 10 calories of heat are added to 10 grams of water. The temperature of the water will increase by how much?

9. Suppose 100 calories of heat are added to 10 grams of water. The temperature of the water will increase by how much?

10. Suppose 50 calories of heat are added to 10 grams of water at 10°C. What will the final temperature be?

Technology Note

Pressure cookers cook food quickly by raising the boiling temperature of water. We can make water boil at a higher temperature by putting it under pressure. When the tightly sealed pot is heated, steam pressure builds up inside. The more pressure, the higher the temperature, and the faster food cooks.

Measuring the Rate of Heat Loss

Purpose

Do different amounts of water cool at different rates? In this investigation, you will measure the cooling rates of different amounts of water.

Procedure

1. Copy the data table on a sheet of paper. Extend the length of the table to fit 15 minutes.

Time	Temperature (°C)	
	Large Jar	**Small Jar**
0 minutes		
1 minute		
2 minutes		
3 minutes		
4 minutes		
5 minutes		

2. Put on your safety glasses.

3. Fill the large jar with hot tap water. **Safety Alert: Do not use water hot enough to cause a burn.**

4. Fill the small jar about halfway with hot tap water.

5. Place the jars next to each other on a flat surface.

6. Place a thermometer in each jar, as shown in the figure on page 261. Immediately read the temperature on each thermometer. Record the temperatures in the section of your data table marked *0 minutes*.

Materials

◆ safety glasses
◆ large jar
◆ hot tap water
◆ small jar
◆ 2 Celsius thermometers
◆ clock or watch
◆ ice water

7. Leave the thermometers in the jars. Use the clock or watch to keep track of the time. Record the temperature of each water sample every minute for 15 minutes.

Questions and Conclusions

1. What was the temperature of the water in each jar the first time you measured it? After 8 minutes? After 15 minutes?

2. How did the amount of water in the jar affect how fast the temperature of the water dropped?

3. What happened to the heat from the water as the water cooled?

Explore Further

Repeat the activity, using a jar of ice water. Then answer these questions.

1. How did the temperature of the water change after 8 minutes? After 15 minutes?

2. Explain the change of temperature that occurred in the ice water.

Think about different ways you can travel, or move, from one place to another. You might walk or run. You might ride a bicycle. You might travel in a car, bus, train, boat, or airplane. Energy also has different ways of moving from warm matter to cool matter.

Radiation

The sun is a very long distance from Earth—150 million kilometers, in fact. Yet the sun heats Earth. How does the sun's energy travel the long distance from its surface to Earth? It must travel through a **vacuum.** A vacuum is a space that has no matter. Energy from the sun reaches us by **radiation.** Radiation is the movement of energy through a vacuum. Radiation can carry energy across space where there is no matter. The energy can heat matter.

Vacuum

Space that contains no matter

Radiation

The movement of energy through a vacuum

Radiant energy from the sun is transferred into chemical energy through photosynthesis. Photosynthesis is the process by which plants use sunlight to make food.

Heat from sources other than the sun can also travel by radiation. You can see this illustrated in the figure. Heat energy from the fire moves into the room by radiation and then heats the air.

Conduction

You probably know that if you hold a strip of metal in a flame it will get hot. Why does this happen? The metal gets hot because of **conduction.** Conduction is the movement of heat energy from one molecule to the next. Heat travels by conduction when molecules bump into each other.

Look at the strip of copper in the figure. Heat from the flame makes the copper particles (atoms) near the flame move faster. As the particles move faster, they hit other particles. These particles then bump into the particles farther up on the strip of copper. They transfer energy. As a result, the slower particles move faster. Eventually, all the particles in the copper are moving fast. In other words, the entire piece of copper becomes hot.

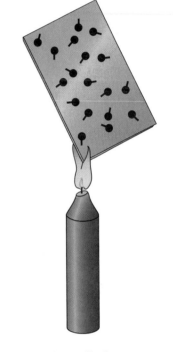

Energy moves easily through some kinds of matter. A substance that allows heat energy to flow through it easily is called a **conductor.** Most metals, such as copper, silver, gold, aluminum, and tin, are good conductors.

A material that does not conduct heat well is called an **insulator.** Energy does not move easily through insulators. Insulators are used in the walls of homes to keep heat out in summer and cold out in winter. Some good insulators are glass, wood, sand, soil, Styrofoam, and air.

Convection

Convection is a method of heat movement that happens when the particles of a gas or a liquid rise. As they rise, they carry heat.

Find the heater in the figure. First, conduction heats the air touching the heater. Then the warm air rises. Cool air moves in to take its place. The heater warms the cool air and it rises. The warm air cools as it moves through the room. Then it flows back to the heater and is warmed again. The arrows show how heat energy flows up and around the room. Convection keeps the air moving.

Convection also happens in liquids. Suppose a pot of cold water is placed on the stove. Heat is conducted from the hot burner to the pot and then to the water at the very bottom of the pot. Then convection heats the rest of the water. The warm water rises and the cooler water sinks.

How do different heating systems work?

How can you control the temperature of your home? The chart describes some types of heating systems. People use these types of heating systems to keep their homes at a comfortable temperature.

Heating Systems		
Type of System	**Description**	**How Heat Travels**
Hot water	A furnace heats the water. A pump circulates the water through pipes to a radiator in each room.	Convection and radiation circulate heat throughout the room.
Steam	A boiler sends steam to pipes. Steam forces the heat through the pipes to radiators in each room.	Radiation and convection circulate heat throughout the room.
Forced air	Air is heated by a furnace. It is then pumped into rooms through vents at the floor of each room.	Forced convection circulates heat throughout the room.
Passive solar	The sun's rays pass through a large door or window. They heat up a large tile or rock wall. Heat radiates into the room from the wall and sets up convection currents.	Radiation and convection distribute heat.
Radiant electric	Electric current heats up wires in baseboards, walls, and/or ceilings.	Heat radiates from these specific places.

1. Which heating systems heat a home by convection?
2. Which heating systems provide radiant heat?
3. Which type of heating system would be more efficient in a hot, sunny climate? Explain your answer.
4. Which types of heating systems would be more efficient in a cold climate? Explain your answer.

Lesson 5   R E V I E W

Write your answers to these questions in complete sentences on a sheet of paper.

1. How does the sun's heat travel to the earth?

2. How does heat move by conduction?

3. Explain how convection heats a room.

4. What is a vacuum?

5. Explain the difference between a conductor and an insulator.

Achievements in Science

Temperature Scales

For 2,000 years, people have used temperature scales. But people used different kinds of scales for different purposes. Only in the 1600s did scientists develop temperature scales like those we use today.

The Fahrenheit temperature scale was introduced in 1724. This scale began at 0°, the freezing point of an ice, water, and salt mixture. It ended at 98°, the normal body temperature. Water's freezing point was 32°. Scientists later adjusted Fahrenheit's scale, making the highest point 212°, water's boiling point.

The Celsius temperature scale was introduced in 1742. It made zero the boiling point of water and 100 the melting point of ice. The scale was divided into 100 units called degrees centigrade. Later scientists changed "centigrade" to "Celsius." They also made 0° the freezing point of water and 100° the boiling point.

The Kelvin temperature scale, introduced in 1848, is based on the Celsius scale. On the Kelvin, zero is the temperature at which the movement of all atoms stops.

■ Heat is a form of energy. It results from the motion of the particles in matter. Heat energy flows from a warmer object to a cooler object.

■ Mechanical, solar, electrical, chemical, and nuclear energy are sources of heat.

■ Heat can cause matter to change from one state to another.

■ Generally, heat (a rise in temperature) causes matter to expand; loss of heat (a drop in temperature) causes matter to contract.

■ Temperature measures how fast particles are moving.

■ The Fahrenheit and Celsius scales are used to measure temperature.

■ The freezing point, the melting point, and the boiling point are important temperatures for all substances.

■ Heat is measured in calories.

■ Heat depends on the temperature and the mass of an object.

■ The number of calories gained or lost by water equals the change in Celsius temperature multiplied by the mass.

■ Heat travels by radiation, conduction, and convection.

Science Words

boiling point, 254	contract, 245	freezing point, 253	nuclear fusion, 242
calorie, 257	convection, 264	heat, 240	radiation, 262
Celsius scale, 251	degree, 251	heat source, 241	temperature, 249
condensation, 244	evaporate, 244	insulator, 263	thermometer, 250
conduction, 263	expand, 245	melting point, 253	vacuum, 262
conductor, 263	Fahrenheit scale, 251	nuclear fission, 242	

Chapter 9   R E V I E W

Word Bank

Celsius scale

conduction

convection

evaporate

temperature

thermometer

Vocabulary Review

Choose a word or words from the Word Bank that best complete each sentence. Write the answer on a sheet of paper.

1. A device that measures temperature is a(n) _____.

2. A measure of how fast an object's particles are moving is _____.

3. The flow of energy that occurs when a warm liquid or gas rises is _____.

4. The movement of heat energy from one molecule to the next is _____.

5. The temperature scale in which water freezes at 0° and boils at 100° is the _____ .

6. To change from a liquid to a gas is to _____.

Concept Review

Choose the answer that best completes each sentence. Write the letter of the answer on your paper.

7. Heat energy can be produced by _____ energy.
   A nuclear   C chemical
   B electrical   D all of the above

8. When frozen water melts and then evaporates, heat energy has caused the water molecules to _____.
   A move closer together   C move farther apart
   B move faster   D both B and C

9. The melting point of a substance is the same as its _____.
   A boiling point   C both A and B
   B freezing point   D none of the above

10. As the temperature of an object increases, the amount of heat in the object _____.
    A increases   C stays the same
    B decreases   D makes the mass increase

11. The freezing point or boiling point of a substance can be changed by _____.

   A reducing the substance's mass

   B increasing the substance's mass

   C heating or cooling the substance

   D mixing the substance with another substance

12. The amount of heat needed to raise the temperature of 1 gram of water by 6°C is _____.

   A 1 calorie   **B** 3 calories   **C** 6 calories   **D** 12 calories

13. A material that keeps heat out of a house in summer and cold out in winter _____.

   A is a good conductor   **C** has a low freezing point

   B is a good insulator   **D** has a high boiling point

Critical Thinking

Write the answer to each of these questions on your paper.

14. Why does ice cream melt faster in a dish that is room temperature than in a dish that has been in the freezer?

15. The objects shown in the figure to the left have the same temperature. Do they give off the same amount of heat? Explain your answer.

Sound and Light

Almost everyone enjoys watching a fireworks display like the one in the photograph. Fireworks help us celebrate special holidays and events. What happens when you view fireworks? First, you see an explosion of bright, colorful light. Then, you hear the explosion's crashing boom or sharp whistle. Why do you see the light before you hear the sound? In Chapter 10, you will learn how sound is produced and how light travels. You also will discover how sound and light are alike and how they are different.

Organize Your Thoughts

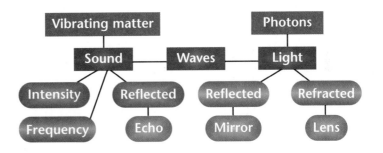

Goals for Learning

◆ To explain how sound is produced

◆ To describe intensity and volume of sound

◆ To tell how sound travels

◆ To describe the nature of light

◆ To explain reflection of light

◆ To explain refraction of light

You hear many kinds of sounds every minute of every day. But do you know what sound is? Sound is a form of energy. Scientists who study sound also study human hearing and the effect of sound on different objects.

How Sound Is Produced

All the sounds you hear are made when matter **vibrates.** To vibrate means to move quickly back and forth. Look at the figure of the bells. When the clapper hits the bell, energy from the clapper causes the bell to vibrate. When the bell vibrates, it moves back and forth. The bell pushes the air around it. You can see in the figure that as the bell vibrates to the right, it pushes together the air particles to the right of the bell. When it vibrates back to the left, the air particles to the right of the bell move apart. Those particles to the left of the bell are squeezed together. As the bell continues to vibrate, the air particles on each side are squeezed together and spread apart many times.

Vibrate

To move rapidly back and forth

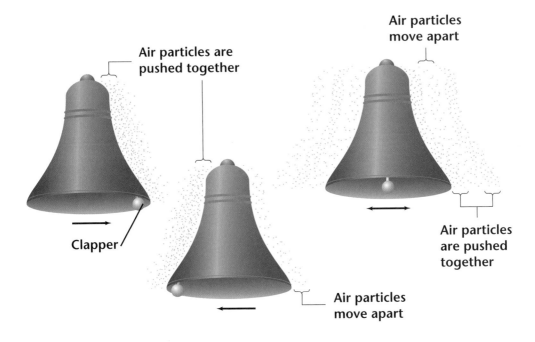

Air particles are pushed together

Air particles move apart

Air particles are pushed together

Air particles move apart

Clapper

How Sound Travels

Sound wave

A wave produced by vibrations

The movement of the air molecules around a vibrating object is a **sound wave.** You cannot see a sound wave. Sound waves move out from the vibrating object in all directions. As the sound waves travel farther from the object, they become weaker. The figures of the wire spring show how sound energy travels in waves. In Figure A, the wire is pinched together at one end. In Figure B, the "wave" moves across the spring.

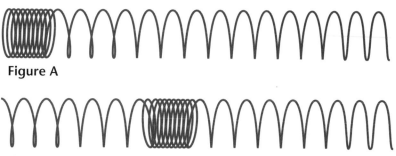

Figure A

Figure B

Some things make sounds even though you cannot see them vibrate. For example, if you strike a tuning fork, you will not see it vibrate. But you will hear the sound it makes. You can see evidence of sound waves by placing the end of a tuning fork that has been struck into a small container filled with water. You will notice water splashing out of the container. The vibrations of the tuning fork cause the water to move about.

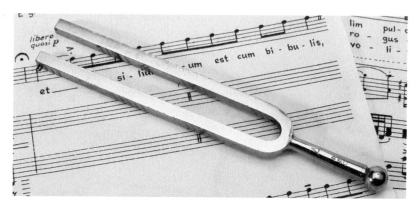

When a tuning fork vibrates, it produces sound waves.

Write your answers to these questions in complete sentences on a sheet of paper.

1. How is sound produced?

2. How does sound travel?

3. What is a sound wave?

4. What word means "to move quickly back and forth"?

5. What happens to the strength of sound waves as they travel farther from the vibrating object?

Intensity
The strength of a sound

Decibel
A unit that measures the intensity of sound

Amplitude is how far particles move from a wave's midpoint to its highest or lowest point. A high amplitude means high energy. The more energy a sound wave has, the more intense the sound.

How would you describe the sounds around you? You might point out that some sounds are loud or soft. You might also describe some sounds as high or low.

Loud and Soft Sounds

You might barely be able to hear the sounds of rustling leaves. The noise made by a jet, however, might make you want to cover your ears. The strength of a sound is known as its **intensity.** A sound wave that carries a lot of energy has a high intensity. A sound wave that carries less energy has a lower intensity.

Scientists measure the intensity of sounds in units called **decibels.** The sound of rustling leaves would be measured at about 20 decibels. The roar of a jet engine would be approximately 135 decibels. You can see the decibel levels of some common sounds below.

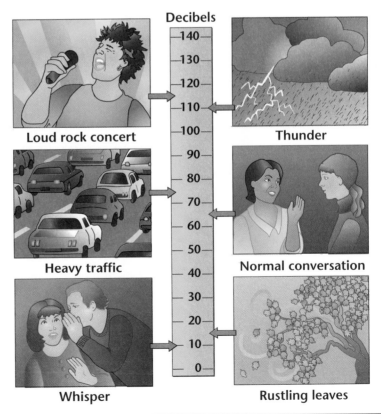

Decibels

Loud rock concert	Thunder
Heavy traffic	Normal conversation
Whisper	Rustling leaves

— 140 —
— 130 —
— 120 —
— 110 —
— 100 —
— 90 —
— 80 —
— 70 —
— 60 —
— 50 —
— 40 —
— 30 —
— 20 —
— 10 —
— 0 —

The point at which a wave is at its highest is called its crest. A wave's lowest point is its trough. The distance between one wave crest and the next crest is called the wavelength.

Your hearing interprets the intensity of a sound as loud or soft. The loudness or softness of a sound is the **volume** of the sound. The more intense a sound, the higher its volume seems.

In some cases, loud sounds can help keep you safe. For example, the siren on a fire truck is loud enough to be heard above other sounds.

Loud sounds can also be harmful. Listening to loud music or other loud sounds for a long period of time can damage your hearing. Sounds above 90 decibels can cause pain to your ears. Sounds above 130 decibels can damage your ears.

Loud sounds can cause pain, and they can damage your ears.

High and Low Sounds

How does the sound of a flute differ from the sound of a tuba? The flute has a high sound. The tuba has a low sound. We say that the flute has a higher **pitch** than the tuba. Pitch is how high or low a sound seems. Look at the sound waves in the figure below. You can see that the sound waves made by the flute are closer together than those made by the tuba. The flute produces more sound waves per second than the tuba.

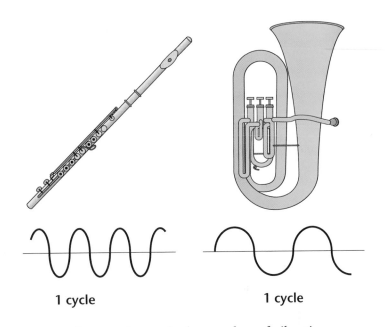

| 1 cycle | 1 cycle |

Pitch

How high or low a sound is

Frequency

The number of vibrations per second of a sound wave

Cycle

The complete back-and-forth motion of a vibration

Hertz, Hz

The unit used to measure frequency of a sound; one Hertz equals one cycle per second

Science Myth

Hitting something harder changes the pitch of the sound that is produced.

Fact: Hitting something harder does not change the sound waves' frequency. The sound might be louder or last longer, but the pitch will not be different.

Frequency of a sound wave is the number of vibrations per second. If an object vibrates 5 times in each second, the resulting sound wave would have a frequency of 5 **cycles** per second. A cycle is one complete back-and-forth motion of a vibration.

We measure frequency in units called **Hertz.** One Hertz equals one cycle per second. For example, an object that has a frequency of 10 Hertz has 10 back-and-forth motions in one second. The abbreviation for Hertz is *Hz*.

Did You Know?

Sometimes people who train dogs use special whistles. Dogs can hear the high-pitched sounds from the whistles, but people cannot hear these sounds.

Although objects can vibrate at many different rates, the human ear can hear only a certain range of frequencies. Generally, the human ear can detect sounds with frequencies ranging from 20 Hz to 20,000 Hz. The range can vary somewhat depending on a person's hearing ability.

The figures below compare the frequencies of sounds that a human can hear with those that some animals can hear.

Frequencies of Sounds Heard	
Sounds Heard by	**Frequencies**
frog	50 to 10,000 Hz
human	20 to 20,000 Hz
dog	15 to 50,000 Hz
bat	1,000 to 120,000 Hz

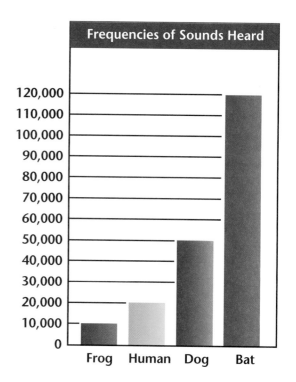

Frequencies of Sounds Heard

Lesson 2   R E V I E W

Write your answers to these questions in complete sentences on a sheet of paper.

1. Describe the intensity of a sound wave that carries a lot of energy.

2. How does volume relate to intensity?

3. How does the frequency of a sound wave affect pitch?

4. What unit is used to measure frequency?

5. What property of sound does a decibel measure?

Achievements in Science

The Doppler Effect

The Doppler effect, described by Christian Doppler in 1842, is an apparent change in wave frequency. The Doppler effect occurs with all types of waves: sound, light, or radio waves. This effect happens when the sound source is moving or when the observer is moving. The relative motion of the waves' source and the observer causes the frequency change.

As the wave source moves forward, the waves in the front of it get crowded. When the waves move closer together, the frequency of the waves increases. As the source of the waves moves away, the waves spread apart. These waves have a lower frequency.

Scientists use the Doppler effect in many ways. They use it to study the speed and direction of a star. They measure the change that motion causes to the frequency of the star's light. Meteorologists use Doppler radar to track storms by finding changes in wind speed or direction. Police use Doppler radar to measure a car's speed. Edwin Hubble used the Doppler effect to show that the universe is expanding.

Suppose you wake up to the roar of a jet plane. It is high in the air. How does the noise from the jet reach you in your home?

Sound Moves Through Matter

Heat energy can move through empty space. Sound energy cannot travel through empty space. In outer space, there are no molecules of matter. You can only hear sound when it travels through matter. Therefore, no sounds can travel through outer space. Sound, however, can travel through air.

Sound travels through all matter in a similar way. Sound waves travel through matter by causing the particles in matter to vibrate. When a particle begins to vibrate, it bumps into another particle. Then that particle bumps into another particle, and so on.

The dominoes in the photo help illustrate how sound travels through matter. As each domino falls, it strikes the next domino, causing it to fall over. Each of the dominoes travels only a short distance. But the effect of one domino's motion can travel a large distance.

The motion of falling dominoes shows how sound travels through matter.

The Speed of Sound

If you put the dominoes closer together, they fall down in less time. In the same way, sound waves travel more quickly through substances with molecules that are closer together.

Chapter 3 described molecules in solids, liquids, and gases. Molecules of matter in solids are closest together. For this reason, sound moves fastest through solids.

Molecules in liquids are farther apart than those in solids. Sound travels more slowly through liquids. Molecules of gases are the farthest apart. Sounds move slowest through gases.

The speed of sound in air depends on the temperature of the air. In higher temperatures, molecules of air move farther apart. As a result, sound travels more slowly. The speed of sound through air is about 346 meters per second (or 700 miles per hour) at a temperature of 25 degrees Celsius. The graph below lists the speed of sound through some different materials.

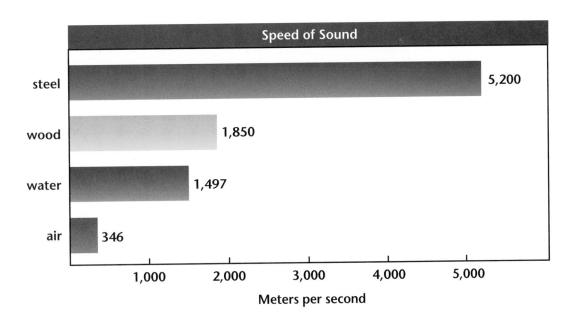

Sound travels quickly, but light travels even faster. Because light travels faster than sound, you will see a flash of lightning before you hear the thunder. You can use the speeds of sound and light to figure out how far away a storm is. Follow these steps to calculate the distance of a storm.

1. When you see a flash of lightning, count the number of seconds until you hear the thunder.

2. Divide the number of seconds by 3 seconds per kilometer. The answer tells you how many kilometers away the storm is. (For example, if it takes 3 seconds for you to hear the thunder, the flash of lightning is about 1 kilometer away.)

Suppose you see a flash of lightning. You find that it takes 6 seconds until you hear the thunder. How far away is the storm?

EXAMPLE

$$\text{distance of storm} = \frac{6 \text{ sec}}{3 \text{ sec/km}}$$

$$\text{distance of storm} = 2 \text{ km}$$

Sound travels quickly, but light travels even faster.

How Sound Bounces

Suppose a radio is playing in the next room. You may hear music from the radio because some of the sound travels through the solid wall. However, some of the sound might not travel through the wall. The matter in the wall might absorb, or trap, some of the sound. For this reason, the sound of the music might seem softer to you than to a person standing next to the radio.

Other sound waves from the radio might be **reflected.** That is, the sound might bounce back from the wall. The figure of the ball bouncing against the wall illustrates how sound can be reflected. Sound that bounces back from an object is an **echo.** Echoes can be heard best when sound bounces from hard, smooth surfaces.

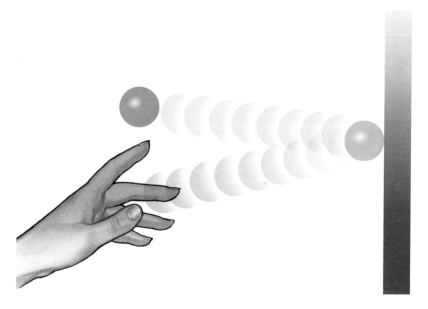

You have probably heard echoes at one time or another. Did you ever call out someone's name in a large, empty room? If so, you might have heard an echo of your voice even after you stopped speaking.

Measuring Distances with Sound Waves

Scientists can use **sonar** to find objects below the surface of water. Sonar is a method that uses sound to measure distances under water. People can use sonar to locate schools of fish, to explore shipwrecks, and to find other underwater objects.

Scientists can use sonar to find out exactly how deep water is at a particular location. The figure illustrates how sonar works. Instruments on the ship send out sound waves. The sound waves are reflected by the ocean bottom back to the surface of the water.

Scientists can measure the time it takes for the sound to reach the bottom of the ocean and return to the surface. Because scientists know how fast sound travels through water, they can tell how far the sound travels. Scientists can use sonar to measure very deep parts of the ocean. They can also use sonar to map the ocean floor.

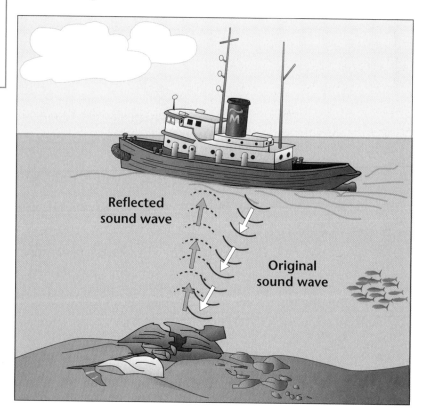

Reflected sound wave

Original sound wave

"Seeing" Inside the Body with Sound

Scientists also use sound waves, called **ultrasound,** to "see" inside the human body. Ultrasound waves are sound waves that humans cannot hear. When these waves are beamed into the body, some are reflected back. Each part of the body reflects the waves a little differently. Ultrasound equipment picks up these reflected waves and makes a picture. By looking at the picture, doctors can tell if an organ is an unusual size or shape. Doctors can also use the picture to find tumors.

Ultrasound is commonly used to study the development of an unborn baby. Ultrasound waves are directed into the mother's body. These waves echo off the unborn baby. The picture below shows an image made by an ultrasound screen. Ultrasound waves do not hurt the mother or the baby.

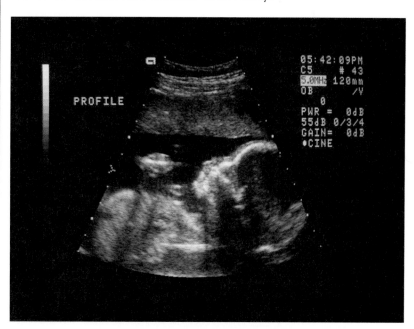

Ultrasound waves are used to make a picture of an unborn baby.

Lesson 3   R E V I E W

Write your answers to these questions in complete sentences on a sheet of paper.

1. How do sound waves move from place to place?

2. Does sound move most quickly through solids, liquids, or gases? Explain your answer.

3. How does air temperature affect the speed of sound?

4. Explain how sonar can be used to measure distances in the ocean.

5. List two ways that sound waves can be used for medical purposes.

Technology Note

Most speakers produce audible sound beams that spread out. Hypersonic speakers produce audible beams that stay narrow. This gives hypersonic speakers an advantage. The sound they produce is directed at a specific target or targets. We can hear sound through these speakers only if we are directly in their path. Ambulances with hypersonic sirens can be heard on the street but not in nearby houses.

Inferring How Sound Waves Travel

Materials

- safety glasses
- pencil with sharpened point
- large plastic-foam cup
- 2 rubber bands (one cut)
- plastic food wrap
- salt
- plastic beaker
- water
- tuning fork

Purpose

Can sound waves travel through matter? This investigation will demonstrate that sound waves are vibrations that travel through matter.

Procedure

1. Copy the data table on a sheet of paper.

How the Rubber Band Was Plucked	Observations

2. Put on your safety glasses.

3. Use the point of the pencil to punch a small hole in the bottom of the cup.

4. Push one end of the cut rubber band through the hole in the cup. Tie a knot in the end of the rubber band so that it cannot be pulled through the hole. The knot should be inside the cup.

5. Stretch a piece of plastic wrap tightly over the top of the cup. Use the other rubber band to hold the plastic wrap in place, as shown in the figure on the next page.

6. Hold the cup with the plastic wrap facing up. Sprinkle a few grains of salt on the plastic wrap.

7. Hold the cup while your partner slowly stretches the rubber band. Gently pluck the stretched rubber band and observe what happens to the salt. Record your observations in the data table.

8. Vary the force used to pluck the rubber band. Notice the difference in sound the rubber band makes as you vary the force.

Questions and Conclusions

1. In Step 7, what happened to the salt when you plucked the rubber band?

2. What do you think caused the salt to move? Explain your answer.

3. In Step 8, how did the force you used to pluck the rubber band affect the sound it made?

4. In Step 8, how did the force you used to pluck the rubber band affect the salt on the plastic wrap?

Explore Further

1. Use a tuning fork and a plastic beaker half-filled with water. Gently tap the tuning fork against the heel of your hand and place the tips of the fork into the beaker of water. What happens to the water?

2. Vary the force used to tap the tuning fork. Notice what happens to the water as you vary the force.

Lesson 4 | What Is Light?

Objectives

After reading this lesson, you should be able to

◆ define light and explain how visible light is produced.
◆ describe the nature of light.
◆ explain how light waves travel.
◆ describe the visible spectrum.

Light

A form of energy that can be seen

Photons

Small bundles of energy that make up light

You see **light** everywhere. You see objects becau[se] reflected from them. But what is light? Light is [] that you can sometimes see. Most visible light is produc[ed] objects that are at high temperatures. The sun is the major source of light on Earth. The sun loses energy by emitting light. The sun's energy arrives as light with a range of wavelengths, consisting of visible light, infrared, and ultraviolet radiation.

Light as a Particle

Scientists have done experiments to gather information about light. Some scientific experiments suggest that light acts like a particle. Evidence tells scientists that light is made up of bundles of energy called **photons.** Photons are like small particles. A single photon is too small to be seen.

Look at the light coming from the flashlight. Streams of photons make up each beam of light. Each photon carries a certain amount of energy.

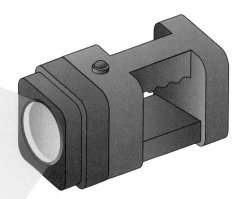

Light as a Wave

Other scientific evidence suggests that, like sound, light travels in waves. As a result of their findings, most scientists agree that light seems to have properties of both particles and waves. Scientists agree that light travels as waves in a straight line. Light is a type of electromagnetic wave. Most properties of light can be explained in terms of its wave nature.

Waves—including waves in water, earthquake waves, sound waves, and light waves—transfer energy when they interact with matter.

Light waves move like water waves.

Light waves move like waves in water. However, light waves travel fastest through empty space. Light waves move more slowly as they pass through matter. In fact, light waves cannot pass through some matter at all.

Light waves travel more quickly than sound waves. Light waves travel about 300,000 kilometers per second. This is the fastest possible speed anything can travel.

Colors in White Light

Visible spectrum

The band of colors that make up white light; the colors in a rainbow

Prism

A clear piece of glass or plastic that is shaped like a triangle; it can be used to separate white light

The light you see from the sun is white light. Did you know that white light is actually made up of many colors of light? If you have ever seen a rainbow, you have actually seen the colors that make up white light.

How is color determined? Usually it is determined by which colors of light an object absorbs or reflects. A red ball is red because it absorbs all colors of the visible spectrum but red.

A rainbow contains all the colors of the visible spectrum.

The band of colors you see in a rainbow is known as the **visible spectrum.** The colors of the visible spectrum always appear in the following order: red, orange, yellow, green, blue, indigo, and violet.

You can use a **prism** like the one in the photo to see the colors in white light. A prism is a piece of glass or plastic shaped like a triangle. A prism can separate white light into the colors of the visible spectrum.

A prism shows the colors in white light.

What are lasers and how do we use them?

A laser is a device that produces a powerful beam of light. Laser light is unique. Wavelengths in ordinary white light differ from one another. They also overlap each other. Wavelengths in laser light are all the same and are in step. The crests, or tops, and the troughs, or bottoms, of the waves are lined up exactly.

Lasers have many uses. We can use lasers to find gas leaks and detect pollutants in the air. Lasers can monitor and identify air pollutants around landfills, factories, and highways. Unlike a flashlight, the concentrated light of a laser can travel miles and miles. So lasers that monitor air pollution do not have to be near the pollution's source. The table shows some other uses for lasers.

Some Other Uses for Lasers	
Communication and entertainment	• transmitting telephone and TV signals • producing and reading compact discs
Business	• identifying bar codes on products • doing sales transactions • making maps • surveying land • printing and scanning
Medicine	• detecting medical problems, diseases, and disorders • doing surgery, such as removing cataracts from eyes, removing cancerous cells, clearing blocked arteries, removing tonsils • treating skin conditions including removal of birthmarks
Scientific research	• collecting data from the moon • studying the atom • studying chemical reactions

Lesson 4   R E V I E W

Write your answers to these questions in complete sentences on a sheet of paper.

1. What makes up a beam of light?

2. How does light travel?

3. Would light travel faster through space or through a window? Explain your answer.

4. What colors make up white light?

5. Explain what a prism does.

Achievements in Science

Electromagnetic Waves and the Electromagnetic Spectrum

In 1864, James Maxwell presented the theory that electromagnetic waves exist. He said visible light is an electromagnetic wave, and there also are invisible electromagnetic waves. In the 1880s, Heinrich Hertz proved Maxwell's theory.

Different electromagnetic waves form the electromagnetic spectrum. Waves with lower frequencies than visible light are radio waves, microwaves, and infrared rays. Waves with higher frequencies than visible light are gamma rays, X-rays, and ultraviolet rays.

Radio waves have the lowest frequencies. They carry broadcast signals. Microwaves have a higher frequency and are used to cook food. Doctors use infrared rays, whose frequencies are just below visible light, to treat skin diseases.

Gamma rays have the highest frequencies. They are used to treat cancer. The frequencies of X-rays are just below gamma rays. X-rays help diagnosis illnesses. Ultraviolet rays have frequencies just above visible light. They are used in sun lamps and fluorescent lights.

Electromagnetic waves travel at the speed of light in a vacuum. They can be reflected and refracted. Their only differences are frequency and wavelength.

Objectives

After reading this lesson, you should be able to

◆ describe how plane mirrors reflect light.

◆ describe how concave and convex mirrors reflect light.

What happens when you look into a mirror? Why can you see yourself? The answers to these questions have to do with the way light waves act.

Light Bounces

When you throw a ball to the floor, it bounces back. Light also bounces back when it hits an object. When light bounces off a surface, we say that the light is reflected. Reflection is the bouncing back of a light wave. Few objects give off their own light. We see most objects only because of the light they reflect.

The figure below illustrates how light is reflected. Like a tennis ball, light waves bounce off a surface at the same angle that they hit the surface.

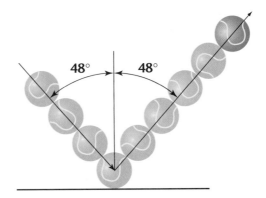

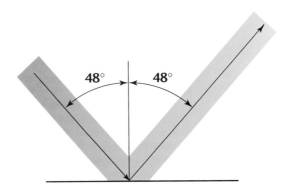

You can see an **image,** a copy or likeness, in a mirror because light waves are reflected. Study the figure. Notice how light from the cup hits the mirror and is reflected toward the observer's eye. Then the eye forms an image. The cup looks as if it is behind the mirror. The image is the same size as the original cup, but it is reversed. The handle of the cup appears on the opposite side when it is seen in the mirror. The angles at which the light reflects back causes this reversal. Follow the lines of light in the figure to see how this happens.

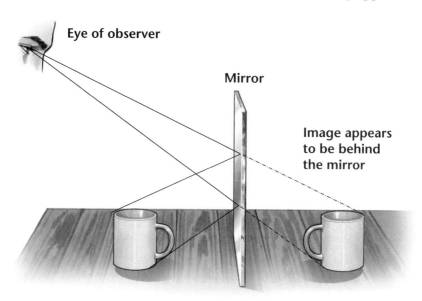

Eye of observer

Mirror

Image appears to be behind the mirror

Plane Mirrors

A mirror with a flat, smooth surface is called a **plane mirror.** The flatter the surface of the mirror, the clearer the image. Few surfaces are completely flat, including surfaces of plane mirrors. The figure below shows how light reflected from a completely flat surface differs from light that is reflected from a surface that is not flat. The small bumps in the surface on the right cause the reflected light to return at many different angles. Therefore, the image is not as clear.

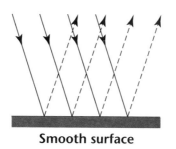

Smooth surface

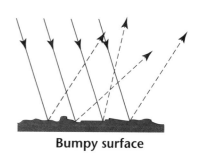

Bumpy surface

Concave Mirrors

Concave mirror

A mirror that curves in at the middle

Focal point

The point where reflected light rays from a concave mirror come together in front of the mirror

Many mirrors have curved surfaces rather than flat surfaces. Look at the curved mirror in the figure. This kind of mirror is called a **concave mirror.** A concave mirror has a reflecting surface that curves inward, like the inside of a spoon. The figure shows how a concave mirror reflects parallel light rays. Notice that the light rays come together at one point, the **focal point.**

Now look at the figure below. The tree is behind the focal point of the mirror. Find the focal point of the mirror in the figure. Rays of light from the tree hit the mirror's surface and are reflected back. Notice how the reflected rays pass through the focal point. If you put a piece of paper at Point A, you could see an image on it. The image would be upside down and larger.

Mirror

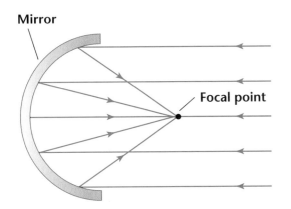

Focal point

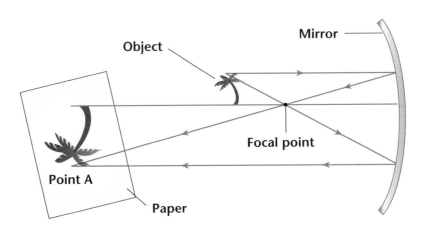

What would happen if the tree were between the concave mirror and the focal point? Look at the figure on the next page. If you follow the rays, you can see that the image of the tree would appear larger, right-side-up, and behind the mirror.

When you use a magnifying mirror to shave or apply makeup, you hold the mirror so that your face is between the focal point and the mirror.

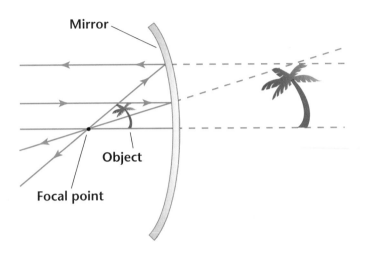

Convex Mirrors

The reflecting surface of some mirrors curves outward like the outside of a spoon. These kinds of mirrors are called **convex mirrors.** A convex mirror creates an image that looks smaller than the real object. However, you can see much more area in a convex mirror. For this reason, rearview and side-view mirrors on vehicles are often convex mirrors.

The side-view mirror on this vehicle is a convex mirror.

Lesson 5   R E V I E W

Write your answers to these questions in complete sentences on a sheet of paper.

1. Why are images reflected from a rough surface not as clear as those reflected from a smooth surface?

2. How does a concave mirror differ from a convex mirror?

3. Why are side-view and rearview mirrors on vehicles often convex?

4. How is the image in a plane mirror different from the object itself?

5. What type of mirror curves inward?

Technology Note

Holograms are lifelike images on film. To make holograms, designers split a laser beam. One beam goes to mirrors and through lenses and reflects off the object being photographed. The other beam goes across the first. The pattern made by their crossing goes to the film. When light shines on holograms, a 3D image appears.

Measuring Angles of Reflected Rays

Materials

- safety glasses
- mirror
- textbook
- masking tape
- unlined white paper
- pencil
- flashlight
- comb
- protractor
- ruler
- sheet of white paper

Purpose

Does the angle of a light ray when it hits a mirror match the angle of its reflection? In this investigation, you will measure the angles at which a light ray hits and is reflected from a mirror.

Procedure

1. Copy the data table on a sheet of paper.

Trial	Angle A	Angle B
1		
2		
3		

2. Put on your safety glasses.

3. Look at the figure. Using masking tape, tape the mirror to the book, as shown.

4. Place the book on its edge on a sheet of paper. Draw a line along the bottom of the mirror.

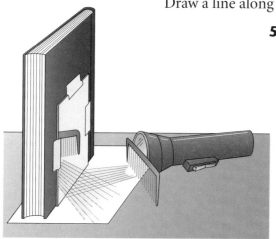

5. Turn on the flashlight. Hold the comb in front of the flashlight. Shine the flashlight on the mirror. Move the light around until you see a pattern of light rays and reflected rays like those shown in the figure.

6. Find a single light ray. Then find the reflected ray for that light ray. Trace both lines on the paper. The point where the two rays meet should be on the mirror line that you drew.

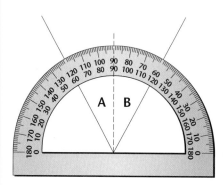

7. Remove the flashlight and turn it off. Move the book and the mirror. Lay the protractor along the mirror line. Place the center of the bottom of the protractor on the point where the rays meet. Draw a line at a right angle to the mirror line, as shown below.

8. Use the protractor to measure angles A and B. Record the measurements.

9. Repeat steps 3 to 7 two more times. Each time, draw rays with different angles.

Questions and Conclusions

1. Which angle—A or B—shows the angle at which the light traveled to the mirror?

2. Which angle shows the angle at which the light was reflected from the mirror?

3. How do angles A and B compare?

Explore Further

On a piece of paper, write the word AMBULANCE backwards as shown below.

ƎƆИА⅃UᗺMA

Hold the paper up to a mirror. How are the letters reflected in the mirror?

Objectives

After reading this lesson, you should be able to

◆ explain how light is refracted.

◆ describe how concave and convex lenses refract light.

◆ explain how lenses in eyeglasses can correct vision.

Refraction

The bending of a light wave as it moves from one material to another

Lens

A curved piece of clear material that refracts light waves

Concave lens

A lens that is thin in the middle and thick at the edges

When light moves from one kind of matter to another, the light waves change speed. As a result, the direction of the light changes. The bending of a light wave as it moves from one material to another is called **refraction.**

Notice that the pencil in the photo appears to be bent. Light travels more slowly in water than it does in air. When light passes from the water to the air, the light waves change speed and change direction. As a result, the pencil seems to bend.

Lenses

A **lens** bends light by acting like the water in the container. A lens is a curved piece of glass or other clear material that refracts light waves that pass through it. Lenses are used in eyeglasses, cameras, magnifying glasses, microscopes, and telescopes. What you see through a lens depends on the kind of lens you use.

Refraction causes the pencil to look like it is bent.

A **concave lens** curves inward. Look at Figure A. The lens is thin in the middle and thick at the edges. Light rays that pass through a concave lens are spread apart.

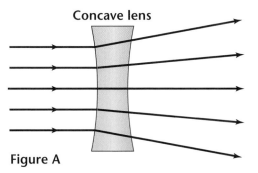

Concave lens

Figure A

When you look through a concave lens, objects appear to be smaller than they really are. Some people say the objects look "sharper." You can see this effect by looking through the glasses of someone who is nearsighted.

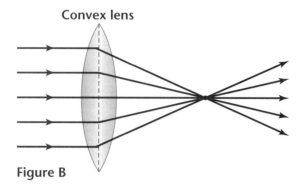

Convex lens

Figure B

A **convex lens** curves outward. Look at Figure B. The lens is thick in the middle and thin at the edges. Light rays that pass through a convex lens are refracted inward. A convex lens focuses light.

If you hold a convex lens close to your eye, the lens will magnify an image. If you hold a convex lens far from your eye and observe an object at a distance, the image appears upside down.

Lenses in Eyeglasses

The human eye has a convex lens. The lens forms an image on the retina, or the back wall of the eye. Figure C on page 303 shows a normal eye. You can see that the image formed is an upside-down image. Your brain interprets the image as right-side-up.

Figure D on page 303 shows the eye of a **nearsighted** person. People who are nearsighted can form clear images of close objects but not of distant objects. Notice that the image is formed in front of the retina instead of on it.

People who are nearsighted wear glasses that have concave lenses. Figure E shows how a concave lens refracts, or bends, light before it enters the eye. As a result, a proper image is formed on the retina.

Figure F shows the eye of a **farsighted** person. A farsighted person can see objects at a distance clearly. The person has difficulty seeing objects that are close. Notice that there is not enough room for the image to be focused properly. The image is focused behind the retina.

Convex lenses are used in eyeglasses for people who are farsighted. Figure G shows how a convex lens changes the focus of the light so that the image is formed properly on the retina.

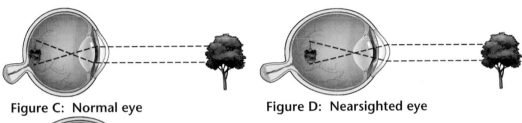

Figure C: Normal eye   **Figure D: Nearsighted eye**

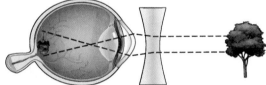

Figure E: Nearsighted eye with concave lens

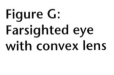

Figure F:
Farsighted eye

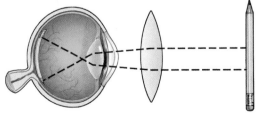

Figure G:
Farsighted eye
with convex lens

Write your answers to these questions in complete sentences on a sheet of paper.

1. What is refraction?

2. How does a concave lens refract light?

3. How does a convex lens refract light?

4. How do concave lenses correct the vision of a nearsighted person?

5. How do convex lenses correct the vision of a farsighted person?

▼◄▲▼◄▲▼◄▲▼◄▲▼◄▲▼◄▲▼◄▲▼◄▲▼◄▲▼◄▲▼◄▲▼◄▲▼◄▲▼◄▲▼◄▲▼◄▲▼

Science at Work

Optician

Opticians fit eyeglasses by following prescriptions written by ophthalmologists or optometrists. They also measure customers' eyes and recommend frames. Opticians write orders to laboratories for grinding and inserting lenses into frames. Some opticians grind and insert lenses themselves. Opticians make sure lenses are correctly ground and frames fit properly. Some opticians specialize in fitting contact lenses.

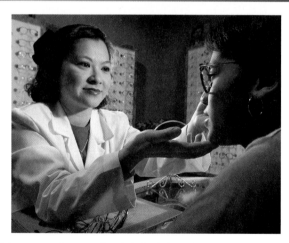

Most opticians complete an apprenticeship or receive on-the-job training. In some states, opticians must be licensed.

Opticians must be courteous, patient, and have good communication skills. They need to work well with their hands and be very detailed. Opticians also must take measurements accurately and have a good understanding of physics.

Chapter 10 SUMMARY

- Sound is caused by vibrations.

- Sound travels in waves.

- The intensity of sound is measured in decibels.

- A person's hearing interprets intensity as volume.

- A pitch is how high or low a sound is.

- Sound travels at different speeds through different kinds of matter.

- An echo is a reflected sound.

- Scientists use sonar to measure distances under water.

- People see objects because light is reflected from them.

- Light is made up of bundles of energy called photons.

- Light has properties of both particles and waves.

- Light waves travel fastest through empty space.

- The visible spectrum makes up white light.

- Refraction is the bending of a light wave.

- A mirror is an object that reflects light.

- Three types of mirrors are plane, concave, and convex.

- Concave and convex lenses refract light and can correct vision.

Science Words

concave lens, 301	farsighted, 303	light, 289	refraction, 301
concave mirror, 296	focal point, 296	nearsighted, 302	sonar, 284
convex lens, 302	frequency, 277	photons, 289	sound wave, 273
convex mirror, 297	Hertz, 277	pitch, 277	ultrasound, 285
cycle, 277	image, 295	plane mirror, 295	vibrate, 272
decibel, 275	intensity, 275	prism, 291	visible spectrum, 291
echo, 283	lens, 301	reflect, 283	volume, 276

Chapter 10 REVIEW

Vocabulary Review

Choose a word or words from the Word Bank that best completes each sentence. Write the answer on a sheet of paper.

1. A(n) _____ is a clear piece of glass or plastic that can be used to separate white light.

2. A(n) _____ is a copy or likeness of something.

3. We use _____ to measure distances under water.

4. A(n) _____ is a curved piece of clear material that refracts light waves.

5. A(n) _____ uses sound waves to study organs inside the human body.

6. A(n) _____ measures the intensity of sound.

7. One _____ equals one frequency cycle per second.

8. A(n) _____ is thick in the middle and thin at the edges.

Concept Review

Choose the answer that best completes each sentence. Write the letter of the answer on your paper.

9. Sounds are made when matter _____.

A rotates

B moves quickly back and forth

C vibrates

D both B and C

10. Light is made of tiny bundles of energy called _____.

A photographs   **C** neurons

B photons   **D** none of the above

11. A straw sticking out of a glass of lemonade looks bent due to _____.

    A light traveling more slowly in water than in air

    B refraction

    C light waves changing speed and direction

    D all of the above

Critical Thinking

Write the answer to each of these questions on your paper.

12. What is the difference between a sound's intensity, volume, pitch, and frequency?

13. How far away is an object whose echo takes 9 seconds to return?

14. Copy the drawing of each of these lenses. Draw lines to show how the light waves are refracted as they pass through each lens. Explain what you drew for each lens. What type of vision can each of the lenses help improve, and why?

15. Explain what is meant when something is called the mirror image of an object.

Test-Taking Tip When answering multiple-choice questions, first identify the questions you know are untrue.

Electricity

The lightning in the photograph is an example of electricity—static electricity. Electricity is all around us. Every day we use electricity. It lights homes and runs appliances. It starts cars and operates traffic signals. There are even electrical signals in our bodies that make our organs work. Do you know how electricity works and where it comes from? In Chapter 11, you will learn what electricity is, how it works, and how it travels.

Organize Your Thoughts

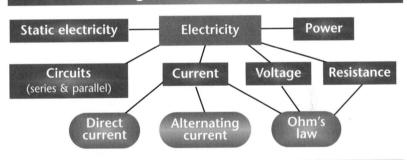

Goals for Learning

◆ To explain how electric current flows through a circuit

◆ To compare insulators and conductors

◆ To tell how resistance is useful

◆ To describe how batteries produce current

◆ To explain direct current and alternating current

◆ To apply Ohm's law

◆ To compare series and parallel circuits

◆ To describe how electricity is measured

Objectives

After reading this lesson, you should be able to

◆ explain static electricity.

◆ explain how electricity moves through a circuit.

◆ compare an open circuit to a closed circuit.

Electricity

Flow of electrons

Static electricity

Buildup of electrical charges

Science Myth

Electricity only flows through wires.

Fact: Electrons (electricity) can flow without wires. The transfer of electrons from fingers to a metal doorknob (as shown in the figure on this page) is one example of this.

In Chapter 3, you read about atoms and the particles that make them. Electrons are negatively charged particles. Under the right conditions, electrons can escape from one atom and move to another one. The atom that loses the electron becomes positively charged. The atom that has picked up the electron becomes negatively charged. In turn, this negatively charged atom can pass the electron on again. This movement, or flow, of electrons is the basis of **electricity.** Electricity is a form of energy.

Static Electricity

Have you ever gotten a shock when you touched metal after walking across a carpet? The shock was caused by a buildup of charge, called **static electricity.** Walking across the carpet caused electrons to leave the carpet and enter your body. When you touched the metal, the extra electrons jumped from your finger to the metal.

When electrons move from one place to another, energy is transferred. Lightning is a discharge of static electricity between clouds or between a cloud and Earth.

Closed Circuits

The movement of electrons from one place to another is called **electric current.** The rate at which electrons move from one place to another can vary. Electric current is measured in **amperes.** An ampere tells how much current is moving past a point in a circuit in one second. One ampere is the flow of about 6 billion billion electrons per second! An ampere is often called an amp.

Currents from static electricity are not easy to control. But an electric current produced by a power source can be controlled and is easy to use.

When electrons travel in an electric current, they follow a path. This path is called a **circuit.** Follow the path of current in the figure below. The circuit begins at the power source. It travels through the wire to the light bulb. It lights up the bulb, and then returns to the power source.

Electrons can only follow a complete, unbroken path. You can see that the path in this circuit is unbroken. This path is called a **closed circuit.** As long as the current continues to flow in the circuit, the light will remain lit.

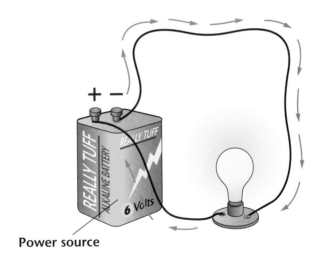

Power source

Open circuit

An incomplete or broken path for electric current

Open Circuits

Suppose you have a light turned on in your room. You decide you want to turn off the light. What do you do? Most likely you turn off a switch. To turn on the light again, you turn the switch on.

How does a switch work? Look at Figure A. You can see that the wires of the circuit are connected to a switch. When the switch is closed, the electrons can flow in an unbroken path. The light stays lit.

In Figure B, the switch is open. The current cannot pass through it. The bulb does not light. This is an incomplete, or broken, path for electric current. It is called an **open circuit.**

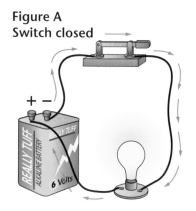

**Figure A
Switch closed**

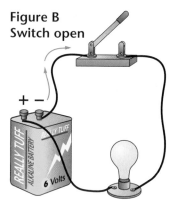

**Figure B
Switch open**

The switches you see in Figures A and B are called knife switches. The switches in your home are different from knife switches, but they work the same way. The switches in your home break the flow of electrons when they are turned off. These three images show some of the switches you might find in your home.

A lamp switch

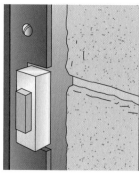

A doorbell switch

A wall switch

Schematic Diagrams

Scientists often use drawings of circuits. To make this job easier, they have developed symbols to show different parts of a circuit. Different symbols represent wires, switches, bulbs, and power sources. You can see some of these symbols in the diagram below.

A diagram that uses such symbols to show the parts of a circuit is called a **schematic diagram.** The schematic diagram below shows a battery in a circuit with a closed switch, wiring, and a bulb.

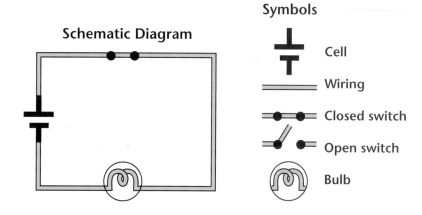

Symbols

Cell	
Wiring	
Closed switch	
Open switch	
Bulb	

Achievements in Science

Van de Graaff Generator

In 1931, Robert Van de Graaff invented the electrostatic generator that is named after him. Van de Graaff generators produce high voltage but low currents.

The top of an electrostatic generator is a hollow metal dome. The base is a motor. The motor turns a conveyor-like belt made of insulating material. The belt carries electrons from the base to the dome. When the electrons reach the top, they gather on the dome's outside surface. As more gather, the dome's voltage increases. The result is a source with very high voltage but low current. It is so low that when someone touches the dome, no harm is done.

Van de Graaff generators can be as small as 2 inches high, producing 5,000 volts. They can be several stories high, producing millions of volts. Scientists use Van de Graaff generators to accelerate charged particles for nuclear physics experiments. Teachers use Van de Graaff generators in classroom demonstrations. You may have seen Van de Graaff generators at work in old movies. This is the machine that makes the mad scientist's hair stand on end.

Write your answers to these questions in complete sentences on a sheet of paper.

1. Explain what happens when you get a shock from a metal doorknob after walking across a carpet.

2. Look at the following schematic diagrams, A and B. Which of the circuits is a closed circuit? Which is an open circuit?

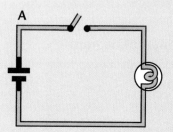
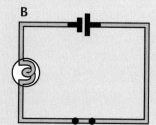

3. In which of the schematic diagrams above would current flow? Explain your answer.

4. What is the name for the path that electrons follow?

5. What unit is used to measure electric current?

Objectives

After reading this lesson, you should be able to

◆ explain the difference between a conductor and an insulator.

◆ give examples of conductors and insulators.

◆ explain what resistance is.

◆ list three things that affect the resistance of a material.

◆ explain how resistance is useful.

Conductor

Material through which electricity passes easily

Insulator

Material through which electricity does not pass easily

Look at the electrical cords that carry electric current in your home. You will notice that the metal wire that carries the electricity is covered with a material. This material is often plastic. Why do you think electrical cords have this covering?

Look at the cross section of the electrical cord in the figure. The wire in the center of the electrical cord is a **conductor.** A conductor is a material through which electrons can flow easily. Electricity passes easily through the wire from a power source to the lamp.

Metals, such as copper, gold, aluminum, and silver, are good conductors. Silver is a very good conductor of the metals. But it is too expensive to use in most wires. Most electrical circuits use copper wire.

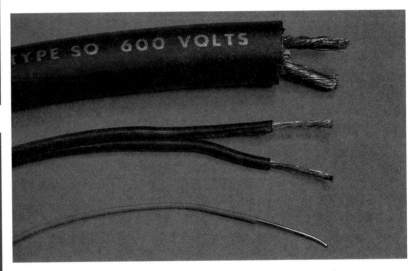

The plastic covering on these electrical cords is a good insulator.

The outer covering of the electrical cord is an **insulator.** An insulator does not conduct electricity well. The electrons in an insulator are not as free to move as the electrons in a conductor. Electricity does not pass through an insulator easily. Examples of good electrical insulators are glass, rubber, wood, and plastic.

Semiconductors are minerals that can be made to act like conductors and insulators. The mineral used most often in semiconductors is silicon. The microchip used in computers is an example of a semiconductor device.

Did You Know?

If your skin is wet, your chance of electrical shock is higher. The water mixed with the salt on your skin lowers your body's electrical resistance. This lets voltage pass more current through your body.

The insulator that covers the electrical cord keeps the electricity flowing in the wire. The covering prevents the current from flowing to places where it might cause fires or electrical shock. For example, if you touch a wire that is carrying an electric current, the electrons are free to travel through your body. You will get a shock. But if the wire is covered with an insulator like the one in the photo on page 315, the electricity cannot flow through your body.

When using electrical cords, be sure to check for worn insulation. If the bare wire is exposed, the cord is dangerous. You should replace or repair the cord. Electrical tapes that are good insulators can be used to repair the area where the wire is exposed.

Resistance

Not all conductors allow electricity to pass through them in the same way. Likewise, not all insulators slow down electricity equally well.

Resistance is a measure of how easy or hard it is for electric current to flow through a material. Resistance is measured in **ohms.** To understand resistance, think about two water hoses. They are the same in every way, except one has a larger hole running down the middle than the other. A pump pushes water through the two hoses equally. Through which of the hoses will more water pass in one minute?

If you answered that more water would pass through the hose with the larger opening, you are correct. The hose with the larger opening offers less resistance to the water flow than the hose with the smaller opening. In a similar way, more current flows through a substance with less resistance than through a substance with more resistance. Insulators have high resistance. Conductors have low resistance.

The resistance of a wire depends on three things.

◆ The material the wire is made of. Some materials have more resistance than others. For example, tungsten has a greater resistance than copper. Tungsten wire is used in lightbulbs.

◆ The length of the wire. The longer a wire is, the greater its resistance. Look at the two wires below. One wire is longer than the other. The longer wire has greater resistance. If you use a long extension cord to plug in a lamp, less electric current will go through the wire to the lamp.

◆ The thickness of the wire. The thinner the wire, the greater its resistance. You can see wires of two thicknesses below. The thinner wire has greater resistance than the thicker wire.

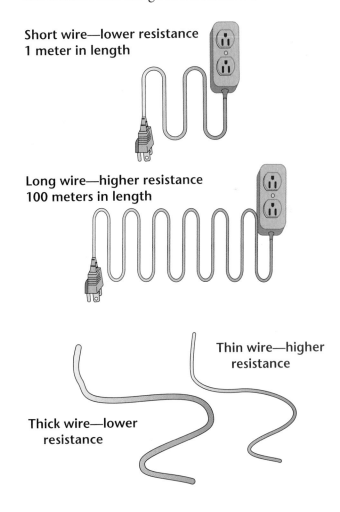

Short wire—lower resistance
1 meter in length

Long wire—higher resistance
100 meters in length

Thin wire—higher resistance

Thick wire—lower resistance

Resistance causes electrical energy to change into heat and light energy. Without resistance, many appliances in your home would not work.

Nichrome is a metal with a high resistance. When electricity passes through a nichrome wire, it gets hot. The wire coils in a toaster are made of nichrome. When electricity passes through the toaster, the wires get hot and toast your bread. Other appliances that use materials with high resistance include curling irons, hair dryers, and irons. Some of these appliances are shown here.

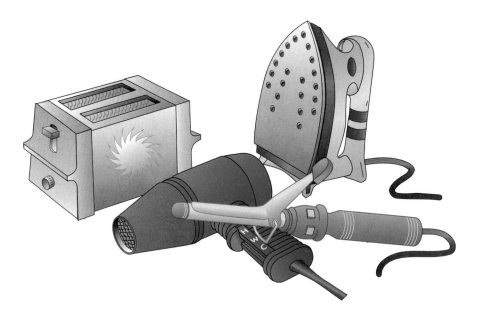

Lesson 2 REVIEW

Write your answers to these questions in complete sentences on a sheet of paper.

1. What is the difference between a conductor and an insulator?

2. Give two examples of conductors and two examples of insulators.

3. Sometimes the insulation on an electrical cord gets destroyed. Why would it be dangerous to use such a cord?

4. What are three things that affect the resistance of a wire? How is resistance useful?

5. List the appliances you have used in the last 24 hours. Put a check behind those that use materials with high resistance to produce heat and light.

▼◄▲▼◄▲▼◄▲▼◄▲▼◄▲▼◄▲▼◄▲▼◄▲▼◄▲▼◄▲▼◄▲▼◄▲▼◄▲▼◄▲▼◄▲▼

Science at Work

Line Installer

Line installers install electrical power, telephone, and cable TV lines. They put up poles and towers and dig trenches to carry wires and cables. They also set up service for customers and maintain and repair wires and cables. In emergencies, they have the important responsibility of restoring utility and communications services.

Most line installers complete several years of on-the-job training. Some have a two-year technical degree and have received on-the-job-training through an apprenticeship.

Line installers must have mechanical ability and a basic knowledge of algebra and trigonometry. They need stamina, strength, and coordination. They must also be comfortable working high above the ground. Good customer service skills are also important.

In order for current to move through a circuit, something has to "push" it. You might compare the flow of current to the flow of water through a hose. Something has to push the water through the hose. A water pump provides this push.

The push that keeps the current flowing in a circuit is called the **electromotive force.** Electromotive force is sometimes written as EMF. Electromotive force is measured in **volts.** A volt tells the amount of push. It also tells how much energy the electrons have. The energy that a power source gives to electrons in a circuit is called the **voltage.** When voltage is high, electrons have more energy available to do work.

Dry-Cell Batteries

Batteries are a common source of voltage. All batteries change chemical energy into electrical energy. One common type of battery is the **dry-cell battery.** This type of battery is called a dry cell because the materials inside the battery are somewhat dry or pastelike. Dry cells are used in flashlights, radios, and other small appliances. These batteries come in many sizes and shapes. D-size dry-cell batteries are used in flashlights and large radios. Smaller dry-cell batteries are used with devices that do not require much power.

Electromotive force

The push that keeps the current (electrons) flowing in an electric circuit

Volt

The metric unit used to measure electromotive force that tells the amount of push

Technology Note

Some batteries can be recharged. Rechargeable batteries work like regular batteries. But they can take electrical energy and store it as chemical energy for later use. Electrons flow in the opposite direction while the batteries are being recharged. The electrons keep flowing until a full charge is reached.

Voltage

The energy that a power source gives to electrons in a circuit

Battery

A source of voltage that changes chemical energy into electrical energy

Dry-cell battery

Electric power source with a dry or pastelike center

Terminal

Points where electrons leave or enter a battery

Batteries or other power sources do not supply electrons. The electrons in a circuit were there before the power source. Power sources move electrons that are already in the circuit. They cause electrons to flow.

The construction of most dry-cell batteries is similar to the one in the figure. Dry-cell batteries are not completely dry. They are made of a zinc container filled with black, moist manganese dioxide powder. In the center of the cell is a long rod made of carbon.

Each dry-cell battery has two **terminals,** or points, where electrons leave or enter the cell. Wires can be attached to the terminals to connect the cell to an electrical device. Larger batteries have both terminals on top.

Dry-Cell Battery

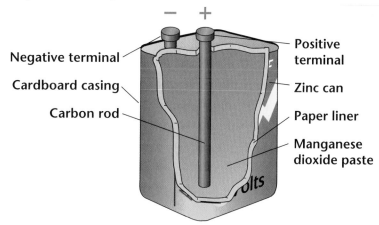

- Negative terminal
- Cardboard casing
- Carbon rod
- Positive terminal
- Zinc can
- Paper liner
- Manganese dioxide paste

The center terminal is the positive terminal. It is attached to the carbon rod. The positive terminal is marked with a plus sign (+). The other terminal is the negative terminal. It is connected to the zinc container. The negative terminal is labeled with a minus sign (−). This terminal is negative because it has an excess of electrons. The "pressure" at the negative terminal "pumps" the electrons along the circuit to the positive terminal.

A smaller dry-cell battery has only one terminal on top. The top terminal is the positive terminal. The negative terminal is located on the bottom of the battery. You would use this kind of battery in an ordinary flashlight.

Wet-Cell Batteries

The lead storage battery that you find in most cars is an example of a wet-cell battery. A wet-cell battery is different from a dry-cell battery because it is an electric power source that is filled with a liquid. Look at the figure below. Most wet-cell batteries have a hard rubber case filled with a solution of sulfuric acid. Plates are placed inside the sulfuric acid. Often, these plates are made of lead or lead dioxide.

A chemical reaction between the acid and the plates causes a series of reactions. As the reactions happen, electrons flow from one plate to another. This produces an electric current.

Did You Know?

The bite of the South American bushmaster snake is sometimes treated with electric shock. The snake bite victim receives a series of short shocks of about 20,000 volts. Sometimes car or outboard motors are used to deliver the voltage.

Wet-Cell Battery

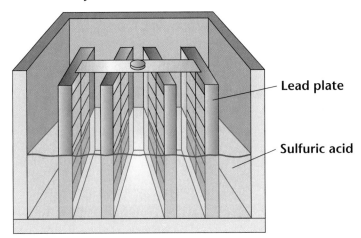

Lead plate

Sulfuric acid

Science Myth

A larger battery makes things run faster.

Fact: A battery's voltage determines how fast things run. A large battery does not necessarily have more voltage than a small battery. Nine-volt batteries are smaller than 1.5-volt D-cell batteries. A 12-volt car battery is much larger than a 9-volt battery. Yet the car battery's voltage is only slightly higher.

Direct and Alternating Current

The current in a wet-cell battery and a dry-cell battery flows in one direction. This type of current is called **direct current.** It sometimes is referred to as DC. The figure below on the left shows direct current. Notice that the arrow points one way. Direct current is not the most common kind of current.

The electricity in your home probably is **alternating current.** Alternating current is also called AC. The figure on the right shows alternating current. The arrow indicates that current moves in two directions. In alternating current, the flow of electrons changes direction regularly. Machines called generators produce alternating current. The generators that produce electricity for your home change the direction of the current about 60 times per second.

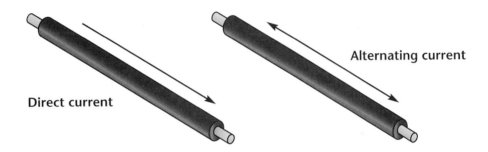

Alternating current

Direct current

Write your answers to these questions in complete sentences on a sheet of paper.

1. What is electromotive force?

2. How is a battery like a water pump?

3. Explain how a dry-cell battery works.

4. How does a wet-cell battery differ from a dry-cell battery?

5. What is the difference between direct current and alternating current?

Achievements in Science

Transistor

John Bardeen, Walter H. Brattain, and William Shockley invented the transistor in 1947. All progress made in electronics since—from vacuum tubes to microprocessors—rests on that invention. Transistors control the flow of electric current in circuits. They switch current off and on and they strengthen current. Transistors are made of a semiconductor material that can conduct and insulate.

Before transistors, vacuum tubes were used in circuits. Vacuum tubes were large, used lots of energy, and created lots of heat. The first electronic computers had vacuum tubes. Transistors dramatically changed the electronics industry. Radios, computers, and hearing aids used to be big and bulky. Now they are quite small thanks to transistors. The first transistor was .5-inch high. Now millions of transistors in integrated circuits sit on silicon chips smaller than a dime.

In 1959, Jack Kilby and Robert Noyce patented the integrated circuit. An integrated circuit is a tiny chip of semiconductor material. Transistors and other electronic parts are built into it. The integrated circuit led to the development of the microprocessors that operate computers today.

Ohm's law

Current equals voltage divided by resistance

In the early 1800s, Georg Ohm, a German schoolteacher, discovered that volts, amps, and ohms in an electrical circuit are all related to one another. To understand Ohm's idea, remember these things that you have learned about electricity:

◆ Power sources, such as batteries, provide the push (voltage) to the current in a circuit.

◆ The rate at which the current flows can be measured in amperes.

The flow of current can be slowed down by the resistance of the material through which the current flows. Resistance is measured in ohms.

Ohm put these relationships into a formula. This formula is known as **Ohm's law.**

$$\text{current (amperes)} = \frac{\text{electromotive force (volts)}}{\text{resistance (ohms)}}$$

The formula is more commonly written as:

$$I = \frac{V}{R}$$

Notice in the equation that the letter *I* is the symbol for current. The symbol for resistance is *R*. The law shows that as resistance increases, current tends to decrease. Using this equation, you can find the current of a circuit if you know the voltage and resistance.

The diagram on this page shows an electric circuit. It has a 1.5-volt dry-cell battery and a lamp, or bulb. A lamp is a resistor. How much current is in the circuit?

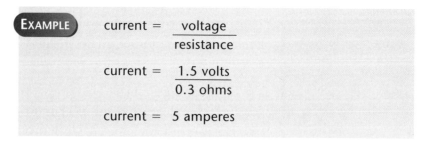

Notice that when you divide volts by ohms, your answer is in amperes.

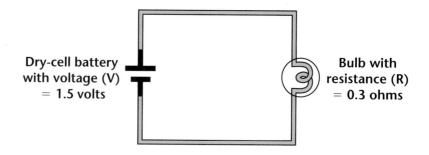

Copy the table on a sheet of paper. Then write the answers in your table.

Find the current in amperes for each circuit in the table. The first one is done for you.

	Voltage (volts)	Resistance (ohms)	Current (amperes) $\dfrac{V}{R}$
1.	10	5	$\dfrac{10 \text{ volts}}{5 \text{ ohms}} = 2 \text{ amperes}$
2.	15	5	
3.	50	5	
4.	35	10	
5.	1.5	10	

Technology Note

Hybrid electric vehicles (HEVs) combine a gasoline-powered engine and a battery-powered electric motor. These high-tech cars switch to electric power when less power is needed. Sometimes, when more power is needed, they use energy from electricity and the engine together. An HEV's computer decides which type of energy to use and when.

Have you ever had a string of decorative lights? You might know that with some strings of lights, if one light burns out, all the remaining lights stay lit. But in other strings, all the lights will go out if one burns out. Then you have to change each bulb on the string until you find the one that is burned out. Why do these strings of lights act differently? The answer is in the way the circuit is made.

Devices in Series Circuits

Look at the circuit in the diagram. It includes a source of energy, such as a battery, and wire to carry the current. It also has different electrical devices attached to it. This kind of circuit is called a **series circuit.** In a series circuit, current (electrons) flows through only one path around the circuit.

Series circuit

A circuit in which all current (electrons) flows through a single path

Series Circuit

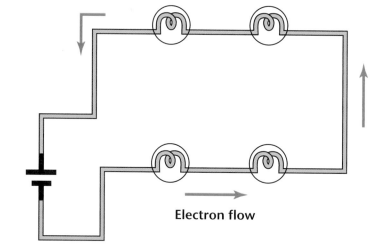

Electron flow

You can see in the circuit on page 328 that all the electrons must pass through each electrical device. In the example of the decorative lights, each light is a separate device. The electrons must pass through each lightbulb.

Series circuits have a disadvantage. If one light is unscrewed or burns out, all of the other lights will go out. That is because the circuit becomes open, and electrons cannot flow.

When electrical devices are connected in series, the current is the same throughout the circuit. That means that adding electrical devices to the series lowers the voltage through each device. Notice in the diagram below that if only one bulb is connected to a dry cell, the bulb may shine brightly. If another bulb is added in series, each of the bulbs will be dimmer than the single bulb was.

Series Circuits

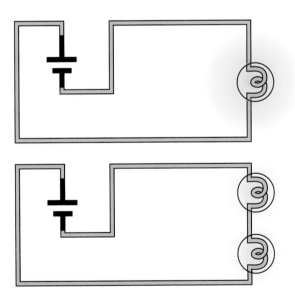

Batteries in Series Circuits

Batteries in a circuit can be connected in series, too. Batteries in series increase the voltage of the circuit. To find the total voltage, add the voltages of the cells together.

In the figure of the circuit shown below, the batteries are in series. A wire connects a positive terminal to a negative terminal. A second wire connects the lamp and switch to the batteries. When batteries are connected in series, they can deliver more energy in the same amount of time. Bulbs in this kind of circuit burn brighter because the voltage is higher.

Cells in Series

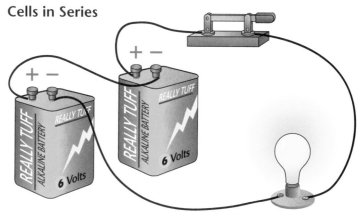

6 volts + 6 volts = 12 volts
Total voltage = 12 volts

In a flashlight, dry-cell batteries are usually connected in series. You can see in the figure below how the positive terminal of one battery touches the negative terminal (the bottom metal plate) of the next battery.

1.5 volts + 1.5 volts = 3 volts

Fuses and Circuit Breakers

Connecting electrical devices in series can be inconvenient. But there are practical uses for series circuits, too. For example, your home is probably protected by fuses or circuit breakers. Fuses and circuit breakers help prevent fires.

Look at the fuse in the drawing. Notice the piece of metal on the top of the fuse. It is designed to melt at a certain temperature. When the wires get too hot, the fuse will melt and break the circuit. When a fuse melts, it must be replaced. A circuit breaker, on the other hand, is a switchlike device that can be reset after the circuit has been repaired.

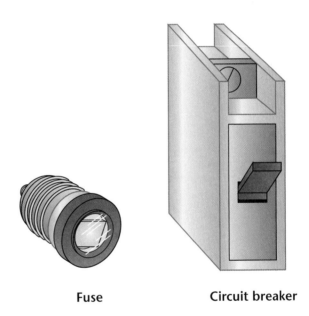

Fuse   Circuit breaker

Write your answers to these questions in complete sentences on a sheet of paper.

1. What is a series circuit?

2. What is one advantage of a series circuit?

3. What happens to the brightness of a bulb when more bulbs are added to the same series circuit?

4. When two cells with the same voltage are connected in series, what happens to the voltage?

5. Compare a fuse and a circuit breaker.

Materials

- safety glasses
- two 1.5-volt dry-cell batteries
- 2 holders for batteries
- 2 flashlight bulbs
- 2 bulb sockets
- 1.5 m-long piece of common bell wire, cut into various lengths
- switch
- 1–3 additional 1.5-volt dry-cell batteries
- 1–3 additional flashlight bulbs

Constructing Series Circuits

Purpose

How would you create a series circuit? In this investigation, you will construct and study a series circuit.

Procedure

1. Copy the data table on a sheet of paper.

Circuit	Schematic Diagram	Prediction	Observations
A			
B			
C			

2. Put on your safety glasses.

3. Draw each of the schematic diagrams shown below in the correct space in the data table. Then label each item in each diagram.

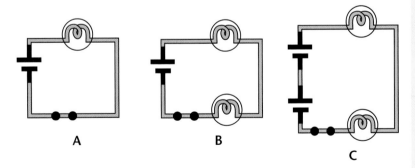

A   B

C

4. Use the materials to construct circuit A. What do you think will happen to the bulb when you close the switch? Write your prediction in the data table. Close the switch. Record how brightly the bulb shines.

5. Take apart circuit A. Construct circuit B. Predict how brightly the bulbs will shine compared to the single bulb in circuit A. Record your prediction. Close the switch. Record your observations.

6. Unscrew one of the bulbs and record what you observe.

7. Construct circuit C. Predict how brightly the bulbs will shine compared to the bulbs in circuit B. Close the switch. Record your observations.

Questions and Conclusions

1. What items make up circuit A? What kind of circuit is it?

2. What items make up circuit B? What kind of circuit is it?

3. How brightly did the bulbs in circuit B shine compared to the bulb in circuit A? Explain your answer.

4. What happened in circuit B when one of the bulbs was unscrewed? Why did that happen?

5. How brightly did the bulbs in circuit C shine compared to the bulbs in circuit B? Explain your answer.

Explore Further

What do you think would happen if you added more bulbs or more batteries to your circuit? Write your prediction on a sheet of paper. Then construct a circuit and find out. Record your observations.

Objectives

After reading this lesson, you should be able to

◆ describe a parallel circuit.

◆ explain what happens to the brightness of bulbs in a parallel circuit when more bulbs are included.

◆ explain what happens to voltage when two batteries with the same voltage are connected in parallel.

Parallel circuit

A circuit in which there is more than one path for current

The lights and appliances in your home are not wired in a series circuit. If they were, every time a bulb burned out, none of the other lights and appliances would work. Instead, most circuits in houses are **parallel circuits.** In a parallel circuit, there is more than one path for the current to follow.

Devices in Parallel Circuits

Look at the following diagram of two lamps connected in parallel. As you can see, there are two paths around this circuit. If one bulb burned out, the other bulb would stay lit. That is because there is more than one path for the electrons.

Parallel Circuit

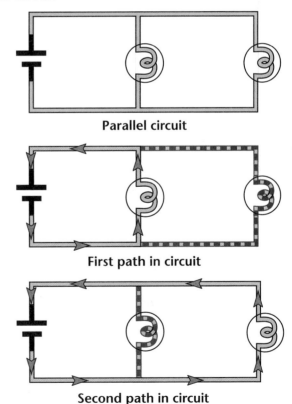

Parallel circuit

First path in circuit

Second path in circuit

When we connect several bulbs in parallel, all the bulbs will remain as bright as just one bulb alone would. However, more current must be drawn from the battery to power the extra bulbs.

When more electrical devices are added to the same circuit, more current runs through the circuit. As current in a circuit increases, wires begin to heat up. If they get too hot, the wires can start a fire in the walls. The fuses you read about in Lesson 5 help prevent this problem.

Batteries in Parallel Circuits

Batteries can be connected in parallel. A parallel connection between batteries allows them to keep providing energy longer. A parallel connection does not increase the voltage.

Look at the figures below. Figure A shows a circuit with only one 6-volt battery. The circuit in Figure B has two 6-volt batteries connected in parallel. The bulb in the circuit will stay lit longer. However, it will not burn brighter than the other bulb. The total voltage is still only 6 volts. The voltage is the same for both circuits in the figure. The two bulbs burn equally bright.

Cells in Parallel

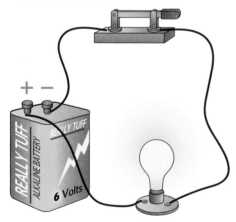

Figure A
Total voltage = 6 volts

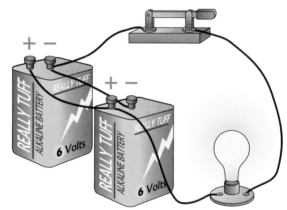

Figure B
Total voltage = 12 volts

Write your answers to these questions in complete sentences.

1. How can you recognize a parallel circuit? What happens to the bulbs in a parallel circuit when one bulb burns out?

2. Determine the number of paths in each of these parallel circuits.

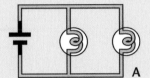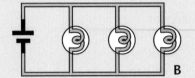

A   B

3. What happens to the brightness of bulbs in a parallel circuit when one bulb is added?

4. When two batteries with the same voltage are connected in parallel, what happens to the voltage?

5. Identify each of these circuits as either a parallel or series circuit.

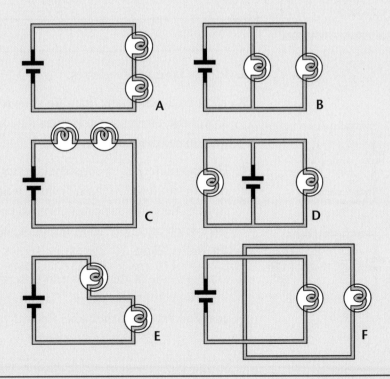

A   B

C   D

E   F

INVESTIGATION

Constructing Parallel Circuits

Materials

- safety glasses
- two 6-volt dry-cell batteries
- 2 holders for batteries
- 3 flashlight bulbs
- 3 bulb sockets
- 1.5 m-long piece of common bell wire, cut into various lengths
- switch

Purpose

How do you know a circuit is a parallel circuit? In the investigation, you will construct and study parallel circuits.

Procedure

1. Copy the data table on a sheet of paper.

Circuit	Schematic Diagram	Prediction	Observations
A			
B			
C			
D			
E			

2. Put on your safety glasses.

3. Draw each schematic diagram shown here and on page 339 in the correct space in your data table. Label each item in the diagram.

4. Use the materials to construct circuit A. How brightly do you think the bulbs will shine when you close the switch? Record your prediction in your table. Close the switch and note what happens. Notice how brightly the bulbs shine.

5. Unscrew one of the bulbs and observe what happens. Record your observations. Then tighten the bulb again and unscrew the other one. Record your observations.

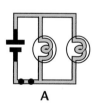

A

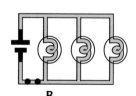

B

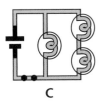

C

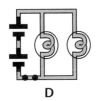

D

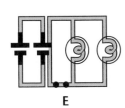

E

6. Take apart circuit A. Construct circuit B. Predict how brightly the bulbs will shine compared to the bulbs in circuit A. Close the switch. Record your observations. Then unscrew different combinations of bulbs. Record your observations.

7. Construct circuit C, and close the switch. Try loosening various combinations of bulbs. Record your observations.

8. Construct circuit D. Predict how brightly the bulbs will shine compared to the bulbs in circuit A. Close the switch. Record your observations.

9. Construct circuit E. Predict how brightly the bulbs will shine compared to the bulbs in circuit D. Close the switch. Record your observations.

Questions and Conclusions

1. What items make up circuit C? What kind of circuit is it?

2. Are the cells in circuit E connected in series or in parallel?

3. How brightly did the bulbs in circuit B shine compared to the bulbs in circuit A? Why?

4. What happened in circuit C when various bulbs were unscrewed?

5. How brightly did the bulbs in circuit D shine compared to the bulbs in circuit A? Why?

6. How brightly did the bulbs in circuit E shine compared to the bulbs in circuit D? Why?

Explore Further

Which circuit—C or D—will stay lit longer? Which uses less power?

Your home has many electrical devices. Every time you turn one of them on, you use electricity. How can you measure how much electricity you use?

Electric Power

Look at the lightbulb in the photo. Notice that the top of the bulb has 100 W stamped on it. The W stands for watt. It was named for James Watt, one of the inventors of the steam engine. You may recall from Chapter 8 that the watt is the unit we use to measure power, including **electric power.** Electric power is the amount of electrical energy used in a certain amount of time. This lightbulb uses 100 watts. It uses four times as much energy each second as a 25-watt bulb.

Electric power

The amount of electrical energy used in a certain amount of time

Kilowatt-hour

A unit to measure how much electric energy is used; it is 1,000 watts used in one hour

Using Electricity

When you pay your electric bill, you are paying for the amount of electricity you use. The electric company measures the amount of electricity you use in **kilowatt-hours.** A kilowatt-hour is 1,000 watts used in one hour. A meter measures the number of kilowatt-hours you use.

The 100 W on this bulb tells how much power it uses.

How can you check your home's electrical safety?

Electricity is helpful but it also can be harmful. Knowing how electricity works can help avoid electrical shock or electrocution. Electric current flows naturally to the ground through anything that will conduct it. Electric current can flow through your body if your body is touching the ground. Grounding circuits is an important safety practice. It lets electric current take another path if an electric device is not working correctly.

The plugs of many electric devices have a third prong. The third prong lets current flow to the ground if the device is not working correctly. Some outlets have a ground-fault circuit interrupter (GFCI). Sensors in GFCI outlets quickly detect tiny changes in current flow. They protect you if you accidentally come in contact with water and an ungrounded appliance. Surge protectors help protect electronic equipment from damage.

Use this checklist to check the electrical safety of your home. Be sure a parent or guardian knows that you are checking the items listed in the checklist. Check off things that are safe and unsafe. If anything is in an unsafe condition, tell a parent or guardian.

Electrical Items	Safe	Unsafe
Check that outlets and extension cords are not overloaded.		
Make sure electric cords are not frayed or cracked.		
Check that lightbulbs are the correct wattage for fixtures.		
Check that lightbulbs fit tightly in the fixtures.		
Make sure plugs fit the outlets into which they are plugged.		
Make sure no third prongs have been removed from plugs to fit an outlet.		
Make sure halogen floor lamps and space heaters are positioned away from materials that can catch fire.		
Make sure all plugged-in appliances are placed away from water.		

Write your answers to these questions in complete sentences on a sheet of paper.

1. A lightbulb has 25 W stamped on it. What does this mean?

2. Which would use more energy, a 50-watt bulb or a 75-watt bulb of the same kind?

3. What is a kilowatt-hour?

4. How is a kilowatt-hour used?

5. What term describes the amount of electrical energy used in a certain amount of time?

Science Myth

Batteries are an inexpensive source of energy.

Fact: The cost per kilowatt-hour of batteries is far higher than the cost per kilowatt-hour of household electricity. A large D-cell battery can cost 2,700 times more than your home electricity. Smaller batteries, like those in watches and cameras, can cost 10,000 to 100,000 times more. People use batteries because they are convenient.

Chapter 11 SUMMARY

- Electricity is the flow of electrons.

- Static electricity is a buildup of electric charge.

- Current, the rate of flow of electricity, is measured in amperes.

- A closed circuit is a complete, unbroken path for current. An open circuit is an incomplete or broken path for current.

- A schematic diagram uses symbols to show the parts of a circuit.

- A conductor is a material through which a current can easily pass. An insulator is a material through which a current cannot easily pass.

- Resistance is a measure of how easily electric current will flow through a material. It is measured in ohms.

- Fuses and circuit breakers prevent electrical wires from getting too hot or causing fires.

- Electromotive force is the force that keeps current flowing. It is measured in volts.

- Batteries are a common source of voltage. Two types of batteries are dry cells and wet cells.

- Two types of current are direct current and alternating current. Direct current flows in one direction. Alternating current changes direction regularly.

- According to Ohm's law, current equals voltage divided by resistance.

- In a series circuit, all current flows through a single path. In a parallel circuit, current flows in more than one path.

- Power is the rate at which work is done. It is measured in watts.

Science Words

alternating current, 323
ampere, 311
battery, 321
circuit, 311
closed circuit, 311
conductor, 315
direct current, 323
dry-cell battery, 321
electric current, 311

electric power, 340
electricity, 310
electromotive force, 320
insulator, 315
kilowatt-hour, 340
ohm, 316
Ohm's law, 325
open circuit, 312
parallel circuit, 335

resistance, 316
schematic diagram, 313
series circuit, 328
static electricity, 310
terminal, 321
volt, 320
voltage, 321
wet-cell battery, 322

Vocabulary Review

Choose a word or words from the Word Bank that best complete each sentence. Write the answer on a sheet of paper.

1. A(n) _____ measures how much electric energy is used.

2. The metric unit used to measure electromotive force is a(n) _____.

3. Electrons leave or enter a battery through the _____.

4. We use a(n) _____ to describe how much electric current flows through a wire.

5. A(n) _____ is a unit used to measure resistance.

Concept Review

Choose the answer that best completes each sentence. Write the letter of the answer on your paper.

6. Lightning is a discharge of _____ between clouds or between a cloud and earth.

   A electric current   **C** static electricity

   B energy   **D** all of the above

7. _____ is an example of a good conductor.

   A Glass   **B** Gold   **C** Rubber   **D** Wood

8. _____ is an example of a good insulator.

   A Aluminum   **B** Copper   **C** Plastic   **D** Silver

9. Of the following materials, _____ has higher resistance.

   A water   **B** rubber   **C** silver   **D** aluminum

10. Wet-cell and dry-cell batteries have _____ current.

    A direct   **B** alternating   **C** series   **D** parallel

11. The formula for Ohm's law is _____.

    A $I = \dfrac{V}{R}$ **B** $V = \dfrac{I}{R}$ **C** $I = \dfrac{R}{V}$ **D** $V = \dfrac{R}{I}$

12. When cells are in _____, the voltage is the sum of the voltages of the cells.

    A parallel   **C** an open circuit

    B series   **D** a closed circuit

Critical Thinking

Write the answer to each of these questions on your paper.

13. What is the effect of resistance on electrical energy?

14. Based on the following schematic diagram, calculate the current.

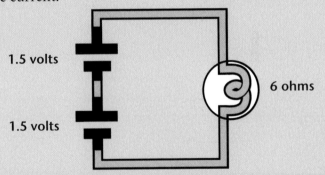

1.5 volts

6 ohms

1.5 volts

15. Explain the circuitry of a string of lights that will not light up if one of the lights is burned out.

Test-Taking Tip Take time to organize your thoughts before writing answers to short-answer tests.

12

Magnets and Electromagnetism

Look at the piece of lodestone in the photograph. Lodestone is a natural magnet made of the mineral magnetite. Years ago, sailors used magnetite to navigate their ships around the world. The sailors discovered that when magnetite was hung from a string it would point north or south. Do you know what causes magnetism? Can a magnet be demagnetized? Are magnets still used to navigate ships? In Chapter 12, you will learn more about magnets and how they work.

Organize Your Thoughts

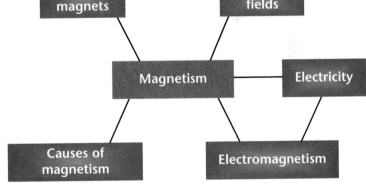

Goals for Learning

◆ To describe various kinds of magnets

◆ To explain what a magnetic field is

◆ To tell what causes magnetism

◆ To describe electromagnetism and its uses

347

After reading this lesson, you should be able to

◆ describe several kinds of magnets.

◆ explain what magnetic poles are.

◆ describe how magnetic poles behave.

You are probably familiar with **magnets.** Magnets attract certain kinds of metals. They pick up metal objects, such as paper clips and other things made from iron. Most of the magnets you have seen are made by people. But there are also naturally occurring magnets such as lodestone. Lodestone, one of a variety of magnetite, is made of iron oxide. It is found naturally in the earth and comes in many sizes and shapes.

Most manmade magnets come in several common shapes. These shapes include the horseshoe, bar, cylinder, and doughnut shapes. You may have seen magnets like the ones in the photo.

Magnet

An object that attracts certain kinds of metals, such as iron

Did You Know?

The ancient Greeks knew about the magnetic properties of lodestone. Lodestone is also called magnetite. The word *magnet* comes from the name Magnesia, the Greek province where the mineral was mined.

Magnets come in a variety of different shapes.

Magnetic Poles

Look at the magnets in the figure. The ends of a magnet are called its **magnetic poles.** Whatever the shape, all magnets have two opposite magnetic poles. The magnetic forces are greatest at the poles. You know this because the ends of the magnet will pick up more paper clips than the center of the magnet.

The poles on a magnet are called the north pole and the south pole. On a marked magnet, the north pole is marked with an *N*. The south pole is marked with an *S*.

You cannot tell whether the end of an unmarked magnet is a north pole or a south pole simply by looking at it. But you can find out by placing the magnet close to another magnet whose poles are marked. Observe whether the poles **attract** (pull together) or **repel** (push apart). To figure out the poles of the unmarked magnet, use the following rules.

Did You Know?

Farmers give their cows magnets to eat. Because cows do not chew their food, they often swallow metal objects. Magnets attract these objects. The magnets hold the metal objects in place in a cow's digestive system so the animal isn't injured by the objects.

Poles of opposite types attract each other.

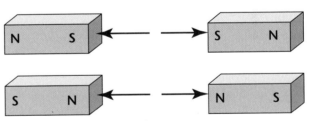

Poles of the same type repel each other.

Write your answers to these questions in complete sentences on a sheet of paper.

1. How can you determine the poles of an unmarked magnet?

2. If two south poles are placed close together, what will happen?

3. If a north and a south pole are placed close together, what will happen?

4. What is lodestone?

5. Name four familiar shapes of magnets.

Achievements in Science

Magnetic Resonance Imaging (MRI)

Scientists first considered using magnetic resonance to make pictures of the human body in 1946. In 1977, the first Magnetic Resonance Imaging (MRI) exam was performed on a human being. Magnetic resonance imaging uses two things to create high-quality cross-sectional images of bodies. Computer-controlled radio waves work with a powerful doughnut-shaped magnet that creates magnetic fields. The magnetic field of an MRI magnet is stronger than an industrial crane magnet.

The protons of hydrogen atoms in the body act like magnetic spinning tops. MRI aligns these hydrogen protons with its magnetic fields. MRI then uses radio waves to move the protons out of alignment temporarily. As the protons return to their original position, they release their own radio waves. These radio waves are used to create a computer image of internal body parts.

MRI shows doctors the difference between healthy and diseased tissues. It lets doctors see into bones and organs without surgery to diagnose illnesses and injuries. MRI is safer than X-rays because it has fewer possible side effects.

A **magnetic field** surrounds all magnets. A magnetic field is an area around a magnet in which magnetic forces can act. The magnetic forces will attract or repel other magnets.

Although you cannot see magnetic fields, you can easily see their effects. Place a bar magnet under a sheet of paper. Sprinkle iron filings on top of the paper. The filings will line up in a pattern of curving lines like those shown in the figure. These lines are called **lines of force.** They are caused by the magnetic field and they show the field. The lines of force reach around the magnet from one pole to another. The lines are closest together near the poles. That is where the field is strongest and the forces are greatest.

Magnetic field

Area around a magnet in which magnetic forces can act

Lines of force

Lines that show a magnetic field

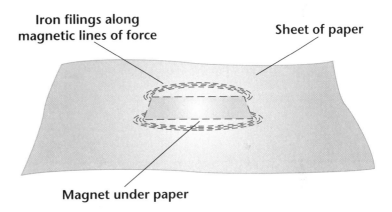

Iron filings along magnetic lines of force — Sheet of paper — Magnet under paper

You can see in the figure below how the lines of force of two magnets affect each other. Notice how they cause the poles of magnets to attract or repel each other.

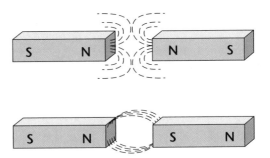

The Earth as a Magnet

You may be surprised to learn that Earth itself is a giant bar magnet. Like other magnets, Earth has magnetic poles. These magnetic poles are located near the geographic north and south poles.

Earth's natural magnetism allows compasses to work. The needle of a compass is a magnet, too. It has a north pole and a south pole. They are located at opposite ends of the needle.

Like magnetic poles repel each other. However, you can see in the figure that the north magnetic pole of Earth attracts the north pole of a compass. This happens because Earth's north magnetic pole is actually like the south pole of a magnet. But it is called the north magnetic pole because it is located near the geographic North Pole. Earth's south magnetic pole is really like the north pole of a magnet.

Earth's magnetic field attracts and lines up the compass needle. The north pole of the magnet in a compass is attracted to the Earth's magnetic pole. As a result, it points north.

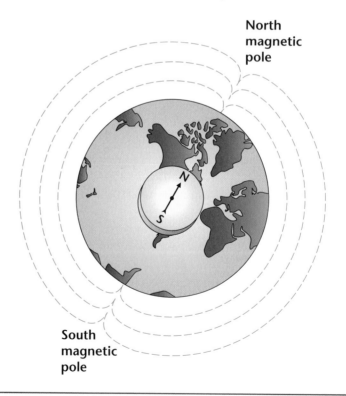

North magnetic pole

South magnetic pole

Write your answers to these questions in complete sentences on a sheet of paper.

1. What is a magnetic field?

2. What pattern is made by magnetic lines of force around a bar magnet?

3. How does a compass work?

4. How can you see the lines of force around a magnet?

5. Where are magnetic lines of force closest?

Science Myth

The earth's magnetic field never changes.

Fact: The earth's magnetic field changes slowly but constantly. Over time, the North and South Poles trade places. This last happened about 700,000 years ago. More than 20 flip-flops have occurred in the past five million years. The ocean floor shows evidence of these changes. Why this happens, however, continues to puzzle scientists.

Observing Magnetic Lines of Force

Materials
◆ safety glasses
◆ 2 bar magnets
◆ 2 horseshoe magnets
◆ 2 sheets of paper
◆ cup of iron filings
◆ metal bar that attracts a magnet

Purpose
Do the lines of force around a bar magnet look different than the lines of force around a horseshoe magnet? In this investigation, you will observe the lines of force around two magnets.

Procedure

Part A
1. Copy the data table on a sheet of paper.

Parts	Bar Magnet	Horseshoe Magnet
Part A		
Part B		
Part C		

2. Put on your safety glasses.

3. Place one bar magnet and one horseshoe magnet on a flat surface. Cover each magnet with a sheet of paper.

4. Sprinkle some of the iron filings on each of the pieces of paper. Do not pour the filings. It is best to sprinkle them lightly from a height of about 31 cm (about 1 foot).

5. Observe the pattern of iron filings made by the lines of force. Record your observations in the data table.

6. Carefully pour the iron filings from each paper back into the cup.

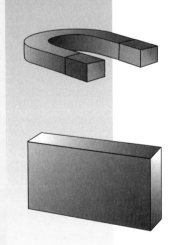

Part B

7. Place the bar magnets end to end with like poles close together.

8. Place a sheet of paper over the magnets and sprinkle with iron filings. Record your observations.

9. Carefully pour the iron filings from the paper back into the cup.

Part C

10. Reverse the poles of one of the bar magnets so that opposite poles are close together. Cover with a sheet of paper.

11. Sprinkle the paper with iron filings. Record your observations.

12. Repeat Part B and Part C with the horseshoe magnets. Record your observations.

Questions and Conclusions

1. Describe the pattern made by the lines of force of the single bar magnet.

2. In Part B, did the poles of the bar magnets attract or repel each other? How did the lines of force show this?

3. In Part C, did the poles of the bar magnets attract or repel each other? How do you know?

4. How were the patterns on the bar magnet similar to those on the horseshoe magnet?

Explore Further

Find a metal bar that is attracted to a magnet. Repeat Parts B and C using the metal bar. Record your observations.

Objectives

After reading this lesson, you should be able to

◆ explain what causes magnetism.

◆ describe how to make a magnet.

◆ describe how magnetism is destroyed.

◆ list materials that are attracted by magnets.

Scientists have observed that some atoms have north and south magnetic poles. In most substances, though, the atoms point in all different directions. As a result, the atoms cancel out each other's magnetism. So these substances are not magnetic. Materials that are not magnetic include wood, copper, plastic, rubber, gold, and glass. In addition, magnets are not attracted to these materials.

Look at Figure A. In a nonmagnetized material, the magnetic fields of atoms do not line up.

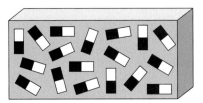

Figure A

Now look at Figure B. In a magnetized material, the magnetic fields of atoms line up.

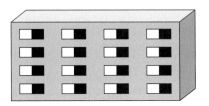

Figure B

In some substances, atoms can be made to line up so that most of them are aligned in the same direction. This arrangement causes the substance to act like a magnet. Only a few materials can be made into magnets. They include iron, nickel, and cobalt. Magnets are attracted to these materials.

Making a Magnet

One of the simplest ways to make a magnet is to take an iron wire and stroke it with a magnet. Hold one of the poles of the magnet at one end of the wire. Slowly stroke the magnet in one direction down the length of the wire. After four or five strokes, the wire will become a magnet. Figure C shows this process.

What do you think would happen if you cut the wire into two pieces? Look at Figure D. Each of the two pieces would become magnets.

Figure E shows that each piece of cut wire still contains atoms that are lined up in the same direction. When a magnet is broken in two, each half is a magnet with a north and a south pole.

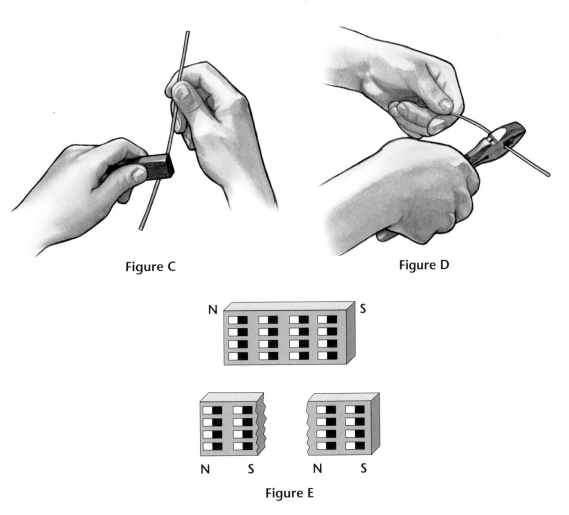

Figure C

Figure D

Figure E

Demagnetizing a Magnet

If you break a magnet in two, you will have two magnets. If you break each of those two magnets in half, you will have four magnets. Each magnet has a north and a south pole. Magnetic poles are always in pairs.

You can break a magnet into two parts. This action will not destroy the magnet's magnetism. Both parts remain magnetic. However, it is possible to destroy magnetism or demagnetize a magnet. Have you ever tried to demagnetize a magnet?

Two common ways to demagnetize a magnet are by heating it or by striking it with a hard blow. The figure below illustrates these two ways to demagnetize a magnet. Both of these actions can cause atoms to rearrange themselves so that they are no longer facing the same direction.

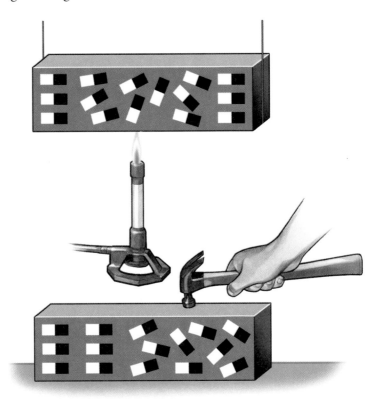

Write your answers to these questions in complete sentences on a sheet of paper.

1. What causes magnetism?

2. What happens when you break a magnet into two pieces?

3. How can you destroy magnetism?

4. Name some materials that can be made into magnets.

5. Name some materials that are not magnetic.

▼◀▲▼◀▲▼◀▲▼◀▲▼◀▲▼◀▲▼◀▲▼◀▲▼◀▲▼◀▲▼◀▲▼◀▲▼◀▲▼◀▲▼

Science at Work

Appliance Service Technician

Appliance service technicians check appliances such as refrigerators, dryers, and ovens for different problems. They perform tests on different parts of appliances, including motors, heating elements, and switches. Because of differences among types of appliances, many appliance service technicians specialize.

Appliance service technicians receive training either through on-the-job experience or a post-high school technical program. Some complete an apprenticeship. Apprenticeships often combine on-the-job training and schooling and may last four to five years.

Appliance service technicians must understand the mechanical workings of machines. They must also be able to work with their hands. In addition, these technicians must enjoy solving problems and managing details.

Magnets are not the only things that can produce a magnetic field. Electricity can also produce a magnetic field. You can see this when you place a compass near a wire that is carrying electricity. The compass needle will turn until it is at right angles to the wire. The current produces a magnetic field around the wire.

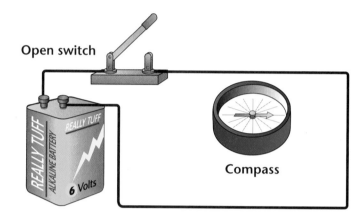

Open switch

Compass

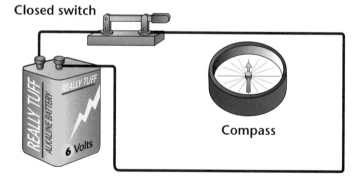

Closed switch

Compass

Electromagnetism

The relationship between magnetism and electricity

Electromagnet

A temporary magnet made by passing a current through a wire wrapped around an iron core

The relationship between magnetism and electricity is called **electromagnetism.** Moving electric charges produce magnetic forces and moving magnets produce electric forces.

Electricity can be used to make a type of magnet called an **electromagnet.** An electromagnet is a temporary magnet. It is made by passing a current through a wire wrapped around an iron core. An electromagnet is magnetic as long as an electric current is flowing.

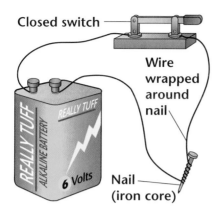

Closed switch

Wire wrapped around nail

Nail (iron core)

6 Volts

REALLY TUFF
ALKALINE BATTERY

An electromagnet, like the one in the figure, can be made with a large nail, some common bell wire, and a 6-volt dry-cell battery. The nail serves as the iron core. The flow of current through the wire surrounding the core creates a magnetic field.

The strength of an electromagnet depends on a number of factors. Power sources with higher voltages make more powerful electromagnets. More turns of wire around the core will also increase the strength of a magnet.

Using Electromagnets

The magnetism that electromagnets produce is the same as the magnetism a magnet produces. An electromagnet has a magnetic field and a north and south pole. Unlike a regular magnet, an electromagnet can be switched off and on. This quality makes electromagnets very useful. Many salvage yards have electromagnets like the one in the photo.

Electromagnets can be turned on and off.

Winding wire into coils makes the wire's magnetic fields stronger. Coiled wire with current flowing through it is called a solenoid. Putting an iron core inside a solenoid creates an electromagnet and even stronger magnetic fields.

When the current is turned on, the electromagnet picks up pieces of metal from piles of scrap. When the current is turned off, the electromagnet loses it magnetism. The metal pieces fall to the ground.

You may not be aware that you use electromagnets every day. Many appliances use electromagnets. Speakers, earphones, and telephones use electromagnets to change electric currents into sound waves.

Find the electromagnet in the figure below. Notice the device that provides electric current to the electromagnet. The level of electric current passing to the electromagnet from this device changes. These changes cause the strength of the electromagnet to change, too. As the strength of the electromagnet changes, the plate located in front of the electromagnet vibrates back and forth. The vibration of the plate creates sound waves.

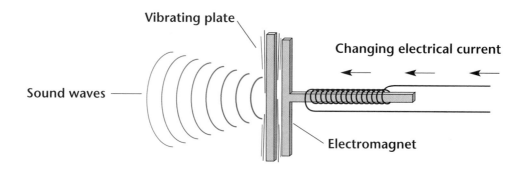

Vibrating plate

Changing electrical current

Sound waves

Electromagnet

Technology Note

Superconducting magnets are electromagnets that produce a very strong magnetic field. Their magnetic field can be 200,000 times greater than the earth's. Superconducting magnets are unique because they are made from materials that have no resistance. The lack of resistance results in greater electric current, which creates a stronger magnetic field.

Motors

Motor

A device that converts electrical energy to mechanical energy

Science Myth

Motors and engines are the same thing.

Fact: Motors and engines are not the same thing. A motor uses magnetic force to change electrical energy into kinetic energy. Motors operate an automobile's starter, heater fan, windshield wipers, and other parts. An engine changes the potential energy of fuel into kinetic energy. An engine uses gasoline as fuel to operate an automobile.

Motors also make use of electromagnetism. A motor converts electrical energy to mechanical energy, which is used to do work. The figure illustrates how a motor works.

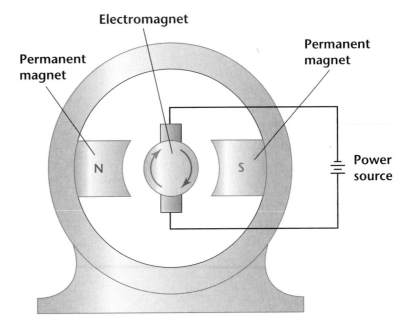

A motor has three basic parts. One part is a permanent magnet that cannot move. A second part is an electromagnet that is free to turn. The electromagnet turns between the opposite poles of the permanent magnet. A third part is a device that supplies alternating electric current to magnetize the electromagnet. As you learned in Chapter 11, alternating current changes direction at a regular rate.

When current is supplied to the electromagnet, each pole of the electromagnet is attracted to the opposite pole of the permanent magnet. This attraction causes the electromagnet to turn so that its poles line up with the opposite poles of the permanent magnet. The constant switch of poles in the electromagnet of a motor causes it to turn.

As the direction of current changes, the electromagnet's poles reverse. As a result, the aligned poles repel each other. And the electromagnet continues to turn. The current in the electromagnet continues to reverse direction after every half turn, causing the electromagnet to continue to turn.

The spinning motion of the electromagnet in a motor can be used to do work or operate other devices. Motors operate cars, refrigerators, electric toys, hair dryers, air conditioners, and many kitchen appliances. Look at the figure below. These items are examples of devices that have motors.

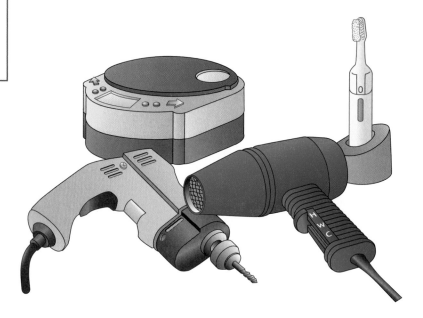

Technology Note

Electric guitars have electromagnetic devices called magnetic pickups. Pickups are bar magnets wrapped with thousands of turns of narrow wire. When the guitar's strings are plucked, they vibrate. Their vibration produces a vibration in the magnet's magnetic field, which creates an electronic signal. An amplifier makes the signal louder. Speakers change the signal into sound waves.

How does magnetism move a train?

Imagine riding in a train that moves on a cushion of air instead of rolling along tracks. Such trains use electromagnetism to travel at very fast speeds. These vehicles are called maglev trains—short for "magnetic levitation." Electromagnetism is used to levitate, or lift up, the train, to move it forward, and to guide it. There is no friction with the track to slow down the train. Maglev trains actually float about 10 centimeters above the tracks.

The maglev train starts out by rolling on rubber wheels. Once the train reaches a faster speed, current is sent through the metal coils on the sides of the train. This current causes the coils to become magnetized. The track also is magnetized. The coils on the train are repelled by the electromagnets in the track. This causes the train to lift off the tracks.

The train moves forward because poles in the magnets in the tracks can be changed. The magnets in the track in front of the train have poles that are opposite to those of the train. The attraction between the train and the track ahead moves the train forward. The repulsion between the train and the track below it keeps the train levitated. By controlling the current to the tracks, a magnetic wave is created that keeps the train moving forward.

In 2002, the world's first public maglev train began running in Shanghai, China. The train reaches 415-km/h speeds along a 32-km route. The route connects Shanghai's financial area with its airport.

Write your answers to these questions in complete sentences on a sheet of paper.

1. What is electromagnetism?

2. Explain how an electromagnet works.

3. Name two devices that use electromagnets.

4. Explain how a motor works.

5. What would happen to the compass needle in the figure on page 360 if the wires attached to the bottom battery were reversed?

Achievements in Science

Electromagnetism

Until the 1800s, the only magnetism known came from natural magnets like lodestone and iron. Scientists believed that magnetism and electricity were unrelated.

This belief changed in 1820 after Hans Oersted made a discovery while doing a classroom demonstration. He saw a wire with electricity running through it make a compass needle move. He discovered that every conductor carrying an electric current is surrounded by a magnetic field.

Oersted's discovery of the connection between magnetism and electricity led Andre-Marie Ampere to experiment further. He found that when current flows through coiled wire, the current acts like a magnet. Ampere's law, published in 1827, is one of the basic laws of electromagnetism. It shows the mathematical relationship between electric currents and magnetic fields.

Oersted's and Ampere's discoveries showed that two forces—electric and magnetic—are associated with electricity. Their work led to the development of the electromagnet. It also led to the prediction of the existence of electromagnetic waves.

INVESTIGATION

Constructing an Electromagnet

Purpose

Is it possible to increase an electromagnet's magnetic properties? In this investigation, you will see how to increase the magnetic properties of an electromagnet.

Procedure

1. Copy the data table on a sheet of paper.

Number of Turns of Wire Coil	Number of Paper Clips
5	
10	
15	
25	

2. Put on your safety glasses.

3. Make a small loop in both ends of the copper wire.

4. Start 10 cm from one end of the wire. Wrap the wire around the nail 5 times, as shown in the figure.

5. Using electrical tape, tape one end of the wire to one end of the battery. Tape the other end of the wire to the other end of the battery.

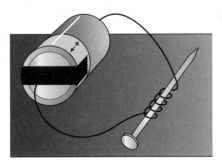

6. Hold the nail near the paper clips. Observe what happens. Record your observations in the right-hand column on the first line of the data table.

Materials

◆ safety glasses
◆ copper wire, 0.5 m long
◆ large nail
◆ metric ruler
◆ electrical tape
◆ 1.5 volt D-cell battery
◆ paper clips
◆ iron filings
◆ sheet of paper

7. Remove one end of the wire from the battery. Wrap the wire around the nail 5 more times. You should now have a total of 10 coils. Tape the end of the wire to the battery again.

8. Hold the nail near the paper clips. Record your observations.

9. Repeat steps 7 and 8, making the coil with 15 turns of the wire. Record your observations.

10. Repeat steps 7 and 8, making the coil with 25 turns of the wire. Record your observations.

Questions and Conclusions

1. In step 7, what happened to the paper clips when you removed one end of the wire from the battery?

2. How did the number of coils in the wire affect the electromagnet?

Explore Further

1. Sprinkle iron filings on a sheet of paper. Hold the paper over the wire when the coil has 25 turns of the wire. Describe the pattern made by the iron filings.

2. Hold the paper with the iron filings over the wire coil when it has 10 turns of the wire. How does the pattern made by the iron filings compare with the pattern you saw in step 1?

3. How does the number of turns in the wire coil affect the magnetic force around the wire?

4. What would happen if you used two batteries in series?

- Magnets can attract materials such as iron. Magnets may be natural, such as lodestone, or manmade.

- A magnet has a north pole and a south pole. Unlike poles of magnets attract. Like poles of magnets repel.

- A magnetic field surrounds a magnet. Magnetic lines of force extend from pole to pole.

- The earth is a magnet. It has a north magnetic pole and a south magnetic pole.

- Materials that can be magnetized and that are attracted to magnets include iron, nickel, and cobalt.

- A magnet can be made by stroking an iron wire with a magnet. Magnets can be destroyed by heat or by hard blows.

- Electromagnetism is the relationship between magnetism and electricity.

- Speakers, earphones, and telephones are devices that use electromagnets.

- Motors make use of electromagnets and permanent magnets to turn electrical energy into mechanical energy.

Science Words

attract, 349	lines of force, 351	magnetic pole, 349
electromagnet, 360	magnet, 348	motor, 363
electromagnetism, 360	magnetic field, 351	repel, 349

Chapter 12 R E V I E W

Word Bank

attract
electromagnet
electromagnetism
lines of force
magnetic field
magnetic poles
motor
repel

Vocabulary Review

Choose a word or words from the Word Bank that best complete each sentence. Write the answer on a sheet of paper.

1. A device that converts electrical energy to mechanical energy is a(n) _____.

2. A temporary magnet made by passing a current through wire wrapped around an iron core is a(n) _____.

3. The area around a magnet in which magnetic forces can act is the _____.

4. The lines that show a magnetic field are the _____.

5. Magnetic poles of opposite types _____ each other.

6. The opposite points or ends of a magnet where magnetic forces are greatest are the _____.

7. The relationship between magnetism and electricity is _____.

8. Magnetic poles of the same type _____ each other.

Concept Review

Choose the answer that best completes each sentence. Write the letter of the answer on your paper.

9. A magnet's lines of force are closest together near the _____.

   A fields   **B** poles   **C** center   **D** edges

10. The magnetic fields of atoms line up in _____.

    A a nonmagnetized field   **C** iron

    B a magnetized field   **D** both B and C

11. A motor is made of a(n) _____.

    A alternating electric current supply

    B electromagnet

    C permanent magnet

    D all of the above

12. An electromagnet is magnetic as long as _____ is flowing through it.

    A air   **B** current   **C** heat   **D** water

Critical Thinking

Write the answer to each of these questions on your paper.

13. What is the difference between a regular magnet and an electromagnet?

14. Explain a way to make a magnet and a way to destroy a magnet.

15. Suppose a bar magnet like the one shown here was cut into three pieces. Explain what would happen to the magnet's poles.

Test-Taking Tip   Read test questions carefully to identify the questions that require more than one answer.

Appendix A: Alternative Energy Sources

Fossil Fuels

We fly through the air in planes. We roll down highways in cars. On the coldest days, our homes are warm. Our stores are full of products to satisfy our needs and wants.

The power that runs our lives comes from fossil fuels. A fossil is the remains of ancient life. Fossil fuels formed from the remains of dead matter—animals and plants. Over millions of years, forests of plants died, fell, and became buried in the earth. Over time, the layers of ancient, dead matter changed. The carbon in the animals and plants turned into a material we now use as fuel. Fossil fuels include coal, oil, natural gas, and gasoline.

Fossil fuels power our lives and our society. In the United States, electricity comes mainly from power plants that burn coal. Industries use electricity to run machines. In our homes, we use electricity to power lightbulbs, TVs, and everything else electric. Heat and hot water for many homes come from natural gas or oil, or from fuels that come from oil.

Of course, cars and trucks run on gasoline, which is also made from oil. Powering our

society with fossil fuels has made our lives more comfortable. Yet our need for fossil fuels has caused problems. Fossil fuels are a nonrenewable source of energy. That means that there is a limited supply of these fuels. At some point, fossil fuels will become scarce. Their cost will increase. And one day the supply of fossil fuels will run out. We need to find ways now to depend less and less on fossil fuels.

Fossil fuels cause pollution. The pollution comes from burning them. It is like the exhaust from a car. The pollution enters the air and causes disease. It harms the environment. One serious effect of burning fossil fuels is global warming. Carbon dioxide comes from the burning of fossil fuels. When a large amount of this gas enters the air, it warms the earth's climate. Scientists believe that warming of the climate will cause serious problems.

Renewable Energy

Many people believe that we should use renewable fuels as sources of energy. Renewable fuels never run out. They last forever.

What kinds of fuels last forever? The energy from the sun. The energy in the wind. The energy in oceans and rivers. We can use these forms of energy to power our lives. Then we will never run out of fuel. We will cut down on pollution and climate warming. Using renewable energy is not a dream for the future. It is happening right now—right here—today.

Energy from the Sun

As long as the sun keeps shining, the earth will get energy from sunlight. Energy from the sun is called solar energy. It is the energy in light. When you lie in the sun, your skin becomes hot. The heat comes from the energy in sunlight. Sunlight is a form of renewable energy we can use forever.

We use solar energy to make electricity. The electricity can power homes and businesses. Turning solar energy into electricity is called photovoltaics, or PV for short. Here's how PV works.

Flat solar panels are put near a building or on its roof. The panels face the direction that gets the most sunlight. The panels contain many PV cells. The cells are made from silicon—a material that absorbs light. When sunlight strikes the cells, some of the light energy is absorbed. The energy knocks some electrons loose in the silicon. The electrons begin to flow. The electron flow is controlled. An electric current is produced. Pieces of metal at the top and bottom of each cell make a path for electrons. The path leads the electric current away from the solar panel. The electric current flows through wires to a battery. The battery stores the electrical energy. The electrical wiring in a building is connected to the battery. All the electricity used in the building comes from the battery.

Today, PV use is 500 times greater than it was 20 years ago. And PV use is growing about 20 percent per year. Yet solar energy systems are still not perfect. PV cells do not absorb all the sunlight that strikes them, so some energy is lost. Solar energy systems also are not cheap. Still, every year, PV systems are improved. The cost of PV electricity has decreased. The amount of sunlight PV cells absorb has increased.

On a sunny day, every square meter of the earth receives 1,000 watts of energy from sunlight. Someday, when PV systems are able to use all this energy, our energy problems may be solved.

Energy from the Wind

Sunlight warms different parts of the earth differently. The North Pole gets little sunlight, so it is cold. Areas near the equator get lots of sunlight, so they are warm. The uneven warming of the earth by the sun creates the wind. As the earth turns, the wind moves, or blows. The blowing wind can be used to make electricity. This is wind energy. Because the earth's winds will blow forever, the wind is a renewable source of energy.

Wind energy is not new. Hundreds of years ago, windmills created energy. The wind turned the large fins on a windmill. As the fins spun around, they turned huge stones inside the mill. The stones ground grain into flour.

Modern windmills are tall, metal towers with spinning blades, called wind turbines. Each wind turbine has three main parts. It has blades that are turned by blowing wind. The turning blades are attached to a shaft that runs the length of the tower. The turning blades spin the shaft. The spinning shaft is connected to a generator.

A generator changes the energy from movement into electrical energy. It feeds the electricity into wires, which carry it to homes and factories.

Wind turbines are placed in areas where strong winds blow. A single house may have one small wind turbine near it to produce its electricity. The electricity produced by the wind turbine is stored in batteries. Many wind turbines may be linked together to produce electricity for an entire town. In these systems, the electricity moves from the generator to the electric company's wires. The wires carry the electricity to homes and businesses.

Studies show that 34 of the 50 United States have good wind conditions. These states could use wind to meet up to 20 percent of their electric power needs. Canada's wind conditions could produce up to 20 percent of its energy from wind, too. Alberta already produces a lot of energy from wind, and the amount is expected to increase.

Energy from Inside the Earth

Deep inside the earth, the rocks are burning hot. Beneath them it is even hotter. There, rocks melt into liquid. The earth's inner heat rises to the surface in some places. Today,

people have developed ways to use this heat to create energy. Because the inside of the earth will always be very hot, this energy is renewable. It is called geothermal energy (*geo* means earth; *thermal* means heat).

Geothermal energy is used where hot water or steam from deep inside the earth moves near the surface. These areas are called "hot spots." At hot spots, we can use geothermal energy directly. Pumps raise the hot water, and pipes carry it to buildings. The water is used to heat the space in the buildings or to heat water.

Geothermal energy may also be used indirectly to make electricity. A power plant is built near a hot spot. Wells are drilled deep into the hot spot. The wells carry hot water or steam into the power plant. There, it is used to boil more water. The boiling water makes steam. The steam turns the blades of a turbine. This energy is carried to a generator, which turns it into electricity. The electricity moves through the electric company's wires to homes and factories.

Everywhere on the earth, several miles beneath the surface, there is hot material. Scientists are improving ways of tapping the earth's inner heat. Some day, this renewable, pollution-free source of energy may be available everywhere.

Energy from Trash

We can use the leftover products that come from plants to make electricity. For example, we can use the stalks from corn or wheat to make fuel. Many leftover products from crops and lumber can fuel power plants. Because this fuel comes from living plants, it is called bioenergy (*bio* means life or living). The plant waste itself is called biomass.

People have used bioenergy for thousands of years. Burning wood in a fireplace is a form of bioenergy. That's because wood comes from trees. Bioenergy is renewable, because people will always grow crops. There will always be crop waste we can burn as fuel.

Some power plants burn biomass to heat water. The steam from the boiling water turns turbines. The turbines create electricity. In other power plants, biomass is changed into a gas. The gas is used as fuel to boil water, which turns the turbine.

Biomass can also be made into a fuel for cars and trucks. Scientists use a special process to turn biomass into fuels, such as ethanol. Car makers are designing cars that can run on these fuels. Cars that use these fuels produce far less pollution than cars that run on gas.

Bioenergy can help solve our garbage problem. Many cities are having trouble finding places to dump all their trash. There would be fewer garbage dumps if we burned some trash to make electricity.

Bioenergy is a renewable energy. But it is not a perfect solution to our energy problems. Burning biomass creates air pollution.

Energy from the Ocean

Have you ever been knocked over by a small wave while wading in the ocean? If so, you know how much power ocean water has. The motion of ocean waves can be a source of energy. So can the rise and fall of ocean tides. There are several systems that use the energy in ocean waves and tides. All of them are very new and still being developed.

In one system, ocean waves enter a funnel. The water flows into a reservoir, an area behind a dam where water is stored. When the dam opens, water flows out of the reservoir. This powers a turbine, which creates electricity. Another system uses the waves' motion to operate water pumps, which run an electric generator. There is also a system that uses the rise and fall of ocean waves. The waves compress air in a container. During high tide, large amounts of ocean water enter the container. The air in the container is under great pressure. When the high-pressure air in the container is released, it drives a turbine. This creates electricity.

Energy can also come from the rise and fall of ocean tides. A dam is built across a tidal basin. This is an area where land surrounds the sea on three sides. At high tide, ocean water is allowed to flow through the dam. The water flow turns turbines, which generate electricity. There is one serious problem with tidal energy. It damages the environment of the tidal basin and can harm animals that live there.

The oceans also contain a great deal of thermal (heat) energy. The sun heats the surface of the oceans more than it heats deep ocean water. In one day, ocean surfaces absorb solar energy equal to 250 billion barrels of oil! Deep ocean water, which gets no sunlight, is much colder than the surface.

Scientists are developing ways to use this temperature difference to create energy. The systems they are currently designing are complicated and expensive.

Energy from Rivers and Dams

Dams built across rivers also produce electricity. When the dam is open, the flowing water turns turbines, which make electricity. This is called hydroelectric power (*hydro* means water). The United States gets 7 percent of its electricity from hydroelectric power. Canada gets up to 60 percent of its electricity from hydroelectric plants built across its many rivers.

Hydroelectric power is a nonpolluting and renewable form of energy—in a way. There will always be fresh water. However, more and more people are taking water from rivers for different uses. These uses include

drinking, watering crops, and supplying industry. Some rivers are becoming smaller and weaker because of the water taken from them. Also, in many places dams built across rivers hurt the environment. The land behind the dam is "drowned." Once the dam is built, fish may not be able swim up or down the river. In northwestern states, salmon have completely disappeared from many rivers that have dams.

Energy from Hydrogen Fuel

Hydrogen is a gas that is abundant everywhere on the earth. It's in the air. It is a part of water. Because there is so much hydrogen, it is a renewable energy source. And hydrogen can produce energy without any pollution.

The most likely source of hydrogen fuel is water. Water is made up of hydrogen and oxygen. A special process separates these elements in water. The process produces oxygen gas and hydrogen gas. The hydrogen gas is changed into a liquid or solid. This hydrogen fuel is used to produce energy in a fuel cell.

Look at the diagram on page 377. Hydrogen fuel (H_2) is fed into one part of the fuel cell. It is then stripped of its electrons. The free electrons create an electric current (e). The electric current powers a lightbulb or whatever is connected to the fuel cell.

Meanwhile, oxygen (O_2) from the air enters another part of the fuel cell. The stripped hydrogen (H+) bonds with the oxygen, forming water (H_2O). So a car powered by a fuel cell has pure water leaving its tailpipe. There is no exhaust to pollute the air.

When a regular battery's power is used up,

the battery dies. A fuel cell never runs down as long as it gets hydrogen fuel.

A single fuel cell produces little electricity. To make more electricity, fuel cells come in "stacks" of many fuel cells packaged together. Stacked fuel cells are used to power cars and buses. Soon, they may provide electric power to homes and factories.

Hydrogen Fuel Cell

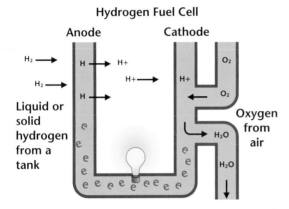

Hydrogen fuel shows great promise, but it still has problems. First, hydrogen fuel is difficult to store and distribute. Today's gas stations would have to be changed into hydrogen-fuel stations. Homes and factories would need safe ways to store solid hydrogen.

Second, producing hydrogen fuel by separating water is expensive. It is cheaper to make hydrogen fuel from oil. But that would create pollution and use nonrenewable resources. Scientists continue to look for solutions to these problems.

Energy from Atoms

Our sun gets its energy—its heat and light—from fusion. Fusion is the joining together of parts of atoms. Fusion produces enormous amounts of energy. But conditions like those on the sun are needed for fusion to occur. Fusion requires incredibly high temperatures.

In the next few decades, scientists may find ways to fuse atoms at lower temperatures. When this happens, we may be able to use fusion for energy. Fusion is a renewable form of energy because it uses hydrogen atoms. It also produces no pollution. And it produces no dangerous radiation. Using fusion to produce power is a long way off. But if the technology can be developed, fusion could provide us with renewable, clean energy.

Today's nuclear power plants produce energy by splitting atoms. This creates no air pollution. But nuclear energy has other problems. Nuclear energy is fueled by a substance we get from mines called uranium. There is only a limited amount of uranium in the earth. So it is not renewable. And uranium produces dangerous radiation, which can harm or kill living things if it escapes the power plant. Used uranium must be thrown out, even though it is radioactive and dangerous. In 1999, the United States produced nearly 41 tons of radioactive waste from nuclear power plants. However, less uranium is being mined. No new nuclear power plants have been built. The amount of energy produced from nuclear power is expected to fall. People are turning toward less harmful, renewable energy sources: the sun, wind, underground heat, biomass, water, and hydrogen fuel.

Fuel That U.S. Electric Utilities Used to Generate Electricity in 2000

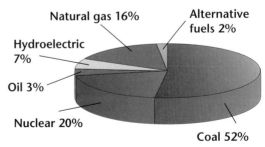

Source: U.S. Dept. of Energy Hydropower Program

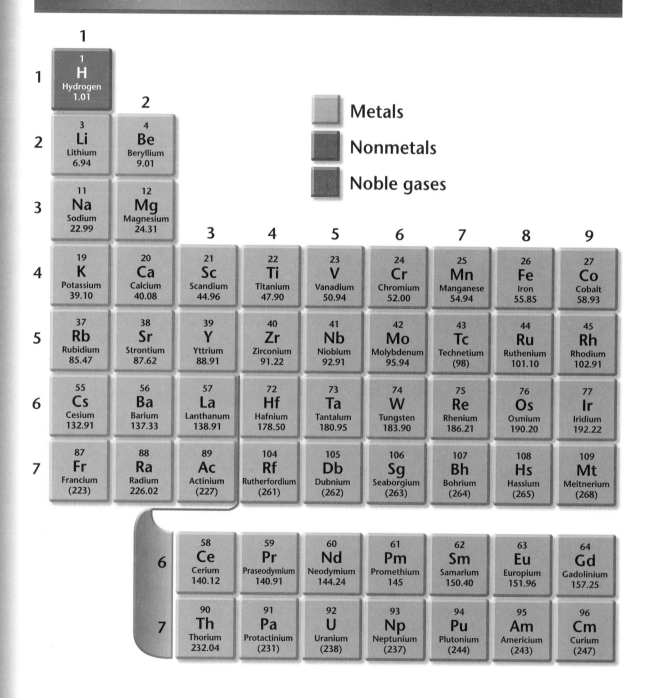

1								
1 **H** Hydrogen 1.01	**2**							

Metals

Nonmetals

Noble gases

| **3**
Li
Lithium
6.94 | **4**
Be
Beryllium
9.01 |
| **11**
Na
Sodium
22.99 | **12**
Mg
Magnesium
24.31 |

3	4	5	6	7	8	9
21 **Sc** Scandium 44.96	**22** **Ti** Titanium 47.90	**23** **V** Vanadium 50.94	**24** **Cr** Chromium 52.00	**25** **Mn** Manganese 54.94	**26** **Fe** Iron 55.85	**27** **Co** Cobalt 58.93
39 **Y** Yttrium 88.91	**40** **Zr** Zirconium 91.22	**41** **Nb** Niobium 92.91	**42** **Mo** Molybdenum 95.94	**43** **Tc** Technetium (98)	**44** **Ru** Ruthenium 101.10	**45** **Rh** Rhodium 102.91
57 **La** Lanthanum 138.91	**72** **Hf** Hafnium 178.50	**73** **Ta** Tantalum 180.95	**74** **W** Tungsten 183.90	**75** **Re** Rhenium 186.21	**76** **Os** Osmium 190.20	**77** **Ir** Iridium 192.22
89 **Ac** Actinium (227)	**104** **Rf** Rutherfordium (261)	**105** **Db** Dubnium (262)	**106** **Sg** Seaborgium (263)	**107** **Bh** Bohrium (264)	**108** **Hs** Hassium (265)	**109** **Mt** Meitnerium (268)

Row 4: **19 K** Potassium 39.10 | **20 Ca** Calcium 40.08
Row 5: **37 Rb** Rubidium 85.47 | **38 Sr** Strontium 87.62
Row 6: **55 Cs** Cesium 132.91 | **56 Ba** Barium 137.33
Row 7: **87 Fr** Francium (223) | **88 Ra** Radium 226.02

6	**58** **Ce** Cerium 140.12	**59** **Pr** Praseodymium 140.91	**60** **Nd** Neodymium 144.24	**61** **Pm** Promethium 145	**62** **Sm** Samarium 150.40	**63** **Eu** Europium 151.96	**64** **Gd** Gadolinium 157.25
7	**90** **Th** Thorium 232.04	**91** **Pa** Protactinium (231)	**92** **U** Uranium (238)	**93** **Np** Neptunium (237)	**94** **Pu** Plutonium (244)	**95** **Am** Americium (243)	**96** **Cm** Curium (247)

																	18
																	2 **He** Helium 4.00

			13	**14**	**15**	**16**	**17**	
			5 **B** Boron 10.81	6 **C** Carbon 12.01	7 **N** Nitrogen 14.01	8 **O** Oxygen 16.00	9 **F** Fluorine 19.00	10 **Ne** Neon 20.18
			13 **Al** Aluminum 26.98	14 **Si** Silicon 28.09	15 **P** Phosphorus 30.97	16 **S** Sulfur 32.07	17 **Cl** Chlorine 35.45	18 **Ar** Argon 39.95

10	**11**	**12**						
28 **Ni** Nickel 58.70	29 **Cu** Copper 63.55	30 **Zn** Zinc 65.39	31 **Ga** Gallium 69.72	32 **Ge** Germanium 72.59	33 **As** Arsenic 74.92	34 **Se** Selenium 78.96	35 **Br** Bromine 79.90	36 **Kr** Krypton 83.80
46 **Pd** Palladium 106.42	47 **Ag** Silver 107.90	48 **Cd** Cadmium 112.41	49 **In** Indium 114.82	50 **Sn** Tin 118.69	51 **Sb** Antimony 121.75	52 **Te** Tellurium 127.60	53 **I** Iodine 126.90	54 **Xe** Xenon 131.30
78 **Pt** Platinum 195.09	79 **Au** Gold 196.97	80 **Hg** Mercury 200.59	81 **Tl** Thallium 204.40	82 **Pb** Lead 207.20	83 **Bi** Bismuth 208.98	84 **Po** Polonium 209	85 **At** Astatine (210)	86 **Rn** Radon (222)
110 **Uun** Ununnilium (269)	111 **Uuu** Unununium (272)	112 **Uub** Ununbium (277)		114 **Uuq** Ununquadium (289)		116 **Uuh** Ununhexium (289)		

65 **Tb** Terbium 158.93	66 **Dy** Dysprosium 162.50	67 **Ho** Holmium 164.93	68 **Er** Erbium 167.26	69 **Tm** Thulium 168.93	70 **Yb** Ytterbium 173.04	71 **Lu** Lutetium 174.97
97 **Bk** Berkelium (247)	98 **Cf** Californium (249)	99 **Es** Einsteinium (254)	100 **Fm** Fermium (257)	101 **Md** Mendelevium (258)	102 **No** Nobelium (259)	103 **Lr** Lawrencium (260)

Note: *The atomic masses listed in the table reflect current measurements. The atomic masses listed in parentheses are those of the element's most stable or most common isotope.*

Appendix C: Measurement Conversion Factors

Metric Measures

Length
1,000 meters (m) = 1 kilometer (km)
100 centimeters (cm) = 1 m
10 decimeters (dm) = 1 m
1,000 millimeters (mm) = 1 m
10 cm = 1 decimeter (dm)
10 mm = 1 cm

Area
100 square millimeters (mm^2) = 1 square
   centimeter (cm^2)
10,000 cm^2 = 1 square meter (m^2)
10,000 m^2 = 1 hectare (ha)

Volume
1,000 cubic meters (m^3) = 1 cubic
   centimeter (cm^3)
1,000 cubic centimeters (cm^3) = 1 liter (L)
1 cubic centimeter (cm^3) = 1 milliliter (mL)
100 cm^3 = 1 cubic decimeter (dm^3)
1,000,000 cm^3 = 1 cubic meter (m^3)

Capacity
1,000 milliliters (mL) = 1 liter (L)
1,000 L = 1 kiloliter (kL)

Mass
100 grams (g) = 1 centigram (cg)
1,000 kilograms (kg) = 1 metric ton (t)
1,000 grams (g) = 1 kg
1,000 milligrams (mg) = 1 g

Temperature Degrees Celsius (°C)
0°C = freezing point of water
37°C = normal body temperature
100°C = boiling point of water

Time
60 seconds (sec) = 1 minute (min)
60 min = 1 hour (hr)
24 hr = 1 day

Customary Measures

Length
12 inches (in.) = 1 foot (ft)
3 ft = 1 yard (yd)
36 in. = 1 yd
5,280 ft = 1 mile (mi)
1,760 yd = 1 mi
6,076 feet = 1 nautical mile

Area
144 square inches (sq in.) = 1 square foot
   (sq ft)
9 sq ft = 1 square yard (sq yd)
43,560 sq ft = 1 acre (A)

Volume
1,728 cubic inches (cu in.) = 1 cubic foot
   (cu ft)
27 cu ft = 1 cubic yard (cu yard)

Capacity
8 fluid ounces (fl oz) = 1 cup (c)
2 c = 1 pint (pt)
2 pt = 1 quart (qt)
4 qt = 1 gallon (gal)

Weight
16 ounces (oz) = 1 pound (lb)
2,000 lb = 1 ton (T)

Temperature Degrees Fahrenheit (°F)
32°F = freezing point of water
98.6°F = normal body temperature
212°F = boiling point of water

To change	To	Multiply by	To change	To	Multiply by
centimeters	inches	0.3937	meters	feet	3.2808
centimeters	feet	0.03281	meters	miles	0.0006214
cubic feet	cubic meters	0.0283	meters	yards	1.0936
cubic meters	cubic feet	35.3145	metric tons	tons (long)	0.9842
cubic meters	cubic yards	1.3079	metric tons	tons (short)	1.1023
cubic yards	cubic meters	0.7646	miles	kilometers	1.6093
feet	meters	0.3048	miles	feet	5,280
feet	miles (nautical)	0.0001645	miles (statute)	miles (nautical)	0.8684
feet	miles (statute)	0.0001894	miles/hour	feet/minute	88
feet/second	miles/hour	0.6818	millimeters	inches	0.0394
gallons (U.S.)	liters	3.7853	ounces avdp	grams	28.3495
grams	ounces avdp	0.0353	ounces	pounds	0.0625
grams	pounds	0.002205	pecks	liters	8.8096
hours	days	0.04167	pints (dry)	liters	0.5506
inches	millimeters	25.4000	pints (liquid)	liters	0.4732
inches	centimeters	2.5400	pounds advp	kilograms	0.4536
kilograms	pounds avdp	2.2046	pounds	ounces	16
kilometers	miles	0.6214	quarts (dry)	liters	1.1012
liters	gallons (U.S.)	0.2642	quarts (liquid)	liters	0.9463
liters	pecks	0.1135	square feet	square meters	0.0929
liters	pints (dry)	1.8162	square meters	square feet	10.7639
liters	pints (liquid)	2.1134	square meters	square yards	1.1960
liters	quarts (dry)	0.9081	square yards	square meters	0.8361
liters	quarts (liquid)	1.0567	yards	meters	0.9144

Appendix D: Decimal, Percent, and Fraction Conversions

Renaming Decimals as Percents

Example   Rename 0.75 as a percent.

Solution   0.75

0.75 = 75%

Step 1   Move the decimal point two places to the right.

Step 2   Then insert a percent symbol.

Example   Rename 0.5 as a percent.

Solution   0.5 = 0.50

0.5 = 50%

Renaming Percents as Decimals

Example   Rename 80% as a decimal.

Solution   80% = 80.%

80% = 0.80

= 0.8 ⟵ You can always drop zeros at the end of a decimal.

Step 1   Move the decimal point two places to the left.

Step 2   Then drop the percent symbol.

Renaming Fractions as Decimals

Example   Rename $\frac{7}{20}$ as a decimal.

Solution   **Method 1**

$$\frac{7}{20} = \frac{7 \times 5}{20 \times 5} = \frac{35}{100}$$

$$= 0.35$$

Choose a multiplier that makes the denominator a power of 10 (10, 100, 1,000, . . .)

Method 2

$$\frac{7}{20} = \begin{array}{r} .35 \\ 20 \overline{)7.00} \\ -6\,0 \\ \hline 1\,00 \\ -1\,00 \end{array}$$

Divide the numerator by the denominator.

Renaming Decimals as Fractions

Example Rename 0.025 as a fraction.

Solution First, read the decimal: "25 thousandths."

Then write the fraction and simplify.

$$0.025 = \frac{25}{1,000} = \frac{25 \div 25}{1,000 \div 25} = \frac{1}{40}$$

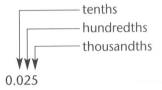

Renaming Fractions as Percents

Example Rename $\frac{9}{25}$ as a percent.

Solution **Method 1**

Write as an equivalent fraction with denominator 100.

$$\frac{9}{25} = \frac{9 \times 4}{25 \times 4} = \frac{36}{100} = 36\%$$

Percent means per 100.
So, 36 hundredths is 36%.

Method 2

$$\frac{9}{25} = 0.36 = 36\%$$

Step 1 Divide the numerator by the denominator.

Step 2 Rewrite the decimal as a percent.

Renaming Percents as Fractions

Example Rename 2% as a fraction.

Solution $2\% = \frac{2}{100}$ ⟵ *Percent* means *per 100.*

$= \frac{1}{50}$ ⟵ Simplify.

Glossary

A

Acceleration (ak sel ə rā′ shən) the rate of change in velocity (p. 187)

Acid (as′ id) a compound that reacts with metals to produce hydrogen (p. 138)

Alloy (al′ oi) a mixture of two or more metals (p. 107)

Alternating current (ȯl tər nā′ ting ker′ənt) current that changes direction regularly (p. 323)

Ampere (am′ pir) the unit used to describe how much electric current flows through a wire (p. 311)

Area (âr′ ē ə) amount of space the surface of an object takes up (p. 15)

Atom (at′ əm) the building block of matter (p. 61)

Atomic mass (ə tom′ ik mas) the average mass of all the isotopes of a particular element (p. 102)

Atomic number (ə tom′ ik num′ bər) a number equal to the number of protons in the nucleus of an atom (p. 82)

Attract (ə trakt′) to pull together (p. 349)

B

Balance (bal′ əns) an instrument used to measure mass (p. 38); to keep the number of atoms the same on both sides of the equation (p. 157)

Base (bās) a compound that contains the hydroxyl (OH) radical (p. 139)

Battery (bat′ erē) a source of voltage that changes chemical energy into electrical energy (p. 321)

Binary compound (bī′ nərē kom′ pound) a compound that contains two elements (p. 134)

Boiling point (boi ling pȯint) the temperature at which a substance changes from a liquid to a gas under normal atmospheric pressure (p. 254)

C

Calorie (kal′ ə re) a unit of heat; the amount of heat needed to raise the temperature of 1 g of water by 1°C (p. 57)

Celsius scale (sel′ sē əs skāl) the temperature scale used by scientists and by people in most countries, in which water freezes at 0° and boils at 100° (p. 251)

Centigram (cg) (sen′ tə gram) a unit of mass in the metric system that is $\frac{1}{100}$ of a gram (p. 25)

Centimeter (cm) (sen′ tə mē tər) a metric unit of measure that is $\frac{1}{100}$ of a meter (p. 10)

Chemical bond (kem′ ə kəl bond) the attractive force that holds atoms together (p. 127)

Chemical change (kem′ ə kəl chānj) a change that produces one or more new substances with new chemical properties (p. 118)

Chemical equation (kem′ ə kəl i kwā′ zhən) a statement that uses symbols, formulas, and numbers to stand for a chemical reaction (p. 155)

Chemical formula (kem′ ə kəl fôr′ myə lə) tells the kinds of atoms and how many of each kind are in a compound (p. 129)

Chemical reaction (kem′ ə kəl rē ak′ shən) a chemical change in which elements are combined or rearranged (p.150)

Chemistry (kem′ ə strē) the study of matter and how it changes (p. 3)

Circuit (ser′ kit) a path for electric current (p. 311)

Closed circuit (klōzd′ sėr′ kit) a complete, unbroken path for electric current (p. 311)

Coefficient (kō′ ə fish′ ənt) a number placed before a formula in a chemical equation (p. 157)

Compound (kom′ pound) a substance that is formed when atoms of two or more elements join together (p. 70)

Concave lens (kon kav´ lenz) a lens that is thin in the middle and thick at the edges (p. 301)

Concave mirror (kon kav´ mir´ ər) a mirror that curves in at the middle (p. 296)

Condensation (kon den sā´ shən) to change from a gas to a liquid (p. 244)

Conduction (kan duk´ shən) the movement of heat energy from one molecule to the next (p. 263)

Conductor (kan duk´ tər) material through which heat travels easily (p. 263); material through which electricity passes easily (p. 315)

Constant speed (kon´ stənt spēd) speed that does not change (p. 179)

Contract (kən trakt´) to become smaller in size (p. 245)

Convection (kən vek´ shən) flow of energy that occurs when a warm liquid or gas rises (p. 264)

Convex lens (kon veks´ lenz) a lens that is thick in the middle and thin at the edges (p. 302)

Convex mirror (kon veks´ mir´ ər) a mirror that curves outward at the middle (p. 297)

Cubic centimeter (cm³) (kyü´ bik sen´ tə mē tər) a metric unit of measure that means centimeter x centimeter x centimeter (p. 201)

Customary (kus´ tə mer´ ē) ordinary (p. 7)

Cycle (sī´ kəl) the complete back-and-forth motion of a vibration (p. 277)

D

Deceleration (dē sel´ ə rā shən) the rate of slowdown (p. 188)

Decibel (des´ ə bəl) a unit that measures the intensity of sound (p. 275)

Decomposition reaction (dē´ kom pə zish´ ən rē ak´ shən) a reaction in which a compound breaks down into two or more simple substances (p. 162)

Degree (di grē´) a unit of measurement on a temperature scale (p. 251)

Density (den´ sə tē) a measure of how tightly the matter of a substance is packed into a given volume (p. 49)

Deuterium (dü tir´ ē əm) an isotope of hydrogen that has one proton and one neutron (p. 99)

Direct current (də rekt´ kėr´ ənt) current that flows in one direction (p. 323)

Displacement of water (dis plās´ mənt ov wo´ tər) method of measuring the volume of an irregularly shaped object (p. 46)

Dissolve (di zolv´) to break apart (p. 151)

Distance (dis´ təns) the length of the path between two points (p. 175)

Double-replacement reaction (dub´ əl ri plās´ mənt rē ak´ shən) a reaction in which the elements in two compounds are exchanged (p. 165)

Dry-cell battery (drī sel bat´ ərē) electric power source with a dry or pastelike center (p. 321)

E

Echo (ek´ ō) a sound that is reflected to its source (p. 283)

Efficiency (ə fish´ ən sē) how well a machine performs (p. 221)

Effort arm (ef´ ərt ärm) the distance between the fulcrum and the effort force of a lever (p. 225)

Effort force (F_e) (ef´ ərt fôrs) the force applied to a machine by the user (p. 218)

Elapsed time (i´ lapsd tim) the length of time that passes from one event to another (p. 174)

Electric current (i lek´ trik kėr´ ənt) movement of electrons from one place to another (p. 311)

Electric power (i lek´ trik pou´ ər) the amount of electrical energy used in a certain amount of time (p. 340)

a	hat	e	let	ī	ice	ô	order	ù	put	sh	she		a	in about
ā	age	ē	equal	o	hot	oi	oil	ü	rule	th	thin	ə	e	in taken
ä	far	ėr	term	ō	open	ou	out	ch	child	ᴛʜ	then		i	in pencil
â	care	i	it	ȯ	saw	u	cup	ng	long	zh	measure		o	in lemon
													u	in circus

Electricity (i lek tris´ ə tē) flow of electrons (p. 310)

Electromagnet (i lek trō mag´ nit) a temporary magnet made by passing a current through a wire wrapped around an iron core (p. 360)

Electromagnetism (i lek trō mag´ ni tism) the relationship between magnetism and electricity (p. 360)

Electromotive force (i lek trə mō´ tiv fôrs) the push that keeps the current (electrons) flowing in an electric circuit (p. 320)

Electron (i lek´ tron) a tiny particle of an atom that moves around the nucleus (p. 76)

Element (el´ ə mənt) matter that has only one kind of atom (p. 65)

Energy (en´ ər jē) the ability to do work (p. 211)

Energy level (en´ ər jē lev´ əl) one of the spaces around the nucleus of an atom in which an electron moves (p. 123)

Evaporate (i vap´ ə rat´) to change from a liquid to a gas (p. 244)

Expand (ek spand´) to become larger in size (p. 245)

Exponent (ek spō´ nənt) a number that tells how many times another number is a factor (p. 15)

F

Family (fam´ ə lē) a group of elements with similar properties, arranged together in a column of the periodic table (p. 103)

Fahrenheit scale (far´ ən hīt skāl) the temperature scale commonly used in the United States, in which water freezes at 32° and boils at 212° (p. 251)

Farsighted (fär´ sī´ tid) able to see objects at a distance clearly (p. 303)

Focal point (fō´ kəl point) the point where reflected light rays from a concave mirror come together in front of the mirror (p. 296)

Force (fôrs) a push or a pull (p. 192)

Freezing point (frēz´ ing point) the temperature at which a liquid changes to a solid (p. 253)

Frequency (frē´ kwən sē) the number of vibrations per second of a sound wave (p. 277)

Friction (frik´ shən) a force that opposes motion and that occurs when things slide or roll over each other (p. 192)

Fulcrum (ful´ krəm) a fixed point around which a lever rotates (p. 218)

G

Gas (gas) a form of matter that has no definite shape or volume (p. 63)

Generator (jen´ ə rā tər) a device used to convert mechanical energy to electrical energy (p. 213)

Graduated cylinder (graj´ ü ā tid sil´ ən dər) a round glass or plastic cylinder used to measure the volume of liquids (p. 43)

Gram (g) (gram) basic unit of mass in the metric system (p. 24)

Gravity (grav´ ə tē) the force of attraction between any two objects that have mass (p. 196)

H

Heat (hēt) a form of energy resulting from the motion of particles in matter (p. 240)

Heat source (hēt sôrs) a place from which heat energy comes (p. 241)

Hertz (Hz) (hėrts) the unit used to measure frequency of a sound; one Hertz equals one cycle per second (p. 277)

I

Image (im´ ij) a copy or likeness (p. 295)

Inclined plane (in klīnd´ plān) a simple machine made up of a ramp, used to lift an object (p. 231)

Indicator (in´ də kā tər) a substance that changes color when in an acid or a base (p. 139)

Inert (in ėrt´) inactive; lacking the power to move (p. 109)

Inertia (in ėr´ shə) the tendency of an object to resist changes in its motion (p. 193)

Insulator (in´ sə lā tər) material that does not conduct heat well (p. 263); material through which electricity does not pass easily (p. 315)

Intensity (in ten´ sə tē) the strength of a sound (p. 275)

Ion (ī′ ən) an atom that has either a positive or a negative charge (p. 127)

Isotope (ī′ sə tōp) one of a group of atoms of an element with the same number of protons and electrons but different numbers of neutrons (p. 99)

J

Joule (jül) metric unit of work (p. 207)

K

Kilowatt-hour (kil′ ə wot our′) a unit to measure how much electric energy is used; it is 1,000 watts used in one hour (p. 340)

Kinetic energy (ki net′ ik en′ ər jē) energy of motion (p. 211)

Kilogram(kg) (kil′ ə gram) a unit of mass in the metric system that equals 1,000 grams (p. 25)

Kilometer (km) (kə lom′ ə tər) a metric unit of measure that is equal to 1,000 meters (p. 11)

L

Law of conservation of energy (lȯ ov kon′ sər vā shən ov en′ ar jē) energy cannot be created or destroyed (p. 214)

Law of conservation of matter (lȯ ov kon′ sər vā shən ov mat′ ər) matter cannot be created or destroyed in chemical and common physical changes (p. 156)

Law of universal gravitation (lȯ ov yü nə vėr′ səl grav ə tā′ shən) gravitational force depends on the mass of the two objects involved and on the distance between them (p. 196)

Lens (lenz) a curved piece of clear material that refracts light waves (p. 301)

Lever (lev′ ər) a simple machine containing a bar that can turn around a fixed point (p. 218)

Light (līt) a form of energy that can be seen (p. 289)

Lines of force (linz′ ov fôrs) lines that show a magnetic field (p. 351)

Liquid (lik′ wid) a form of matter that has a definite volume but no definite shape (p. 62)

Liter (L) (lē′ tər) basic unit of volume in the metric system (p. 21)

M

Magnet (mag′ nit) an object that attracts certain kinds of metals, such as iron (p. 348)

Magnetic field (mag net′ ik fēld) area around a magnet in which magnetic forces can act (p. 351)

Magnetic pole (mag net′ ik pōl) the end of a magnet, where magnetic forces are greatest (p. 349)

Mass (mas) the amount of material an object has (p. 2)

Mass number (mas num′ bər) a number equal to the sum of the numbers of protons and neutrons in an atom of an element (p. 83)

Matter (mat′ ər) anything that has mass and takes up space (p. 2)

Mechanical advantage (MA) (mə kan′ ə kəl ad van′ tij) factor by which a machine multiplies the effort force (p. 224)

Melting point (melt′ ing pȯint) the temperature at which a solid changes to a liquid (p. 253)

Meniscus (mə nis′ kəs) the curved surface of a liquid (p. 43)

Metal (met′ l) one of a group of elements that is usually solid at room temperature, often shiny, and carries heat and electricity well (p. 106)

Meter (m) (mē′ tər) the basic unit of length in the metric system; it is about 39 inches (p. 9)

Meterstick (mē′ tər stik) a common tool for measuring length in the metric system (p. 10)

Metric system (met′ rik sis′ təm) system of measurement used by scientists (p. 7)

a	hat	e	let	ī	ice	ȯ	order	u̇	put	sh	she		a	in about
ā	age	ē	equal	o	hot	oi	oil	ü	rule	th	thin	ə	e	in taken
ä	far	ėr	term	ō	open	ou	out	ch	child	ᴛʜ	then		i	in pencil
â	care	i	it	ȯ	saw	u	cup	ng	long	zh	measure		o	in lemon
													u	in circus

Milligram (mg) (mil´ ə gram) a unit of mass in the metric system that is $\frac{1}{1,000}$ of a gram (p. 25)

Milliliter (mL) (mil´ ə lē tər) a metric unit of measure that is $\frac{1}{1,000}$ of a liter; it equals one cubic centimeter (p. 22)

Millimeter (mm) (mil´ ə mē tər) a metric unit of measure that is $\frac{1}{1,000}$ of a meter (p. 10)

Mixture (miks´ chər) a combination of substances in which no reaction takes place (p.150)

Model (mod´ l) a picture, an idea, or an object that is built to explain how something else looks or works (p. 75)

Molecule (mol´ ə kyül) the smallest particle of a substance that has the same properties as the substance (p. 60)

Motion (mō´ shən) a change in position (p. 174)

Motor (mō´ tər) a device that converts electrical energy to mechanical energy (p. 363)

N

Natural element (nach´ ər əl el´ ə mənt) an element found in nature (p. 66)

Nearsighted (nir´ sī´ tid) able to see objects that are close up clearly (p. 302)

Neutron (nü tron) a tiny particle in the nucleus of an atom that is similar to a proton in size (p. 77)

Newton (nüt´ n) the metric unit of weight (p. 37)

Noble gas (nō´ bəl gas) one of a group of elements made up of gases that do not combine with other materials under ordinary conditions (p. 109)

Nonmetal (non met´ l) one of a group of elements with properties unlike those of metals (p. 107)

Nuclear fission (nü´ klē ar fish´ ən) the reaction that occurs when the nucleus of an atom splits and energy is released as heat and light (p. 242)

Nuclear fusion (nü´ klē ar fyü´ zhan) the reaction that occurs when atoms are joined together and energy is released (p. 242)

Nucleus (nü´ klē əs) the central part of an atom (p. 76)

O

Ohm (ōm) the unit used to measure resistance (p. 316)

Ohm's law (ōmz lȯ) current equals voltage divided by resistance (p. 325)

Open circuit (ō´ pən ser´ kit) an incomplete or broken path for electric current (p. 312)

P

Parallel circuit (par´ ə lel ser´ kit) a circuit in which there is more than one path for current (p. 335)

Periodic table (pir ē od´ ik tā´ bəl) an arrangement of elements by increasing atomic number (p. 97)

pH (pē āch) a number that tells whether a substance is an acid or a base (p. 140)

Photons (fō´ tonz) small bundles of energy that make up light (p. 289)

Physical change (fiz´ ə kəl chānj) a change in which the appearance (physical properties) of a substance changes but its chemical properties stay the same (p. 119)

Physical science (fiz´ ə kəl sī´ əns) the study of matter and energy (p. 2)

Physics (fiz´ iks) the study of how energy acts with matter (p. 3)

Pitch (pich) how high or low a sound is (p. 277)

Plane mirror (plān mir´ ər) a flat, smooth mirror (p. 295)

Plasma (plaz´ mə) a very hot gas made of particles that have an electric charge (p. 63)

Potential energy (pə ten´ shəl en´ ər jē) stored energy (p. 211)

Power (pou´ ər) the amount of work a person does within a given period of time (p. 209)

Precipitate (pri sip´ ə tāt) a solid that is formed and usually sinks to the bottom of a solution (p. 165)

Prism (priz´ əm) a clear piece of glass or plastic that is shaped like a triangle; it can be used to separate white light (p. 291)

Product (prod´ əkt) a substance that is formed in a chemical reaction (p. 155)

Property (prop´ ər tē) a characteristic that helps identify an object (p. 32)

Proton (prō´ ton) a tiny particle in the nucleus of an atom (p. 76)

Pulley (pul´ ē) a simple machine made up of a rope, chain, or belt wrapped around a wheel (p. 229)

R

Radiation (rā de ā´ shən) the movement of energy through a vacuum (p. 262)

Radicals (rad´ ə kalz) a group of two or more atoms that acts like one atom (p. 131)

Reactant (rē ak´ tənt) a substance that is altered in a chemical reaction (p. 155)

Reflect (ri flekt´) to bounce back (p. 283)

Refraction (ri frak´ shən) the bending of a light wave as it moves from one material to another (p. 301)

Repel (ri pel´) to push apart (p. 349)

Resistance (ri zis´ təns) measure of how easily electric current will flow through a material (p. 316)

Resistance arm (ri zis´ təns ärm) the distance between the fulcrum and resistance force of a lever (p. 225)

Resistance force (F$_r$) (ri zis´ təns fôrs) the force applied to a machine by the object to be moved (p. 218)

S

Schematic diagram (ski mat´ ik di´ ə gram) a diagram that uses symbols to show the parts of a circuit (p. 313)

Screw (skrü) a simple machine made up of an inclined plane wrapped around a straight piece of metal (p. 232)

Series circuit (sir´ ēz sėr´ kit) a circuit in which all current (electrons) flows through a single path (p. 328)

Simple machine (sim´ pəl mə shēn´) a tool with few parts that makes it easier or possible to do work (p. 218)

Single-replacement reaction (sing´ gəl ri plās´ mənt rē ak´ shən) a reaction in which one element replaces another in a compound (p. 164)

Solid (sol´ id) a form of matter that has a definite shape and volume (p. 62)

Solute (sol´ yüt) the substance that is dissolved in a solution (p. 151)

Solution (sə lü´ shən) a mixture in which one substance is dissolved in another (p. 151)

Solvent (sol´ vənt) a substance capable of dissolving one or more other substances (p. 151)

Sonar (sō´ när) a method of using sound to measure distances under water (p. 284)

Sound wave (sound wāv) a wave produced by vibrations (p. 273)

Speed (spēd) the rate at which the position of an object changes (p. 175)

Standard mass (stan´ dard mas) a small object that is used with a balance to determine mass (p. 38)

State of matter (stāt ov mat´ ər) the form that matter has—solid, liquid, or gas (p. 63)

Static electricity (stat´ ik i lek tris´ ə tē) buildup of electrical charges (p. 310)

Subscript (sub´ skript) a number in a formula that tells the number of atoms of an element in a compound (p. 130)

Symbol (sim´ bəl) one or two letters that represent the name of an element (p. 92)

Synthesis reaction (sin´ thə sis re ak´ shən) a reaction in which elements combine to form a compound (p. 160)

a	hat	e	let	ī	ice	ȯ	order	ù	put	sh	she	ə {	a	in about
ā	age	ē	equal	o	hot	oi	oil	ü	rule	th	thin		e	in taken
ä	far	ėr	term	ō	open	ou	out	ch	child	ᴛʜ	then		i	in pencil
â	care	i	it	ȯ	saw	u	cup	ng	long	zh	measure		o	in lemon
													u	in circus

T

Temperature (tem´ pər ə char) a measure of how fast an object's particles are moving (p. 249)

Terminal (tėr´ mə nəl) points where electrons leave or enter a battery (p. 321)

Thermometer (thər mom´ ə tər) a device that measures temperature (p. 250)

Tritium (trit´ ē əm) an isotope of hydrogen that has one proton and two neutrons (p. 99)

U

Ultrasound (ul´ trə sound) a technique that uses sound waves to study organs inside the human body (p. 285)

Unit (yü´ nit) a known amount used for measuring (p. 6)

V

Vacuum (vak´ yü əm) space that contains no matter (p. 262)

Velocity (və los´ ə tē) the speed and direction in which an object is moving (p. 182)

Vibrate (vī´ brāt) to move rapidly back and forth (p. 272)

Visible spectrum (viz´ ə bəl spek´ trəm) the band of colors that make up white light; the colors in a rainbow (p. 291)

Volt (vōlt) the metric unit used to measure electromotive force that tells the amount of push (p. 320)

Voltage (vōl´ tij) the energy that a power source gives to electrons in a circuit (p. 321)

Volume (vol´ yəm) the amount of space an object takes up (p. 20); the loudness or softness of a sound (p. 276)

W

Watt (wät) the unit used to measure power (p. 209)

Wedge (wej) a simple machine made up of an inclined plane or pair of inclined planes that are moved (p. 232)

Weight (wāt) the measure of how hard gravity pulls on an object (p. 37)

Wet-cell battery (wet sel bat´ ərē) electric power source with a liquid center (p. 322)

Wheel and axle (wēl and ak´ səl) a simple machine made up of a wheel attached to a shaft (p. 233)

Work (wėrk) what happens when an object changes its position by moving in the direction of the force that is being applied (p. 206)

Work input (wėrk in´ put) work put into a machine by its user (p. 221)

Work output (wėrk out´ put) work done by a machine against the resistance (p. 221)

Index

Photo and Illustration Credits

Cover photos: background–© Royalty-free/ Fotosearch Stock Photography; left inset– © Royalty-free/Comstock Images; top inset–© Roz Woodward/Getty Images; right inset–© Royalty-free/Comstock Images; pp. iii, xviii–© James Randklev/Image Bank; p. 2–© Jerome Wexler/ Visuals Unlimited; pp. 3, 106–© Michael Newman/ PhotoEdit; p. 6–© Mike Doebel/Masterfile; p. 17– © Jean Miele/Corbis; p. 30–© Tom Benoit/Stone; pp. 32, 33, 38–© Stock Montage; p. 34–© AP/Wide World Photos; p. 58–© Phil Degginger/Animals Animals; p. 61–© Mark E. Gibson/Visuals Unlimited; p. 62–© Dean Conger/Corbis; p. 72– © Michael L. Abramson/TimePix; p. 90–© Roberto de Gugliemo/Science Photo Library/Photo Researchers, Inc.; p. 94–© Stephen Agricola/Stock Boston; p. 109–© Richard Cummins/Corbis; p. 116–© Ralph White/Corbis; pp. 118, 315–© E.R. Degginger/Color-Pic Inc.; p. 118–© Izzy Schwartz/ PhotoDisc; p. 128–© Roger Tully/Stone; p. 132– © Peter Gridley/Taxi; p. 136–© Photri-Microstock; p. 141–© Kevin Miller/Stone; p. 148–© W. Wayne Lockwood, M.D./Corbis; p. 150–© Stapleton Collection/Corbis; p. 152–© Gibson Stock Photography; p. 152–© Lawrence M. Sawyer/ PhotoDisc; pp. 161, 164, 171–© Stephen Frisch Photography; pp. 161, 190–© Tony Freeman/ PhotoEdit; p. 163–© Roger Ball/Corbis; p. 172– © P. Sharpe/OSF/Animals Animals; p. 187–

© Robert Brenner/PhotoEdit; p. 188–© Phil Degginger/Color-Pic Inc.; p. 195–© Ted Kawalerski Photography/Image Bank; p. 204–© Dann Coffey/ Image Bank; p. 206–© Digital Vision; p. 208– © Casey McNamara/Index Stock Imagery; p. 212– © Stephen Wilkes/Image Bank; p. 214–© Jose Carillo/PhotoEdit; pp. 232, 238, 372, 374, 375– © Royalty-free/Corbis; pp. 240, 249–© David Young-Wolff/PhotoEdit; p. 241 Barbara Stitzer/ PhotoEdit; p. 246–© John Feingersh/Stock Boston; p. 250–© J. K. West/Rainbow; p. 270–© Jeff Hunter/Image Bank; p. 273–© John Foxx/ Alamy.com; p. 276–© Dave Bartruff/Corbis; p. 280–© Stacy Pick/Stock Boston; p. 282–© Roger Archibald/Animals Animals; p. 285–© Russell D. Curtis/Photo Researchers, Inc.; p. 290–© Don Bensey/Stone; p. 291–© Craig Tuttle/Corbis; p. 291– © Chris Ryan/Taxi; p. 292–© Bob Daemmrich/ Stock Boston; p. 297–© Alan Schein Photography/ Corbis; p. 301–© Bill Beatty/Visuals Unlimited; p. 304–© Charles Gupton/Stock Boston; p. 308– © Pete Turner/Image Bank; p. 319–© Chuck Keeler, Jr./Corbis; p. 340–© Julie West/Rainbow; p. 341– © D. Yeske/Visuals Unlimited; p. 346–© Larry Stepanowicz/Visuals Unlimited; p. 348–© Andrew Lambert/LGPL/Alamy.com; p. 359–© Susan Van Etten/PhotoEdit; p. 361–© Coco McCoy/Rainbow; p. 365–© AFP/Corbis; illustrations by Stephanie Pershing and Kathy Kruger